NEURAL MECHANISMS OF HIGHER VERTEBRATE BEHAVIOR

NEURAL MECHANISMS O

IIGHER VERTEBRATE BEHAVIOR

BY J. S. BERITOFF (BERITASHVILI), D.Sc.

PROFESSOR OF NEUROPHYSIOLOGY, TIFLIS STATE UNIVERSITY, AND
HEAD OF THE DEPARTMENT OF GENERAL PHYSIOLOGY, INSTITUTE OF
PHYSIOLOGY OF THE ACADEMY OF SCIENCES OF THE GEORGIAN S.S.R.,
TIFLIS, U.S.S.R. MEMBER OF THE ACADEMY OF SCIENCES U.S.S.R.,
THE ACADEMY OF MEDICAL SCIENCES, U.S.S.R., AND THE ACADEMY
OF SCIENCES OF THE GEORGIAN S.S.R.

TRANSLATED AND EDITED BY W. T. LIBERSON, M.D., Ph.D.

PROFESSOR OF PHARMACOLOGY AND CHIEF OF SECTION OF PHYSICAL MEDICINE
AND REHABILITATION, STRITCH SCHOOL OF MEDICINE, LOYOLA UNIVERSITY,
CHICAGO; CHIEF OF THE PHYSICAL MEDICINE AND REHABILITATION SERVICE,
VETERANS ADMINISTRATION HOSPITAL, HINES, ILLINOIS

Little, Brown and Company, Boston

Other Books by J. S. Beritoff

Studies on Basic Elements of the Central Coordination of the Skeletal Muscles. Petrograd, 1916.

Individually Acquired Activity of the Central Nervous System. Tiflis, 1932.

General Physiology of Muscular and Nervous Systems. Moscow-Leningrad, 1937.

On Basic Forms of Nervous and Psychonervous Activity. Moscow, 1947.

General Physiology of Muscular and Nervous Systems. Moscow: Vol. 1, 1947; Vol. 2, 1948.

General Physiology of Muscular and Nervous Systems, 3rd revised ed., Vol. 1. Moscow, 1959.

Nervous Mechanisms of Spatial Orientation of Mammals. Tiflis, 1959.

Studies on the Nature of Man in Ancient Georgia (IV-XIV centuries). Tiflis, 1961.

Published in Great Britain
by J. & A. Churchill Ltd., London
PRINTED IN THE UNITED STATES OF AMERICA

FOREWORD TO THE ENGLISH EDITION

The name of Professor Beritoff (Beritashvili in his native Georgian), the dean of Russian neurophysiologists, is known to physiologists the world over. He has been an inspiring participant of International Physiological Congresses and the leading scientist in his field in Russia for several decades. He is the author of one of the most comprehensive Russian textbooks on neurophysiology. However, his name may not be familiar to neurologists, psychiatrists and psychologists in this country, inasmuch as most of his publications have appeared only in Russia. For these readers, the following brief account of his scientific career may be helpful.

Born in 1885 in Vedgini, Georgia, U.S.S.R., he became a student of the internationally known Russian physiologist Wedensky at the University of St. Petersburg. He started his experimental work in 1909 and received additional postgraduate training under the direction of Samoiloff, who introduced Russian physiologists to the string galvanometer at the beginning of this century, and Magnus, the famous Dutch physiologist from Utrecht. After a short period of teaching at the University of Odessa, he was appointed (1919) Professor and Chairman of the Department of Physiology at the University of Tiflis. The Department later merged with the Physiological Institute of the Georgian Academy of Sciences, where Professor Beritoff continues to spend unbounded energy as author, teacher and researcher at the age of eighty.

Professor Beritoff is one of the rare neurophysiologists who has had the curiosity and determination to explore all facets of central nervous system activity. He is as familiar with the spinal cord mechanisms as he is with the highest behavioral functions and at each stage of his work has made important contributions to our knowledge in these different fields.

He started his scientific work with the study of reciprocal inhibition of spinal and postural reflexes (1911–1915). It was at this time that he disclosed the phenomena of widespread inhibition which is the subject of current studies by leading Western neurophysiologists. More recently (1936–1937), he conducted experiments and formu-

v

lated hypotheses which ascribed to neuropil in general and dendritic structures in particular a modulating function of the central nervous system. Processes of dendritic excitation are still very much in the foreground of neurophysiological research. Although remaining controversial, some of Beritoff's concepts, such as the anelectrotonic nature of inhibition which he conceived as the major dendritic function, have inspired many physiologists to make fruitful explorations.

Professor Beritoff did not limit himself to the investigation of the simple reflex action of the central nervous system. Following the example of his celebrated senior colleague I. P. Pavlov, he turned his inquiring mind to the physiological analysis of animal behavior. Obviously, the importance of Pavlov's discoveries inspired Beritoff to undertake his own experiments in this domain, although he preferred to use Bechterev's method of conditioned paw withdrawal instead of the Pavlovian technique of salivation. However, it soon became obvious to him that the Pavlovian concepts were not sufficient to explain many types of animal behavior. For example, a dog who sees a piece of meat thrown from the second floor laboratory window will run downstairs and find the meat. According to Beritoff, there must be something—some image-substitute, if not the food-image itself—that guides the animal on his way down toward the meat.

It furthermore is difficult to account for the following repeated observations within the narrow framework of classic conditioning theories: A single perception of a "vitally important" object may lead to conditioned image-driven behavior; conversely, each of us knows on the basis of his own subjective experiences that despite many repetitions of the perception of an object within a familiar environment, a mere view of the object alone does not produce in the mind a representation of the whole environment where this object is usually located. Repeated associations are therefore not sufficient for conditioning.

Thus, mental representation of the goal-object, banished from behavioral theories by the Pavlovian school of conditionists, somehow had to be reinstated in order to be subjected to experimental analysis. This led Beritoff to consider "image-driven" behavior as a behavior distinct from that of automatized conditioning.

It has been customary among Russian Pavlovians to consider conditioned reflexes as an expression of the "highest activities" of the central nervous system. Yet the observation of the formation of conditioned behavior shows that awareness of the artificiality of the experimental setup is sufficient to suppress the appearance of these reflexes in man. There are therefore higher levels of behavior, including the planned behavior discussed by Beritoff.

These important observations and many others led Beritoff and his associates to design and conduct multiple experiments starting in the early 1920's. Their experiments paralleled the research of Western investigators and considerably enlarged the scope of behavioral studies. Thus, they discovered that concussion may differentially affect various forms of conditioning. Similar results were obtained by the functional splitting of the brain in pigeons, a technique which anteceded those described more recently in this country. Their painstaking observations of the microcephalic girl Peta, the ingenious experiments of activating conditioned reflexes in man by diverting the attention of the subject from the conditional stimulus, their experimental control of "setting" influences—all this work revealed a wealth of new information largely unknown in this country.

More recently conducted experiments of Beritoff and his associates in ablating different parts of the brain seem to confirm the importance of a differentiation of various forms of conditioning. They showed that a cat without the neocortex is unable to form food-approach behavior after only one feeding (which is common in a normal cat). Yet in such cats other forms of conditioned behavior may be formed without the presence of the neocortex. In the light of his concepts, Beritoff analyzed the experiments of his colleagues in relation to the emotional components of conditioned behavior. While he remains in the mainstream of Pavlovian concepts and reaffirms the primary role of the cortex in the conditioning of normal behavior, Beritoff is ready to accept the notion that emotional components of such behavior may be conditioned with the participation of subcortical brain mechanisms integrated by the paleocortex.

Beritoff was led to formulate three different kinds of individually acquired conditioned behavior: automatized conditioning behavior, image-driven behavior and planned behavior. Contrary to the usual Pavlovian concepts of an increased complexity of behavior superstructured on the basis of automatic conditioned reflexes, Beritoff proposes the possibility, in certain cases, of an inverse development. Namely, he postulates a primary emergence of an image-driven behavior and its subsequent automation.

One of the major prerequisites of image-driven behavior is the ability of the animal to orient himself in space in order to find the goal-object. Consequently, most of the recent experimental work of Beritoff has been devoted to the analysis of the mechanisms of spatial orientation in man and animals. He analyzed the effects of passive transport of animals, blindfolded or not, before and after a variety of surgical procedures aimed at the destruction of the vestibular apparatus and of different brain structures, particularly ablations of discrete cortical areas. He also studied children and adults, including blind and deaf-mute individuals, as well as patients with affected labyrinths. From this comprehensive experimentation emerged a great deal of new knowledge concerning the activity of the "vestibular analyzer" in goal-directed spatial orientation in normal and blind individuals.

Beritoff has not limited his activities to the experimentation which led him to many discoveries and general behavioristic concepts. He welcomed the possibility of a more specific investigation of the "black box." He was in part responsible for the introduction in Russia of electrophysiological techniques for exploring processes of conditioning—research which placed Russian neurophysiologists in a leading position in this field. He also attempted to answer the following question: Which one of the different cortical structural elements is most probably the neurophysiological substrate of the highest form of behavior, image-driven behavior?

Obviously, no precise experimentation has so far been devised to answer this question with a comfortable degree of probability. However, Beritoff has boldly speculated (at least to stimulate further inquiries) that the stellate neurons of the neocortex, which have a rich pericellular network, are the most "eligible" candidates for the task of sustaining images of the perceived world. He uses arguments of an evolutionary, developmental and functional nature to support this speculation. Indeed, these cells seem to be the most capable of relatively independent self-stimulation, of maintaining a focus of excitation and of memorization. No mechanism has so far been found capable of inhibiting these cells, although their physiological tone may be modulated by the nonspecific structures of the brain stem. Beritoff focuses our attention on the fact that, while a conditioned reaction may be inhibited, the conscious perception of the conditioned stimulus persists unperturbed.

This hypothesis is only one of a series of speculative attempts of Beritoff presented in this monograph. One of his earliest suggestions (1920) refers to the formulation of "reverse connections" which he postulated to be present in the process of the establishment of conditioned reflexes. The experimental counterpart of this suggestion is the possibility that conditioned reflexes can be formed with a conditional stimulus succeeding rather than preceding the unconditional one. For Beritoff, this Pavlovian experiment confirmed the presence of "reverse connections" and was a starting point for speculations on the role of these connections in the process of internal inhibition. This hypothesis, together with the concept of reinforcement, preceded the cybernetic concept of "negative" and "positive" feedback which is now the most promising theoretical basis for understanding behavior.

Continuing his hypothesizing, Beritoff linked external inhibition to the widespread inhibition discovered by him at the beginning of his scientific career. He reports in this monograph related experiments involving the spinal cord and proposes a theory of a modulating action of the substantia gelatinosa, thus contributing to the present thinking concerning this structure. Unfortunately, at the time this book was written, the more recently acquired facts concerning presynaptic inhibition had not been disclosed; therefore, some of Beritoff's theorizing in relation to the initially known facts concerning this phenomenon may have to be revised or completed. However, in his attempts to integrate the knowledge acquired by experimentation at different levels of central nervous system activities, he produced a comprehensive hypothetical blueprint which can help future theorists to modify the scheme as our knowledge progresses.

In the meantime he reviewed a monumental number of experimental findings of Russian as well as Western and Japanese physiologists. Many of these findings may be new to the average reader of this book. It is regrettable that Beritoff's analysis of the American literature covers only recent neurophysiological research. Most of the previous work on learning by American experimental psychologists, which in so many ways is related to Beritoff's own disclosures, is not discussed in this monograph. Obviously, this literature had not been fully accessible to Russian readers; the time has come when this lack of mutual information needs to be corrected.

It is a matter of public record that during the dark days of Stalinism Professor Beritoff was submitted to the indignities of investigating committees for holding unorthodox views on the limitations of Pavlovian concepts in explaining some of the neural mechanisms of animal behavior. Despite this, Beritoff kept defending his views and published a great number of articles and books on the subject. At the present time he is a member of the U.S.S.R. Academy of Sciences, the Academy of Medicine, U.S.S.R. and the Georgian Academy of Sciences. In December, 1964, the Soviet government honored him with one of its highest awards. He is also an honorary member of the American Electroencephalographic Society and of the New York Academy of Sciences.

I have followed Professor Beritoff's work with great admiration for several decades. My own thinking was influenced by him as well as by such other Russian physiologists as A. Ouchtomsky and N. Bernstein. I acknowledged his influence in my early attempts at theorizing about "peripheral closure" and "peripheral confirmation," which ante-ceded both cybernetic speculations and Anokhin's more recent concept of "acceptors of action," discussed in this book.° It was therefore with great pleasure and a sense of responsibility that I accepted the request of Professor Beritoff seven years ago to translate and edit his book. My work on this project progressed rather slowly due to my other com-mitments, and Beritoff published his monograph in Russia two years ago in a slightly enlarged form. With his permission, I undertook the task of a complete rearrangement of the material in a form that I believe is more suitable for Western readers. For example, Russian readers are more acquainted with Beritoff's experiments and with those of other Russian conditionalists. The major emphasis of the Russian edition was on the new theoretical concepts; they were pre-sented starting with the very first chapter of the book.

I felt that in the English edition the factual material should be re-ported at the beginning, starting with studies in experimental psychol-ogy and continuing with an account of the more strictly physiological research. Theoretical concepts, which unavoidably are more open to controversy, occupy the concluding chapters of the English edition. Although this was authorized by Professor Beritoff, I must take the full responsibility for the rearrangement of the material.

All in all, this is a remarkable work covering the spinal, subcortical and cortical mechanisms of the central nervous system. Not only does this book provide the reader with firsthand information concerning the achievements of Russian behavioral sciences; it constitutes a unique testimony of the indefatigable lifework of one of the leading neurophysiologists of this century.

Chicago   W. T. LIBERSON

°1. Liberson, W. T.   Attitude mentale et rythme des mouvements volontaires. C.R. Soc. Biol. (Paris) *118:* 1047, 1935.
  2. Liberson, W. T.   Quelques points de vue physiologiques en psychiatrie. l'Un. Med. Canada *78:* 648–658, 1949.

PREFACE

This monograph summarizes all the findings and theoretical concepts that I and my associates have discovered and formulated during our half century of studies of the central nervous system (CNS). We have investigated the coordinating and integrating function of the CNS in simple as well as in more complex reflexes, in elementary inborn behavioral acts and in a higher level activity which, in our opinion, should be thought of as image-driven behavior. We have attempted to reveal the principles governing each of these types of CNS activity and to determine how much it is influenced by the environment and how much by the state of the organism itself and its needs and emotions.

We have analyzed the complex CNS phenomena in terms of the well-known principles of the elementary reflex action. When a phenomenon under our consideration could not be explained by these well-known mechanisms of the nervous system, we attempted to determine its qualitative characteristics and to spell out novel concepts capable of explaining the particular phenomenon. We did this for the first time when, after studying inborn reflexes of decerebrate and spinal animals, we turned to the study of individually acquired conditioned behavior in intact animals. Novel concepts were again required when we started to investigate animal behavior under conditions of free locomotion. In order to understand its underlying mechanisms, we had to note qualitative characteristics of such behavior and to define corresponding new principles governing it.

All elementary and complex reflexes and behavioral acts are accomplished with the participation of the entire CNS. However, the involvement of different parts of the system may be characteristic of each reflex or behavioral act. Our goal has been to determine the role played by different segments of the nervous system in a given behavioral act.

Functional specificity of each segment of the brain is closely dependent upon its structure. This is why we have attempted to correlate different functional characteristics with the structure of a given segment of the brain. Obviously, with the development of our knowledge of these brain structures and their interconnections, our understanding of the role of participating elements of each of the brain segments in the genesis of certain reflexes or behaviors became more precise.

Initially, our basic methodology in investigating the nervous system consisted of recording contractions of the antagonistic muscles, as was done by Sherrington, and of preparing electrograms of muscles and nerves with the help of a string galvanometer. During our study of conditioned reflexes, we used and further developed the technique of W. M. Bechterev. Later on we turned to the study of feeding and defensive behavior with free locomotion of animals in the laboratory. More recently we studied voluntary movements of the animals orienting themselves in the room with the help of object-images projected into space; during this investigation, we tried to elucidate the roles of different receptors and of different cortical and subcortical structures of the brain in the implementation of a given behavior. We used oscillographic techniques for a more penetrating analysis of the basic neural processes of excitation and inhibition during conditioned and unconditioned reflex activities.

In conclusion, we have also tried to relate our work to that of our many colleagues. However, to review all the facts and concepts formulated by many competent investigators in the field would have transgressed the limits of this monograph. From a great number of publications we therefore have selected only those which had to be discussed for the completeness of the presentation of our factual material and for its better understanding.

Tbilisi   J. S. Beritoff

CONTENTS

INTRODUCTION

The behavior of higher vertebrates is aimed at the satisfaction of their needs. It is directed by the cerebral cortex but is implemented with the participation of the entire central nervous system. Thus, a hungry animal continually moves around in order to find food. In this food-searching behavior, chemical characteristics of the blood of a hungry animal constitute the main factors activating the animal's movements. Under the influence of hunger, certain neural mechanisms of the interbrain and of the paleocortex are activated. These mechanisms are responsible for the feeling of hunger, for they produce a corresponding emotional state and they generate searching behavior. This behavior is usually goal-directed: the animal moves toward the usual feeding places.

Orienting movements toward feeding places imply the involvement of higher functions of the brain, i.e., the animal experiences a mental representation of food-images and then projects these images into the environment. This higher function is generated by the cerebral cortex, but other divisions of the brain participate also, since many parts of the brain play an important role in the accomplishment of higher functions. Not only does the animal project food images into the environment, but also its locomotion is directed toward them. The oriented locomotion is acquired through individual experience and implies participation of the neocortex and paleocortex as well as other divisions of the brain and spinal cord.

Any behavioral act is generated through activation of a certain functional interconnected system of neural structures of the brain and spinal cord, resulting in the satisfaction of a specific organic need. One such system leads to the satisfaction of alimentary needs, i.e., it is responsible for feeding behavior. Another system is responsible for the protection of the organism from injurious stimuli; it generates defensive behavior. A third system satisfies the needs of reproduction and governs sexual and parental behavior.

In addition to these basic functional systems, there are other systems as well, including those responsible for the satisfaction of the need for physical development (play), for the satisfaction of the need for restoration of function (resting posture), and for the satisfaction of the need to avoid aimless loss of energy.

As each of these systems is activated, the others are actively suppressed. This is why, during a certain behavioral act, the generation of another act is made more difficult. This active suppression of some neural mechanisms during the activation of others takes place in the entire central nervous system, from the cerebral cortex down to and including the spinal cord. This is how the integrated function of the central nervous system is expressed in each behavioral act.

It is not our intention to submit each and every one of these systems to a systematic analysis in this monograph. Our goal is to show functional and structural characteristics of several systems in order to reveal neural and psychoneural laws governing these systems and their interaction. We shall consider primarily the functional system responsible for the satisfaction of the alimentary needs and its interaction with other systems.

J. S. BERITOFF

PART 1 CHARACTERISTICS AND ORIGIN OF HIGHEST FORMS OF BEHAVIOR

1 DIFFERENT TYPES OF BEHAVIOR: INBORN, CONDITIONED AND IMAGE-DRIVEN

The behavior of higher vertebrates reveals their adaptation to the outside world or their actions to modify the environment in order to make it more suitable to their needs. A pattern of behavior may be inborn and therefore instinctive, or it may be individually acquired.

Instinctive and Individually Acquired Behavior

Instinctive behavior depends upon the inborn organization of the central nervous system. Each behavioral act of this type consists of a chain of neural processes, each of these processes being generated by those which precede it. It is elicited through interoceptors and exteroceptors, sometimes by biochemical substances resulting from the antecedent activity in the central nervous system. The direction of the whole pattern, the transition from one segment of the behavioral chain to the next one, is predetermined by a corresponding organic need. Such acts may be simple, for instance, the behavior of the newborn foal sucking maternal nipples, the act of pecking at all kinds of small objects by a newly hatched chick, the search for food by a hungry animal, or more complex, for instance, the behavior of birds in building a nest, laying eggs, and getting food for the nestlings.

While the initial accomplishment of these behavioral acts in the higher vertebrate is entirely instinctive, this behavior becomes modified with repetition. Thus, the chicken pecks only grain and no longer is interested in mere spots or inedible objects. The bird chooses for its future nest a concealed spot where food is abundant. It selects better building material, avoids dangerous places or certain animals, etc. These new behavioral manifestations may consist of reactions to newly acquired specific images of the vitally important objects and their spatial relationships in the environment. With further repetition of the same behavioral act, these segments of the chain of behavioral events become conditioned; namely, certain objects representing food become conditional signals for preferential flight of birds toward them, while some places, particularly those indicating the presence of men or dangerous animals, become conditional signals for avoidance and escape.

Image-Driven Individually Acquired Behavior

It is important to recognize a type of behavior of the higher vertebrates which is developed entirely from individual experience and depends upon the activity of the central nervous system functionally reorganized in the process of biological adaptation. This behavior is also composed of many successive phases, each of which is accomplished by means of conditioned and unconditioned mechanisms. But the most important characteristic of behavioral acts of this type is that segments of this behavior may be generated as a result of the neural processes which are responsible for evoking images of goal objects. Following reproduction of an image of some object and its location spatially projected to a certain environmental area, e.g., food in the case of food-getting behavior, one observes an orienting movement of an animal's head toward this area just as if food were actually seen. Then, the animal approaches this object along the shortest possible route avoiding all obstacles that may be in his way. However, if the image of a vitally dangerous object is reproduced, the animal avoids places where such objects have been present. Such reaction develops on the basis of inborn self-defense behavior.

Biologic Mechanisms of Image-Driven Behavior

The following physiologic activities of the central nervous system are presumed to occur during food-getting behavior. When the animal is hungry, there is an increasing excitability of cortical and subcortical centers corresponding to digestion, and of the centers which coordinate locomotion, searching movements, and the alimentary act. When food is sensed, certain activated complexes of cortical neurons are responsible for the formation of an image of food, and of its projection into space, while others are responsible for orienting the head movement toward food with a simultaneous activation of alimentary centers. Due to the activation of these centers, certain locomotive mechanisms also become involved and the animal's movement toward food is coordinated with the orientation of his head. Then the olfactory centers, those generating searching movements, the center of salivation, and other centers integrated in the feeding act and digestive functions are also activated.

If food is not actually present, the hungry animal turns his head toward the place where food has been found previously, and then moves in that direction. In this case, the initial food-getting behavior is presumed to occur as follows:

Under the influence of some components of the environment, the food image is elicited and projected to a definite location in space. No matter where the animal is located, since the excitability of the corresponding motor mechanisms in the hungry animal is high, he will turn his head toward the projected location of food and will move in that direction as if he perceived food directly.

If on the way toward food the animal encounters an obstacle, he will avoid it by going around it or jumping over it and yet reach the food, precisely localizing it in the space. This overcoming of obstacles will be done by the animal on the basis of his previous experience. Thus, for instance, an adult dog may try to open a door by pressing it with its muzzle or paws, while a puppy is unable to do so. Opening a door by simple procedures has been learned by dogs and cats (Beritoff, Beburishvili, and Tsereteli, 1934). After overcoming an obstacle, the animal again turns his head toward the imagined location of food, goes to the exact spot, sniffs around, and salivates even if there is no trace of food (Beritoff and Kalabegashvili, 1944). All this shows that the orientation and locomotion of the animal are determined not only by the immediate perception of the environment, but by a conjoint influence of the environment and of the images of the presumed location of food. The reproduced image of food, projected to a particular place may continually direct the animal toward this spot just as if he actually saw the food there.

We believe that the central nervous system activity which is responsible for behavioral acts of this type, i.e., image-driven behavior, is qualitatively different from the activity involved in behavioral acts of the instinctive type. In both cases, components of the behavioral act are carried out according to the principles of reflex action. In both cases behavioral acts are determined by internal and external influences. But there is an important difference between them, namely, that the second type of behavior requires a kind of neural activity which allows for the emergence of an image in order to direct the animal's behavior. This neural activity, although based on the principles involved in conditioning, is not entirely subject to its laws. Specific principles governing image-driven activity may be revealed when this type of behavior is investigated directly. These laws are related basically to the formation and reproduction of images of the outside world and their role in the integration of behavioral acts. All the qualitative peculiarities of such behavioral acts are determined by these images, more exactly, by the cortical neural systems responsible for the formation of these images. This is why the specific laws of image formation and image reproduction may be called psychoneural laws in contradistinction to the purely neurologic principles involved in automatized conditioned behavior to be considered in Chapter 2.

CHARACTERISTICS OF PSYCHONEURAL ACTIVITY IN IMAGE-DRIVEN BEHAVIOR

We call the neural processes which sustain image-driven behavior "psychoneural processes" and the behavior, itself, "psychoneural behavior." The whole complex of neural processes which are involved in producing the mental image is called "psychoneural complex."

Our investigations revealed the following principles governing psychoneural behavior of dogs (1934 and 1937).

1. Psychoneural activity is able to integrate elements of a certain environment into a whole, lived-through experience, generating an integrated image or mental representation. For this the animal need be subjected to a situation only once.

2. The psychoneural complex may be very easily reproduced under the influence of only one component of the corresponding environment or a stimulus closely related to this environment. Furthermore, a reproduction of this image is even possible as a result of spontaneous activation of receptive areas of the brain or of the brainstem centers, that is, without any discernable activation of exteroceptors.

3. Dynamic nature and plasticity is characteristic of a psychoneural complex which may change continually under the influence of a variety of external and internal events.

4. The psychoneural complex of a given image can be reproduced several days, a week, or even months after its original generation.

5. Eliciting the reproduction of the image of the vitally important objects will immediately activate the whole organism; images have an extremely potent driving strength.

6. There is a great facility for establishing temporary connections between the psychoneural complexes of the mental image and the motor centers of the cortex and the subcortex. This is why the individually acquired reactions are easily automatized.

7. The driving strength of the reproduced image depends upon the time elapsed since its generation. The more recent its formation, the more pronounced is the strength.

8. The driving strength of the reproduced image depends upon the importance of the significant elements of this image in the animal's life. Thus, for a dog the psychoneural processes responsible for an image of meat and its projection into space will have more activating strength than those representing bread, etc.

9. The driving strength of the mental image depends upon the distance separating the animal from the projected goal object.

10. The psychoneural activity in the dog's behavior dominates the other types of behavior. It takes precedence over the automatized individual behavior (see below) and inborn reflex behavior, suppressing them each time when they cease to serve the needs of the organism.

Some of these characteristics permit one to differentiate the "image-driven" psychoneural behavior from another type of individually acquired behavior to be considered in Chapter 3.

We believe that the neural matrix sustaining the generation of mental images is located in the cerebral cortex and that it is probably represented by the complexes of stellate cells with short axons found in the fourth and third layers of the primary receptive areas of a larger cortical, specific receptive field which Pavlov called "analyzer." These cells, which are the most recently acquired elements of the brain of higher vertebrates, seem to be the most appropriate candidates for this function, as will be discussed in detail in Part III. The level of their excitability is determined also through the bombardment by impulses elicited by the nonspecific activating reticular formation.

In order to generate a specific image of an object, a certain group of stellate cells of one or several activated analyzers is integrated in a functional system through the complex loops made of association neurons and internuncials. The cells of these neurons are located predominantly in the association areas, between the specific analyzers, and also at the periphery of the analyzers themselves, outside their primary receptive area in the middle layers of the cerebral cortex.

As we will see, image-driven behavior may become automatized, carried out according to the principles of a chain conditioned reflex. The formation of both an object image and a conditioned reflex is based upon the establishment of the temporary connections. We believe that during the perception of the outside world, temporary connections among the receptive stellate cells, as they are excited simultaneously or consecutively, are formed at once. This is what leads to the creation in the neocortex of the images of the environment capable of being reproduced during the remaining life span.

On the other hand, temporary connections between the stellate cells of the neocortex and the large pyramidal effector cells are established only after several associations. We believe that this is the neuronal mechanism of the formation of the conditioned reflexes. Thus, functionally and structurally, the formation of images and the establishment of conditioned reflexes seem to constitute distinct processes. Temporary connections originating from the analyzers receiving the stimuli, generating the initially conditioned behavior and running toward other analyzers will be called "forward connections." These connections are formed mainly with the effector pyramids of the motor area. The connections established in the reverse direction will be called "reverse connections." Mechanisms involved in this system, permitting the integration of the behavior as a whole, taking into consideration the extreme complexity of external and internal stimuli and of the whole environmental set," will be analyzed experimentally and theoretically all through this book. In the following chapters we will discuss these problems as they were observed in our laboratories.

2 CONDITIONED REFLEXES

Formation of Defensive Conditioned Reflexes

First let us summarize some of the factual material in order to illustrate the formation of the conditioned reflexes. We studied the defensive conditioned reflexes using the apparatus schematically represented in Figure 1. We elicited defensive conditioned reflexes consisting of a flexion of one or several extremities. For this purpose, indifferent stimuli were paired with the reflex flexion of the leg elicited by the electrical stimulation.

The defensive conditioned reflex to any of these indifferent stimuli is formed in dogs during the very first day of training after only a few trials. Thus, for instance, in one experiment where there was a pairing of the musical tone of 200 c./sec. with an electrical stimulus to the foreleg followed by a defensive flexion of the leg, this tone alone elicited after only a few trials a head movement, a yelp and the leg withdrawal. Figure 2 shows the record obtained at the tenth and eleventh associations of stimuli. The tone of 200 c./sec. (experiments *1* and *5*) elicited a very strong movement of the leg as well as an orienting turning of the head. The same effect was at first obtained by a tone of 500 c./sec. (experiments *2* and *3*); it also occurred spontaneously (experiment *4*); it could not, however, be elicited by an extraneous tone of 512 c./sec. produced by another instrument.

However, after several days the dog would not show any spontaneous movement of the leg in the experimental room (Figure 3), and would not react even to the tones of 215 c./sec. (experiment *1*) showing reflexes only to the conditional tone of 200 c./sec. (experiment *2*). An unusual tone of 300 c./sec. was ineffective.

During the establishment of the conditioned defensive reflex, the method usually applied is to stimulate the leg not only when the animal fails to withdraw his leg, but also after withdrawal. Therefore, a proprioceptive stimulation of the reacting leg is also associated with the unconditional stimulus. For this reason the proprioceptive stimuli became conditional signals to the leg withdrawal. This explains why

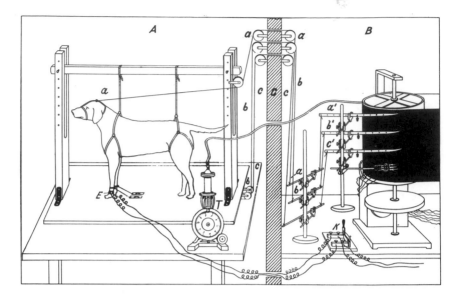

Fig. 1

Schematic representation of the experimental set-up for studies of conditioned motor reflexes. The dog in room A is placed on a table and attached to a stand by straps. Its head, as well as its left and right forelegs are connected by strings (*aaa, bbb, ccc,*) passing over pulleys to the myographic stylets (*a', b', c'*). The kymograph and experimenter are in room B. The tone variator, *T*, is connected through rubber tubing to a pump located in the other room. A switch, *K*, from a secondary coil of a faradic stimulator is connected with electrodes, *E*, for stimulation of the paw. (Beritoff, 1922b.)

in Figure 3 after raising the leg in response to the conditional signal, the animal keeps the leg suspended for the duration of the signal and even for a certain time afterward.

In certain cases when the leg lifting is elicited several times after the onset of a conditional signal, a rhythmic conditioned reflex is established following repeated electrical stimulation. In such cases, the leg would show a rhythmic flexion at a conditional signal (Figure 4). We must assume that such a reflex, started under the influence of the external conditional signal, acquires its rhythmic characteristics because of the proprioceptive stimuli. It seems that the proprioceptive stimuli, set up as the leg is being lowered, become the conditional stimuli for the repeated leg raising.

During the process of establishment of a conditioned defensive reflex, one must keep in mind the fact that a systematic application of

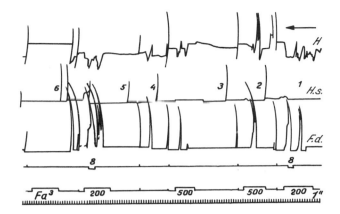

Fig. 2

Dog "Bob." Conditioned defensive reflex of right foreleg to tone of 200 c./sec. Movements of the head, *H*, the left hindleg, *H.s.*, and the right foreleg, *F.d.*, are recorded. Upper signal, electric stimulation. FA^3, an extraneous tone of 512 c./sec. (Beritoff, 1927.)

painful electrical stimuli to the leg during the conditioned withdrawal does not lead to the further reinforcement of the conditioned reflex, but rather to its weakening or even its disappearance (Bregadze, 1953). One should apply the stimulation after the conditioned movement ends, or when the movement is not produced. This was what we did in our experiments. However, one may also arrange the experimental design in such a way that after the onset of the conditional signal, the leg is stimulated only when it still supports the body, so that the stimulation is suspended with the lifting of the leg. In this case, the conditioned withdrawal of the leg becomes very stable and is maintained during several seconds while the animal perceives the conditional signal (Bregadze, 1953).

FORMATION OF TEMPORARY CONNECTIONS

Let us now consider the formation of temporary connections. When any indifferent stimulus, e.g., the ringing of a bell, coincides in time with an unconditioned inborn reflex, e.g., the defensive movement of the leg elicited by electrical stimulation of the skin, several cortical neuronal complexes enter into mutual interaction. These are the elements belonging to the somesthetic and motor analyzers. The motor

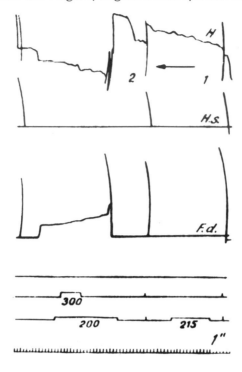

Fig. 3

The same dog as in Figure 2, but at the stage of complete differentiation of the conditioned reflex in which only the 200 c./sec. tone was effective. Symbols same as in Figure 2. (Beritoff, 1927.)

analyzer is activated through the somesthetic analyzer, as well as directly by leg movements. Each activated complex of neurons generates a process of excitation, spreading over the cortex and affecting almost all other neuronal complexes, whose excitability is increased under the influence of relevant stimuli, and which otherwise would remain in the subliminal fringe. Under the influence of this spread of excitation over the cortex, other additional foci of heightened excitability are formed. There is increased activity in groups of neurons located in the association field found between the above-named analyzers. Temporary connections are formed among all the neuronal complexes with increased excitability. Furthermore, as we stated as early as 1920, there is generally a formation not only of forward directed connections, but also of the reverse ones. For instance, in addition to forward connections running from the neuronal complexes of the acoustic analyzer, in the case of auditory conditional stimulation, to the neuronal complexes of the

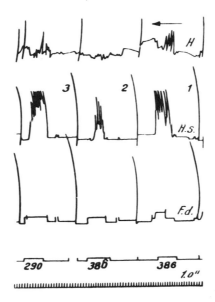

Fig. 4

Dog "Belka." Rhythmic reflex in response to a conditional tone of 290 c./sec. Fifth day of study. In experiments *1* and *2* the reflex is elicited by an unusual tone of 386 c./sec. In experiment *3* it occurs in response to the usual tone. Symbols the same as in Figure 2. (Beritoff, 1927.)

somesthetic and motor analyzers, there are also reverse connections from the latter to the neuronal complexes responding to the conditional auditory stimulation. In this way, neural circuits or loops of the forward and reverse temporary connections are formed (Beritoff, 1920 to 1922).

The temporary connections among the contiguous activated areas of the same analyzer must be made mostly with the participation of the internuncial neurons remaining within the limits of the cortex. The temporary connections among different analyzers and in general between distant areas of the cortex of one hemisphere may be formed with the participation of the association neurons with fibers running through the subcortical white matter. This may explain the observation of Asratyan (1937), that after a section made deeply in the cortex but without serious injury to the underlying white matter, classical conditioned foot-getting and defensive reflexes formed before the operation reappeared very soon after the operation; after 21 days all the reflexes were restored. Asratyan found in this way that isolated, but not undercut, cortical areas mutually interacted as far as both inhibiting and facilitating processes were concerned. However, after the operation, the conditioned reflexes were of lesser intensity and stability than those found in normal animals. Apparently the integrative functions were diminished. These results, of course, show that the temporary connections between the analyzers are also established through the intermediary neurons in the cortical layers themselves, as well as through the association neurons with fibers running through the subcortical white matter.

It is quite possible that during the first trial of pairing the conditional stimuli with the unconditional electrical stimulation of the leg, i.e., during the period of generalization of the defensive conditioned reflex, temporary connections are established with the motor analyzer through the somesthetic analyzer by means of the internuncial neurons in the gray matter.

Since at the very first association of stimuli the integration of the stellate cells, located in the receptive layers of the cortex and receiving the conditional and unconditional stimuli, as well as all the other environmental information, takes place through internuncial pyramidal neurons, one may assume that the primary behavior elicited in response to the conditional stimulation (orienting of the animal, head turning, increased motor activity, yelping, general motor reaction of escape) is the result of an activation of these neurons. In other words, as will be suggested and discussed later, the activation of the whole integrated system of stellate cells is probably effected through these internuncial neurons. This predetermines the reproduction of the integrated image of the paired stimuli, as well as the activation of those extrapyramidal pathways which transmit the excitation to the subcortical centers for the orienting response, yelping and increased respiration; the general motor reaction of escape follows from this occurrence.

Later in the conditioning process, when a conditioned reflex is expressed only by a slight orienting reaction and is limited to a lifting of the leg, one may assume that this occurs as a result of the participation of connections through the association neurons with fibers running in the white matter of the subcortex from the analyzer of the conditional stimulation directly to the motor analyzer without the participation of the somesthetic analyzer. After the formation of the elementary direct connections, the conditional stimulus may activate both types of neuronal connections. The specific movement of the leg may then be accompanied by yelping, increased respiration and even violent escape reaction (Beritoff, 1927).

The fact that, in general, excitation spreads over the cortex through the internuncial neurons may very well be shown by oscillographic investigations. When there is local stimulation of the cortex, as shown by Burns and Grafstein (1952), a disturbance of electrical activity spreads along the entire slab of undercut cortex that has been isolated from the white matter without injury to the circulation. After sectioning this isolated cortical slab through its entire thickness, these potentials are no longer transmitted.

Formation of Reverse Temporary Connections

In the formation of a conditioned reflex, the forward and reverse temporary connections develop simultaneously. However, the rapidity and degree of their development may not be the same. Such difference would be a function of the strength and duration of the paired stimuli, the degree of excitability of the neurons receiving given stimuli, the frequency of stimuli and the character of various extraneous stimuli. In view of all these various conditions, some temporary connections develop earlier than others.

First we may consider the physiologic effects of the intensity and duration of the unconditional stimulus on the rapidity and degree of development of forward connections. It is known, for example, that the weaker the alimentary unconditional stimulus is, the slower the formation of the corresponding conditioned salivary reflex.

It is also known that with the same unconditional stimulation, each new conditioned reflex established to a new signal is developed earlier and becomes stable more rapidly than conditioned reflexes established for the first time in a given animal. This must be because the formation of the first conditioned reflex heightens the excitability of neuronal complexes of the cortex, activated by the unconditional stimulus to such a degree that the formation of the new conditioned reflexes is significantly quickened. Thus, for instance, after the formation of a defensive conditioned reflex using one leg, a threshold stimulation of the other leg will elicit withdrawal of the leg with which the reflex was originally formed (Figure 5).

Similarly, it is known that the formation of a conditioned reflex depends also upon the strength and physiologic effects of the conditional stimulus. For example, the reflex formed to a bell will be developed quicker than the one to light. This is probably because of the more intense excitatory effects elicited by the bell on cortical elements,

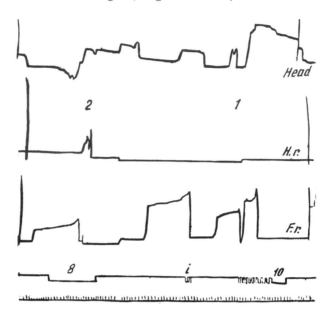

Fig. 5

Reflex flexion of the right foreleg, *F.r.*, in response to electrical stimulation of right hindleg, *H.r.* Stimulation of the hindleg and time in seconds are shown in bottom two traces. The reflex had been formed on the right foreleg. In the first experiment, stimulation of the hindleg was slight, 10 cm. distance between the coils of the inductorium; it elicited a lifting of the foreleg which was originally conditioned as a response to a ringing of a bell. In experiment 2, more intense stimulation (8 cm.) elicited, at first, a flexion of the hindleg and then the lifting of the foreleg. (Beritoff, 1924c).

than those elicited by the light emitted by an ordinary electric bulb (25 watts).

The rapidity and degree of the development of reverse connections is determined first of all by the duration and intensity of the conditional stimulus. For example, the reverse connections are better developed by prolonged rather than brief ringing of a bell. In other words, a conditional stimulus of relatively greater intensity or duration creates greater and longer lasting excitability changes in the corresponding analyzer. Furthermore, a stronger conditional stimulus interacts more rapidly with the effects of the unconditional stimulus. A stronger conditional stimulus will result in more stable forward and reverse connections. However, either the former or the latter connections may be more strongly developed, and therefore, be more functional. We came to the conclusion that when the conditioned reflex is extinguished in the absence of the unconditional stimulation, this means that the reverse connections are more strongly developed and, therefore, they function better than the forward connections.

It is not difficult to determine the presence of forward or reverse connections in a given reflex. It is particularly obvious when an unconditional stimulus is, itself, used as a conditional one, for instance when eating of sugar powder is paired with electrical stimulation of the leg. As is known, from experiments of this type carried out by the Pavlovian school, electrical stimulation begins to elicit alimentary reactions, while the sugar begins to produce defensive reactions (Savich, 1913).

Recently, in our Institute of Physiology, special investigations were conducted in order to study reverse temporary connections. Djavrishvili (1956), using a dog, paired a forced passive flexion of the leg with eating food in one series of experiments; while in another series, the food was given only during an active flexion initiated by the animal itself. The raising of the leg preceded the feeding. After a series of such associations, the passive flexion itself could elicit an alimentary reaction, namely, salivation; there were also associated changes of respiration. This was a manifestation of the forward connections. The passive lifting of the leg after some time was followed by its active raising; after feeding, the dog would raise the leg, which was passively lifted prior to feeding; it raised the conditioned leg when the empty foodbox was shown. In the last two cases, the raising of the conditioned leg was evidence of the functioning of reverse temporary connections.

In Figure 6, experiment *A*, lifting of the right foreleg previously was not associated with feeding; the alimentary reaction was not present and the leg was lowered immediately after the end of the passive lifting. In experiment *B*, on the twentieth association of passive lifting of the left leg with feeding, alimentary reaction occurred, characterized by movements of the mouth, exaggerated respiration and slight salivary secretion; at the same time, the flexed leg remained lifted for a long time.

After the formation of the alimentary reflex to the passive raising of the leg, a previously conditioned auditory signal was given. At this signal the dog reacted, not only with an ordinary response but also by actively raising the passively lifted leg (Figure 7). It follows that the reverse temporary connections become so active that during the functioning of the forward connections involved in the alimentary reaction, the reverse connections also become activated leading to the raising of the paw.

We believe that in the case of the conditional proprioceptive stimu-

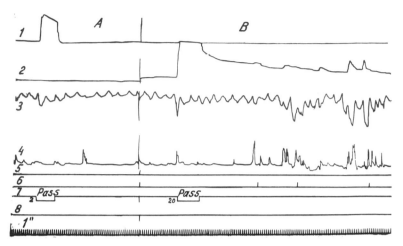

Fig. 6

Conditioned alimentary reaction to a passive lifting of the left foreleg at the earliest developmental stages of conditioning. *1,* Movement of right foreleg; *2,* movement of left foreleg; *3,* respiratory movements of chest; *4,* Mouth movements; *5,* salivation from right parotid gland; *6,* salivation from left parotid gland; *7,* signal of conditional stimulus; *8,* signal of unconditional stimulus; bottom trace, time in seconds. (Djavrishvili, 1956.) (See text for details of experiments.)

lation resulting from a passive raising of the leg, the leg is actively raised because impulses, sent through the reverse connections into the motor analyzer, increase there the excitatory state of neuronal complexes to such a degree that the descending pyramidal pathways of the corresponding leg are activated. In other words, it is as if the motor analyzer was as activated by the reverse connections as it would be by stimulating the proprioceptors of the raised leg during a noxious stimulation.

Furthermore, Djavrishvili paired tactile stimulation of the thigh with a subsequent painful electrical stimulation of a tooth (Figure 8). After a series of associations, the tactile stimulation elicited a head-turning reaction to the side where this stimulation was applied. At the same time, the dog would raise the stimulated leg. This must have been achieved through reverse connections. Figure 8 shows the recording of the third and fourteenth trials of the experiments in which a tactile stimulation of the thigh was associated with electrical stimulation of a tooth.

The tactile stimulation of the left thigh produced mouth movements through the forward connections and at the same time the leg move-

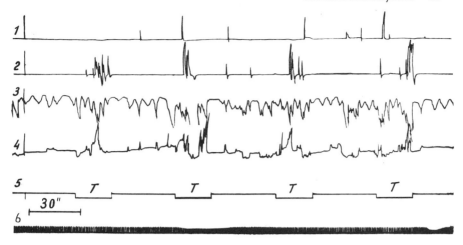

Fig. 7

Conditioned alimentary reaction and lifting of the conditioned leg concomitant with a trial of an old alimentary auditory signal. *1*, Movements of right foreleg; *2*, movements of left foreleg; *3*, respiratory movements of chest; *4*, mouth movements; *5*, signal for conditional stimulus (tone); *6*, time in seconds. The tone was repeated four times; each time it elicited increased respiration, mouth movements and lifting of left foreleg. (Djavrishvili, 1956.)

ment occurred at the rhythm of the applied tactile stimulation due to the reverse connections.

It appears from these facts, that during the association of two stimuli, one of which would elicit alimentary or defensive reactions, the cortical temporary connections are formed in both directions, the forward ones from the analyzers of the conditional stimulation to those of the unconditional one; and the reverse connections from the unconditional analyzer to the conditional one.

Finally, Djavrishvili associated a light, emitted by an electric bulb, and the sound of a bell, each of which separately elicited an orienting reaction in a dog. The electric bulb was located on the right side at the level of the head, while the bell was on the left side. At first the light was turned on for 5 seconds and immediately afterward the bell was activated, also for 5 seconds. Initially, the dog would turn the head to the right in response to the light, and to the left, in response to the bell. In one dog these orienting reactions disappeared with the repetition of the stimuli. In another dog, before the disappearance of these reactions, the following behavior was observed: following the optic stimulus, the dog would turn its head toward the bell and then toward the light. After 10 to 20 such associations, only the light was

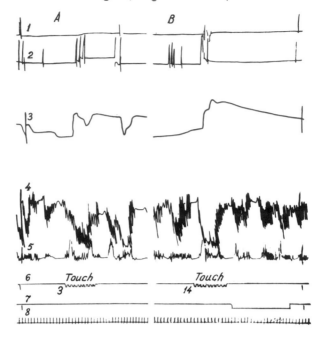

Fig. 8

Formation of a conditioned reaction to skin stimuli in a dog (in a conditional cabin). *1*, Right foreleg; *2*, right hindleg; *3*, movement of head in the horizontal plane (upward deflections correspond to movements to the left side, and downward deflections to movements to the right); *4*, respiratory movements; *5*, mouth movements; *6*, signal for the conditional stimulus; *7*, signal for the unconditional electrical stimulus applied to a tooth; *8*, time in seconds. Experiment *A:* Trial of skin stimulation after the third association with painful stimulation of a tooth. Experiment *B:* Fourteenth association of the skin stimulation with painful stimulation of a tooth. In both cases, skin stimulation applied to the left side would make the dog turn its head to the left, *3*, and lift its left hindleg, *2*; lifting of the leg was accomplished (experiment *A*) to the rhythm of the skin stimuli. (Djavrishvili, 1956.)

associated with feeding. Following the formation of a salivary conditioned reflex to the light after 40 consecutive reinforcements, the sounding of the bell elicited salivation. This showed that during the pairing of light and sound, reverse connections were formed between the corresponding neural structures.

Another of our associates, Bregadze (1956), specifically studied the possibility of the formation of connections during the association of two indifferent stimuli, when the orienting reaction was extinguished prior to the experiment. For example, a sound lasting 5 seconds was produced and then immediately another kind of auditory stimulus was emitted or, in lieu of this, a tactile stimulation was used, also for 5 seconds. After a repetition of 25 to 30 associations, Bregadze reinforced the first stimulus either by food (thus forming a conditioned alimentary reflex) or by electric stimulation of the leg (formation of a conditioned defensive reflex). After this, the previously paired second stimulus, another sound or the skin stimulation also produced a conditioned reflex. This indicated that reverse connections were formed between these two stimuli. Extraneous sounds and other extraneous stimuli did not reproduce the conditioned reflex in these experiments. Thus, it was shown that when two originally indifferent stimuli were merely associated, i.e., without the presence of any unconditional stimulus or reinforcement, connections were formed in the cortex in both directions, forward and reverse.

The formation of so-called reverse associations was proved in experimental psychology by a great number of experiments (Ebbinghaus and his associates, 1911). If, for instance, one learns a series of nonsense syllables in a certain order, the learning of the same syllables in the reverse order will require approximately one-third the time, 24 hours after the original learning. The reverse connections are found not only between the consecutive members of the series of learned syllables, but also between those that do not follow one another immediately. Characteristically, the reverse connections between the "neighboring" members are much more stable than the direct connections between noncontiguous members of the series.

Thus, one may assert that during each association of two stimuli, whether or not they elicit orienting reactions, temporary connections are formed in the cortex over which interactions may occur in either direction, forward or reverse. Figure 9a shows a schematic representation of neural connections in the case of a conditioned defensive reflex to an auditory stimulus.

The Pavlovian school, over a long period of time, recognized only the formation of forward connections, running from the focus of the weaker conditional stimulus to the one of the stronger unconditional stimulus, as if the latter had an ability to attract impulses from the weaker focus. However, in the last years of his life, Pavlov did recognize the formation of reverse temporary connections in addition to the forward ones.

Pavlov conceived of the formation of the neuronal connections in both directions between different cortical centers in the following way:

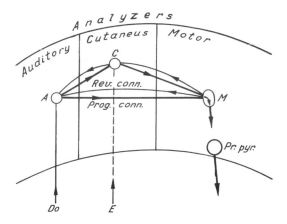

Fig. 9a

Schematic representation of a motor defense conditioned reflex of the right foreleg to an auditory stimulus, *Do*. On this figure are represented a complex temporary connection from the auditory to the motor analyzer via the cutaneous, and a short connection shortcutting the skin analyzer. *A*, Complex of stellate cells perceiving the auditory stimulus; *C*, complex of stellate cells perceiving noxious effects, *E*, on stimulation of the right foreleg; *M*, complex of stellate cells perceiving proprioceptive impulses resulting from movement of the stimulated leg. All these neuronal complexes are joined by dual connections, forward, *Prog. conn.*, and reverse, *Rev. conn.*, the latter being less developed than the former. The connection between *M* and the projection pyramidal neurons, *Pr. pyr.*, eliciting movement of the foreleg is innate, but may be more or less developed by training during the entire postembryonal life span.

When two neuronal foci are connected and become united, the nervous impulses run between them in both directions. If one considers, as an absolute rule, a unidirectional conduction of neuronal events in all the structures of the central nervous system, then one should assume additional connections in a reverse direction between such structures. In other words, one has to assume the presence of additional neurons interconnecting the foci in order to explain the observed facts.

He illustrates this by the following observations:

When after the raising of its leg, the animal is fed, the stimulation undoubtedly spreads from the kinesthetic center to the alimentary center. When this connection is formed in a dog, an alimentary stimulation itself will make the animal raise its leg; therefore, it is obvious that a stimulus spreads in the opposite direction. I cannot understand the foregoing fact in any other way. (Pavlov, 1949d.)

From this quotation, it is obvious that Pavlov recognized the actual possibility of the occurrence of two independent connections between active cortical foci and that he considered the whole nature of the conditioned reaction to be a result of the activities of the forward and reverse directives.

At one time the Pavlovian school held the opinion that in order to form a conditioned reflex it was necessary that the conditional stimulus precede the unconditional one. When the pairing was done in the reverse order, such as when the conditional stimulus is elicited during or soon after the unconditional one, they claimed that then the conditioned reflex is not formed. In other words, in spite of the fact that the unconditional stimulation gives rise in the cortex to a strong focus of excitation, the latter does not result in the formation of the temporary connections with the following indifferent stimulus. This opinion was held in the Pavlovian school as a consequence of a study of Krestovnikov (1913). However, after investigating the defensive reflexes we came to the conclusion that they may also be formed with the reverse order of associations. We formed conditioned reflexes in this way in dogs and pigeons (Beritoff, 1922-1926, Bajandurov, 1926) as well as in humans (Schnirmann, 1925). However, the formation of a reflex in this way requires a great number of associations and the reflex is not as stable and not as intense as when the usual order of associations is given. Also, the conditioned reflex is not always formed with the reversed order of association. To achieve this, it is necessary that the unconditional stimulation be relatively weak and that the conditional stimulus be presented only after the unconditional stimulation has ceased.

In the Pavlovian laboratories the alimentary conditioned reflex was formed in the reverse order of association by Pimenoff in 1907. However, for a long time following the study of Krestovnikov (1913) the results obtained by Pimenoff were not taken into account. Only after the experiments of Kreps (1933) and Pavlova (1933) was there recognition of the possibility of forming the conditioned reflexes with the reverse order of association.

But if temporary connections may be formed in any conditioned reflex in both directions, how can one explain the difficulty in the formation of the conditioned reflex when the reverse order of association is used, i.e., when the reverse connections are established from the focus of the conditional stimulus to the focus of the preceding unconditional one?

As we indicated above, the most favorable condition for formation of temporary reverse connections is realized when the unconditional stimulus is relatively weak, and the conditional stimulus is presented only after it has ended. These observations indicate that under such conditions a strong unconditional stimulus hampers the formation of the temporary connections. We believe that this phenomenon may be explained by the presence of a general inhibition elicited in the nervous system by a strong unconditional stimulus which blocks the transmission of impulses in the cortex arising from the conditional stimulus. However, we shall discuss this later on in more detail.

Formation of a Conditioned Reflex to a Complex of Stimuli

At each particular moment the influence of external and internal stimuli upon the "analyzers" of the cerebral cortex is very complex functionally and structurally. One may ask then how the integration of cortical activity can be implemented in response to complex influences of the outside world. We believe that each component of the external environment at first activates in a corresponding analyzer a certain number of stellate cells with small axons and also a certain number of internuncial and association pyramidal neurons. Then, as the processes of excitation spread, additional neurons become involved, in particular those which were activated only subliminally. These additionally activated intermediate and association neurons inter-react with all those neurons which perceive the external unconditional stimuli as well as with those which are excited in general during the subsequent unconditioned reaction. In this manner, the activity of the cortex as a whole becomes integrated during the perception of the outside world. Such a conclusion has been made on the basis of a great number of experiments which were carried out by us under the ordinary conditions of conditioned reflex studies as well as by the open field method. In order to illustrate these conclusions, we will consider some of our observations made during experiments on alimentary behavior conducted by this method.

Complex of sounds. A complex of four simultaneous sounds was used: a 340 c./sec. tone and a 680 c./sec. tone each made by a Hornboster's tonometer and two types of bell ringing, bell 1 and bell 2. At this complex sound, the animal was taken from its cage to the foodbox and fed. At that time, the sounds were suspended and after the closing of the foodbox, the animal was taken back to its usual place. After several feedings according to this routine, not only the complex of these sounds, but each of its components could elicit the food-getting behavior expressed by the animal going to the foodbox. However, the animal was not fed when these components were presented separately, so that after a while it would run to the foodbox only in response to the entire complex. Moreover, if the components were sounded not simultaneously but one after the other, the animal did not go to the foodbox. Even when one component was sounded initially, with the other three then being added simultaneously, the animal would not go to the foodbox (Beritoff and Bregadze, 1929). Therefore, while the complex of sounds activated the animal and elicited movements toward the foodbox, each separate component acted negatively with the ensuing avoidance of the foodbox.

In another series of experiments, we also produced the complex of sounds, but in these experiments fed the animal only when the components were presented separately. When the dog learned to run toward the foodbox at the sound of each component, we purposely did not reinforce the complex of all four sounds. The animal soon stopped reacting to the complex of stimuli and would approach the box only when each component of the complex stimulus was given separately.

In yet another series of experiments, food-getting behavior in response to a musical tone was established with an approach reaction to a foodbox (box 1) located to the left of the dog, while the sounding of another tone was followed by the feeding of the dog from box 2 located to the right of the dog. When both tones were presented simultaneously, the animal would run at first to one of the two foodboxes then to the other, but was not fed. Consequently, the induced avoidance of any approach behavior was achieved when both sounds were presented simultaneously. At the same time, of course, if only one component was sounded, the dog would approach the corresponding foodbox. Moreover, we discovered that not only did the combination of sounds fail to elicit the food-getting behavior, but also it affected this behavior negatively. Thus, for instance, if very soon after the complex stimulus, one tried only one component, the latter sometimes failed to elicit movement toward the foodbox (Beritoff and Bregadze, 1930).

Complex optic stimulus. Analogous results were obtained during the formation of an individual food-getting behavior in response to a complex optic stimulus. In this case, presentation of a complex pattern was paired with feeding while the components were made ineffective by nonreinforcement. The same responses occurred when the alimentary behavior was formed to a complex visual and auditory stimulus. The dog was fed only when the complex was presented, and the lack of effectiveness of the auditory and visual stimuli presented separately resulted from selective nonreinforcement (Bregadze, 1930).

Consecutive auditory stimuli. Food-getting behavior was also formed in response to two or three consecutive auditory stimuli. For instance a series of tones such as Do^3, Sol^3, Do^4, each lasting 5 seconds, was presented; then, after a few seconds, the dog was taken to the foodbox. Initially, the food-getting behavior would be obvious during sounding of the tones. However, the animal was fed only after the end of the complex. As a result of this after several trials the animal would go to the foodbox only after the end of the complex stimulus. The sounds produced separately stopped eliciting the food-getting behavior. Moreover, a trial of an analogous series with higher or lower sounds was ineffective in some cases initially and in others after several nonreinforced trials (Beritoff, 1932).

From the results of such observations, we concluded that formation of food-getting behavior to a complex of simultaneous or consecutive stimuli is generated at first by all the intervening components individually rather than by the complex. Furthermore, it was clear that these component reactions were more stable when the physiologic action of the corresponding components was stronger. Thus, at the beginning of the formation of the positive food-getting behavior in response to a complex stimulus, each component produces the approach behavior toward the foodbox through its own connections, while the complex elicits it through the temporary connections of all of the intervening components. However, in the following period of training, after repeated reinforcements only while a given complex is presented, the individual components stop eliciting food-getting behavior and even begin to act negatively on this behavior, so that we cannot consider the integrated positive response to the composite stimulus as a mere sum of component reactions. This is particularly clear when these components are observed to exercise a negative effect on the food-getting behavior elicited by the complex of stimuli. Also, one cannot claim a mere summation of the effects of stimuli when food-getting behavior cannot be elicited in other experiments by the complex of the stimuli but only by the individual components, the complex having been applied without reinforcement. In other words, the negative reaction elicited by the complex of the stimuli cannot be a sum of positive component effects.

On the basis of this reasoning, during the stage of differentiation of a conditioned reaction to a complex stimulus, when the complexes are positive and components are not, or when, conversely, the components act positively while the complex does not, we feel that the formation of new temporary connections takes place between those neuronal complexes which are activated exclusively by the composite stimulus. That is, we assume that each component stimulus will elicit not only activation of a certain neuronal complex of the cortex, but also the same component stimulus will increase excitability of some other neuronal complexes by a subliminal influence upon them as a result of the spread of cortical excitation. If these additional neuronal complexes are submitted simultaneously or successively from different sides to such a subliminal influence, they become excited and thus interact with neural elements activated by conditional and unconditional stimuli. It may then be understood that if some complexes of stimuli form effective temporary connections, and their components do not, it is because in the former case the additive neuronal complexes become a starting point for independent neuronal connections. Thus, the combination of stimuli will produce its own effect independent from the component reactions through neuronal connections which are formed only by the simultaneous action of all the components.

In other words, a complex stimulus produces a physiologic activity which will always be more complete and widespread than the sum of physiologic activities of the components, because of the activation of those neuronal elements which are stimulated subliminally by the components. This additional involvement of new neuronal elements confers to the cortical activity an integrated character in any instance of the application of a complex stimulus. But when, in addition, this complex stimulus is associated with a vitally important reflex action, while the components are not, then specific temporary connections are formed linking the effectors with additional neuronal elements activated in the previously described additive fashion. It may also be understood that according to the character of the reinforcement of the complex stimulation, this neuronal substrate for the additive affects may form temporal connections with either the positive or the negative external stimuli.

Figure 9b shows a schematic representation of neuronal connections in the case of a conditioned defensive reflex to a complex of auditory stimuli. It was formed in association with electrical stimulation of the paw. An additional neuronal complex made of subliminal fringes, if activated only by the complex of auditory stimuli, is linked by temporary connections with the motor analyzer; the latter is in turn linked to the projectional pyramids through the permanent connections.

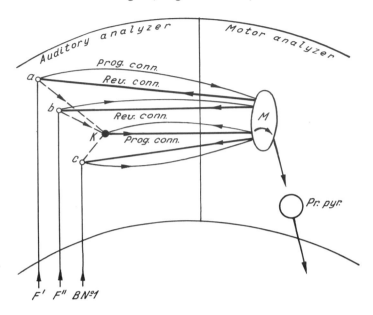

Fig. 9b

Diagram of temporal connections of a motor conditioned reflex to the complex of the auditory stimuli. F' and F'', different tones; $BN\underline{o}1$, sounding of a bell; $a, b, c,$ complexes of afferent stellate neurons with short axons which perceive these sounds; $K,$ an additional complex of neuronal elements composed of intermediary pyramidal neurons activated by the simultaneous effects of all the components; $M,$ complex of afferent stellate neurons of the motor analyzer perceiving the proprioceptive stimuli from the movement of the stimulated leg. The skin analyzer with the complex of afferent stellate neurons activated by electrical stimulation of the leg is not represented in this figure as at this stage of an established defensive conditioned reflex, the participation of this complex is not necessary. Connections extending from the complex of the neuronal elements of the motor analyzer to the projectional pyramidal neurons, *Pr. pyr.,* are mostly inborn connections; *Prog. conn.,* progressive, forward connections; *Rev. conn.,* reverse connections. (Beritoff, 1932.)

Figure 10 is a diagrammatic representation of the temporary connections of automatized alimentary behavior. To one musical tone, A, the animal ran to one foodbox and to another tone, B, to the other foodbox. During the simultaneous presentation of both sounds, the animal remained at its place.

These figures introduce the reader to our concept of the formation of temporary connections. This subject will be considered in more detail after our analysis of the basic neuronal processes and structures.

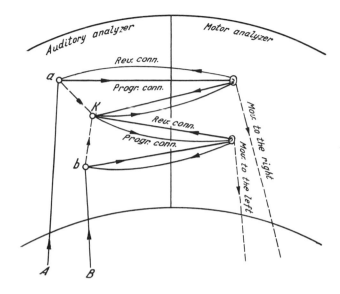

Fig. 10

Diagram of temporary connections for complex food-getting behavior. At the occurrence of tone *A*, the dog went to the right foodbox and at tone *B*, to the left. To the complex of *A* + *B*, the dog remained at its place. One complex of the afferent cortical neurons, *a*, has its temporary connections with the projectional pyramids which elicit the approach of the animal to the right foodbox. The other complex, *b*, is connected with another group of pyramids eliciting the approach to the left foodbox. The complex *a* + *b* activated an additional neuronal complex, *K*, connected with the same pyramids. Their inhibition was elicited through the latter connections. (Bcritoff, 1932.)

Conditioned Reflexes and Conscious (Planned) Psychoneural Activity

Automatization of Conscious Behavior

It is known that the conscious behavior of man is characterized by the mental formation of a plan of action and the anticipation of its results prior to the onset of the actual behavior. However, every conscious behavior, if repeated many times in the same environment, is rapidly automatized and begins without awareness according to the principle of a chain reflex.

In modern factories with the extreme division of work, the same movements are repeated hundreds of times during the working day, with each movement lasting only for a few seconds. During such activity, the qualified worker does not have a constant awareness of the purpose of each separate motor act, which occurs automatically in a machine-like fashion. However, this becomes the case only after training of the worker. Each of us knows from our own personal experience as we learn a new skilled act, that a mental representation of it is formed at first. This representation precedes the movement and makes us aware of the act. However, after a period of training when these movements are well learned, their mental representation disappears, and we may no longer be aware of performing them.

Moreover, during specialized skilled work, one activity may replace another also without the awareness of the individual. A good pianist or an excellent typist may perform a very delicate task without thinking at all about the movements of his fingers. The eyes see notes and letters succeeding each other, and the hands perform corresponding movements one after the other without any awareness. When we consider these movements, it is not difficult to see that they occur according to the principle of an automatized reflex, with the involvement of temporary connections. In certain cases one feels an original stimulus, though one has no mental representation of following movements, while in other cases even such signals are not perceived subjectively (Beritoff, 1934b).

However, such an automatization, without awareness of the transition of one activity into another, does not occur at the beginning of this form of work. Initially, the subject planned these transitions, and actively participated in each change of his motor behavior. Only after repeated training, awareness ceased to determine these changes, and one movement started to succeed another through the formation of temporary connections according to the principle of a conditioned reflex. Therefore, in the activity of a specialized worker, we deal with the formation of a conditioned chain reflex.

However, this does not imply that one is entirely unaware of such behavior. The activity of a worker without a continuous participation of his consciousness is impossible under any conditions or for any degree of training. For one thing, no matter how well trained an activity is, it cannot be repeated invariantly. The state of the central nervous system changes from moment to moment under the influence of continuously changing external stimuli and, to a greater degree, under the influence of an incessant change of the inner organic states, those in particular which are determined by the work itself. This leads to more or less significant variations in the pattern of movement; in its form, rapidity or intensity. And, if the working process is not completely disturbed and therefore interrupted, this must be due to an immediate conscious correction of the movement each time it varies, this being effected with the participation of a corresponding mental representation. An uninterrupted course of working processes cannot be conceived of without continuous conscious control; therefore, during specialized activity the worker is constantly monitoring the results or product of his work. Any impaired production signals a deviation from the standard conditioned movements and elicits the corresponding mental representation for its correction. The shifting of attention or of conscious consideration from movements to their results could be an index of the formation of the appropriate temporary connections with the cortical motor centers, i.e., an index of the worker's skill (Beritoff, 1934b, 1947b).

Conditioned motor reflexes have been studied in man not only in regard to behavior in a specialized work situation, but they have also been studied by the method of associating indifferent stimuli with an electrical stimulus of the skin as in animal research. During the study of conditioned reflexes in humans, scientists immediately found that these reflexes were not as readily formed as in animals; in other words, they required a greater number of associations. For example, in the case of the formation of a conditioned defensive movement of the hand through the association of indifferent stimuli with a painful electrical stimulation of the finger, these studies showed that a conditioned motor reflex is not established in man as rapidly as in higher mammals. In adolescents 16 to 17 years of age, the reflex is formed after 14 to 16 pairings, in some instances the range being 1 to 100 associations (Osipova, 1926). However, in younger children, the reflexes are formed on the average, more quickly. One finds the most rapid formation of conditioned reflexes in retarded children, on the average, after only five associations. In adults, the speed of formation of conditioned motor reflexes is extremely variable. In various experiments from the Bechterev Institute, they were formed in some instances after 10 associations, while in others, only after hundreds of trials; and in some cases they could not be established even after several hundred associations. In some subjects, a conditioned reflex could be formed during the first day of training after only a few associations (Luckina, 1925, Missischev, 1925, Schnirmann, 1925).

These facts suggest that conscious activity involving planning constitutes an obstacle to quick formation of the conditioned motor reflexes, using procedures ordinarily applied to animals.

RELATION BETWEEN CONDITIONED AND CONSCIOUS BEHAVIOR

We specifically investigated the relation of the inborn, conditioned, and conscious psychoneural activity of the adult (Beritoff and Dzidzishvili, 1934b). In our experiments, the subject (a student) was placed in an isolated chamber, and the experimenter and recording instruments were located outside of the chamber. We established conditioned reflexes of the leg to sounds by associating the latter with painful electrical stimulation of the sole of the foot. The movement of one or the other leg as well as the respirations and sometimes pulse and muscle tone of the stimulated leg were recorded on a kymograph. A conditioned reflex consisted of leg withdrawal, inhibition of respiratory movements, tachycardia and general wincing of the body. It was formed in some subjects the first day after only a few associations; in others, it was established during the following days after a number of associations. The defensive movement of the leg was not very strong, and only rarely did its amplitude reach the value of the reflex flexion produced by the direct electrical stimulation (Figure 11).

In both experiments (Figure 11), the onset of the auditory stimulus elicited a conditioned leg lifting. In experiment A, the sound lasted for 20 seconds and was suspended immediately after the third electrical stimulus; a low-amplitude, proprioceptive conditioned reflex (see base line) occurred after the first and second electrically induced defensive movements, whereas, after the third defensive movement, the proprioceptive reflex was not elicited. In experiment B, the sound was continued 10 seconds after the end of the electrical stimulation. In this experiment, the proprioceptive reflex occurred following each defensive movement; after the third one, it lasted until the cessation of the sound and the leg showed a clonic contraction at times.

Electrical stimulation of the foot elicited not only the motor reaction, but also a subjective feeling, since the applied stimulation was very painful. It produced a perception of intense pain, something like a pricking or burning. When the stimulation was of relatively low intensity, these sensations were localized to the stimulated points; with a more intensive stimulation, they seemed to originate farther from the electrode and were also perceived in various distant parts of the body. The subject reported sensations such as a feeling of creeping, or a cold shower on his back, shoulders and arms. Sometimes the painful excitation spread in waves from the stimulated sole of the foot to the big toe (the electrodes were made of a copper ring with a cathode in the middle).

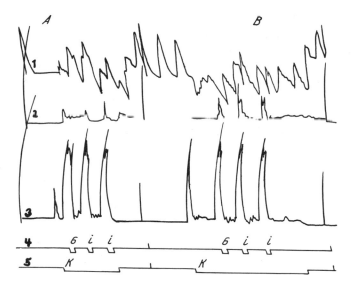

Fig. 11

Conditioned motor reflex in man (subject SK). Recording at the twenty-fifth and twenty-sixth association of a complex of sounds, *K*, (sounding a bell and combined tones of 580 c./sec. and 6905 c./sec.) associated with an electrical stimulation of the sole of the foot repeated three times. Intensity of the electrical stimulus was 6 cm. between the coils of an inductorium each stimulation lasting several seconds and the interval between stimulations being 3 to 5 seconds. *1*, Chest movements; *2*, movements of the left leg; *3*, movements of the right leg; *4*, signal, electrical stimulation; *5*, signal, auditory stimulation; *i*, in this and following figures, an identical stimulation to the preceding one. (Beritoff and Dzidzishvili, 1934b.)

After a few associations, the conditional sounds alone were also able to elicit subjective feelings, such as a perception of paresthesia or cold shower, or heart palpitation, and a perception of tremor in the leg, in the shoulders and "all over the body." After repeated associations, in the course of the experiment for several days afterward, these feelings, elicited by the conditional stimulus, decreased in intensity and finally became limited to an unpleasant tense state of expectation of the electrical stimulation. What seems to be of particular interest is that the subject never experienced a feeling of pain or burning at the sounding of the conditional stimulus comparable to the sensation which occurred during the electrical stimulation itself (Beritoff and Dzidzishvili, 1934b).

All these objective and subjective effects were extinguished if the conditional stimulus was repeated without association with electrical stimulus. Moreover, these effects could become differentiated, in other words, unusual auditory stimuli would not elicit them.

From our observations we concluded that the generally known delay in the formation of conditioned motor reaction of the leg on the basis of the electrical stimulation of the skin in normal adults results from the subject's awareness that the movement of the leg is elicited by the electrical stimulation and not by the sound. Based upon our own observations, the explanation seems to be that although the temporary connection is formed rather rapidly after only a few pairings, its external manifestation at the signal is actively inhibited as an unnecessary movement since it does not prevent the electrical stimulation from occurring immediately afterward. This can be inferred from the following experiment. When the subject regularly did not show a conditioned withdrawal of the leg to the sound, it could be produced by distracting her attention. We asked the subject to perform the Bourdon test, instructing her to cross out the letters A and C and to indicate by her pencil the beginning and the end of the conditional stimulus. As seen in the comparison of two experiments shown in Figure 12, when she was working on the Bourdon test (experiment A), not only did the conditioned reflex cause leg withdrawal, but at the same time the unconditioned reflex to the stimulus was considerably decreased. Conversely, when the subject concentrated her attention on the electrical stimulus (experiment B), the unconditioned reaction was favored and the conditioned movement to the sound was inhibited.

The conditioned leg withdrawal became more regular when the temporal connections were considerably reinforced; characteristically, it then occurred at the very beginning of the conditional stimulus, during the first seconds of its duration. It apparently occurred entirely without the subject's will or awareness. The subject did not perceive the beginning of the movement, and it seemed to occur before she consciously acknowledged the presence of the sound. When the subject became aware of the sound, then the movement ceased. All other objective and subjective reactions to the sound continued for a relatively longer time, and manifested themselves more regularly than the movements of the leg (Beritoff and Dzidzishvili, 1934).

These observations show again that in man, as in other higher vertebrates, the temporary connections for the conditioned movements of the leg may be formed through neuronal elements which do not participate in the psychoneural activity and do not give rise to a conscious perception of a conditioned sound. According to the theory which we will develop below, this initial conditioned movement of

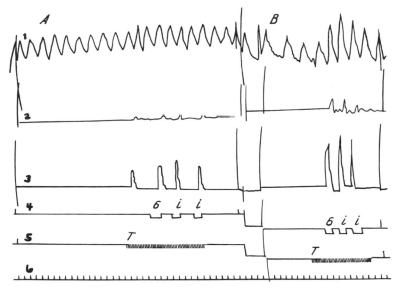

Fig. 12

Influence of mental activity upon conditioned and unconditioned reflexes (subject NB). *1*, Respiration; *2*, tension of the right gastrocnemius; *3*, movement of the same leg; *4*, signal, electrical stimulation; *5*, signal, conditional stimulus (tone of 1000 c./sec.); *6*, time in seconds. (Beritoff and Dzidzishvili, 1934b.) (See the text for explanation.)

the leg, which is not consciously perceived, may be formed through the internuncials of the fourth and third layers of the cerebral cortex, where the specific afferent fibers from the diencephalon terminate, as we will discuss in detail in a later chapter of this book. This also seems to be true in the case of some psychogalvanic reflexes studied by Gershuni.

INFLUENCE OF CONSCIOUS BEHAVIOR ON CONDITIONED AND UNCONDITIONED REFLEXES

We also investigated the influence of different types of conscious psychoneural activity upon the conditioned as well as unconditioned reflexes. We conducted several experiments. For instance, we asked our subject to voluntarily inhibit any movements elicited by the electrical stimulation. These movements could be arrested fully even when the stimulation was extremely painful. This was done not by an immobilization of the leg through a generalized contraction of the

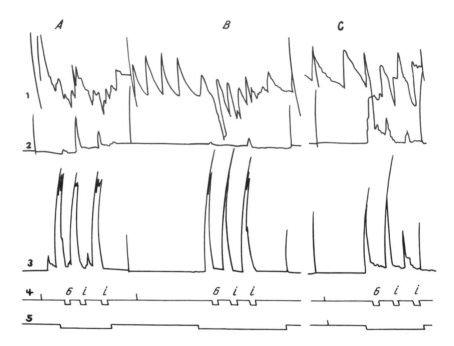

Fig. 13

Influence of distraction of attention upon conditioned and unconditioned reflexes (subject SK). Symbols the same as Figure 12. (Beritoff and Dzidzishvili, 1934b.) (See text for explanation.)

muscles, but by a central inhibition, since all the muscles of the leg were relaxed.

In Figure 13 experiment *A* shows the usual effect during the associative trial. One can note a conditioned reaction to the sound, as well as to the proprioceptive stimulation. In experiment *B*, the same association is found after instruction to "move the leg only during electrical stimulation." Under such conditions, all the conditioned reflexes disappeared while the unconditioned ones increased in intensity. In experiment *C*, the subject was instructed to read. Prior to this, the subject was told to read very attentively so that he could later on recite or summarize the story. Now, the conditioned reactions disappeared and the unconditioned ones were considerably decreased probably because of the particularly intense mental work.

Characteristically, the negative influence of the conscious activity was directed mostly upon movement. Subjective feelings elicited by electrical stimulation as well as by the conditional stimuli did not change or if they did, were decreased only slightly.

On the other hand, the unconditional electrical stimulation as well as the conditional stimulus, if they were able to elicit an intense reflex, would then inhibit conscious activity. For example, during the Bourdon test, the movements of the hands became more laborious, mistakes were very often made and reading was disturbed.

These observations, therefore, showed that the neuronal substrate in the cortex sustaining the inborn and the conditioned activity cannot be the same as the one which sustains conscious willed activity. These substrates, differing in quality, form an integrated system and show mutual interactions according to the general principles governing the activity of the central nervous system. Yet in adults, conscious willed activity predominates over all the other varieties of nervous activity; inborn and conditioned, as well as psychoneural image-directed behavior.

As was indicated above, the conscious activity fully suppressing the conditioned motor reaction, is not able to suspend unpleasant subjective feelings which arise during conditional and unconditional stimulation. I believe that this is due to the fact that the neural substrate of the conscious activity as well as of the conditioned activity is located in the neocortex, and therefore all the described interactions are carried out through the neocortex, while the unpleasant subjective feelings and other emotional experiences arise through the activity of neuronal elements of the paleocortex, as will be discussed in more detail later on. Possibly this difference constitutes one of the explanations of why consciousness exercises so little control over emotional experiences.

It follows from the above discussion that the conditioned activity of a skilled worker is generally controlled by conscious willed activity. Also, the conditioned motor activity elicited by electrical stimulation of the foot is regulated in man by the same type of psychoneural activity.

However, we also know some other facts which show that certain types of conditioned reflexes escape the control of awareness. This, for instance, is very well seen in relation to secretional reflexes. Thus, Lentz (1934) formed in an adult a stereotype of complex conditioned reflexes, using a series of positive and negative signals. He then stopped reinforcing the positive signal by food, while the negative ones, on the contrary, were now reinforced. The salivary reaction was recorded by the Lashley method. The subject recognized the change during the first trial following the first reinforcement of the negative signals and the nonreinforcement of the positive ones. However, the saliva continued to be elicited as before during this day, as well as during the following days, despite the awareness of the change. Only after several days of retraining could a new stereotype be formed. Generally, intellectual activity did not affect the salivary reflexes, reading a newspaper for example. On the contrary, this only increased salivation. We know very well from our every day life that salivation, or any other secretional activity of the alimentary glands, does not stop even during intense intellectual work. Obviously, the conditioned vegetative reflexes, just as the inborn vegetative reactions, are not regulated by consciousness.

It is true that the conditioned secretional reflexes, just as many other autonomic reactions, may very easily be either increased or inhibited under the influence of conditional or unconditional stimuli. However, this regulation of the autonomic reactions is accomplished according to the laws of inborn and conditioned activity, without the participation of the consciousness or the will of the subject.

3 ORIGIN OF IMAGE-DRIVEN BEHAVIOR

Concepts of Image-Driven Behavior

The ability of higher vertebrates to have mental images of environmental objects or events was recognized by Setchenov, Pavlov and many of the latter's pupils (Kupalov, 1938 and Anokhin, 1958). It is recognized also by contemporary psychologists such as Teplov (1949), Leontiev (1949), Uznadze (1949) and Roginsky (1948). Setchenov (1878) spoke of sensory images, or concrete object thinking in animals. According to Setchenov, this most simple psychological occurrence directs behavior in animals and in children. Setchenov (1878) explicitly pointed out that these feelings (mainly perceptions and representations) act by directing movements. In other words, the former elicit the latter and modify them by adjusting their amplitude and direction. Pavlov (1949b) also considered the presence in the cortex of such "stimuli and their traces" which each of us recognizes as impressions, perceptions and representations. Kupalov, one of the outstanding pupils of Pavlov, says, "Some dogs disclose by all their behavior that they expect the occurrence of a certain positive conditional stimulus followed by feeding." These and many other facts suggest the presence in dogs of concrete images and object thinking, so to speak, corresponding to definite configurations and to a regular succession of neuronal states.

However, Pavlov and Kupalov, although recognizing in animals the ability to form concrete images of the outside world, did not consider these images as having a specific biologic significance and did not study them in detail in order to find out the role they play in animal behavior. Anokhin (1958), who systematically studied different types of animal behavior, was the only disciple of Pavlov who acknowledged the fundamental controlling action of the psychoneural process responsible for the reproduction of concrete images. However, in order to avoid the psychological terminology of image and mental representation, he coined a new term, "acceptors of action," to represent a residual complex of afferent traces, remnant of previous reinforcements which are reproduced in the animal at the time of a conditioned signal. Obviously, the "acceptor of action" constitutes a psychoneural process of image representation which emerges in an animal in a given situation during reinforcement. Anokhin writes, "Being formed under the influence of the external events and being a part of each conditional stimulus, the 'acceptor of action' plays a determining role in adaptive behavior. On the basis of different impulses affecting sense organs, it determines the degree of precision and adequacy of the resulting act, elicited by the original stimulus." This means that the spatial image of eating in a particular location, triggered by the conditioned stimulus, determines the ensuing alimentary behavior of the animal.

In contradistinction to the conditioned reflexes of Pavlov, many authors have considered the following aptitudes to be at the basis of the highest forms of animal behavior: ability to grasp the relationship among objects (the occurrence of an environmental insight); possibility of an immediate generation of a new behavior after only one opportunity for grasping temporospatial relationships; perception of a whole situation with ensuing adaptive behavior. The speed of acquiring an adaptive behavior is usually considered as the most significant differential sign discriminating between learning by trial and error and learning on the basis of an immediate grasp of relationships. Furthermore, the perception of temporospatial relationships is considered as an elementary inborn quality which is found at the basis of the total perceptual ability and reactivity of the organism (Thorpe, 1950). Konorski (1950) expressed himself in the same way when discussing insight learning at a recent symposium devoted to animal behavior.

It is easy to see that insight learning (i.e., the grasp of relationships) means, in the above interpretation, the same ability which in our concept is expressed by the formation, reproduction and governing action of images of the environment and of significant objects.

Konorski cites observations of Spence and Lippit made on rats which constitute a good illustration of latent learning, a concept related to the ensuing "insightful behavior." A Y-shaped maze was made of two compartments, one containing food and the other water. The rats were introduced into the maze every day after being fed and provided with fluid. The rats ran through the maze and often visited the compartments containing food and water. This was repeated for several days. Then the rats were deprived of either food or water. When hungry, the animal immediately ran toward the food compartment and when thirsty, toward the compartment containing water. This, concluded Konorski, means that the animals expressed insight.

According to our concept, the rats which visited the maze after being fed acquired, on the basis of visual, vestibular and kinesthetic stimuli, an image of the total organization of the maze with its spatial relationships relative to the location of food and water. This is why, when the animals were introduced into the maze, after being deprived of either food or water, they directed themselves toward either food or water; i.e., each time the image of both lures was reproduced, the rats behaved as if they actually saw these lures.

Obviously, cognizance or the presence of images of the outside world in higher vertebrates is expressed by an insight, and correctly oriented behavior is directed by the reproduced image of the environment.

It is regrettable, however, that the authors who explained animal behavior by an insightful mechanism did not try to elucidate the physiopsychological basis for this ability. They usually limited themselves to calling this behavior intelligence or an expression of latent learning.

Many authors, conducting various types of behavioral experiments in mammals, have concluded that behavior is goal-directed. Buytendijk (1936) considered this behavioral attitude related to a visual image. The visual image according to him does not arise at once, but is built up progressively after repeated perception. The resulting behavior is then considered to be goal-directed and it is implied that there is an intention to reach the goal by the shortest possible way preceding orientation of the animal in the appropriate direction. All such spatial relationships are implied in our concept of images of the outside world.

Buytendijk shares the belief that a dog recognizes objects which it has not seen for a considerable lapse of time. He, too, believes that insightful behavior originates each time an animal overcomes obstacles on its way toward a goal. During the subsequent experiments, the animal will run around obstacles at once, without any searching movements. That is, there is cognizant penetration into a given situation, into its structure and relationships.

Buytendijk states several times that the nature of insightful behavior is not known, but he also is inclined to believe that we are dealing with the ability of an animal to represent objects and events mentally.

In recent literature, one also finds concepts explaining the behavior of higher vertebrates by psychoneural activity of the brain. In a symposium devoted to the brain mechanisms and consciousness (1955), several papers deal with the mechanisms of animal behavior. Thus, a well-known psychologist, Hebb, finds that image-driven activity of the brain (i.e., that activity which is expressed in the mental representation) plays a considerable role in the behavior of higher vertebrates. Such activity is reflected by the ability of the animal to retain the traces of a great number of stimuli for some time before reacting to them with purposeful behavior. With this, Hebb stresses that the phenomenon of purposeful behavior and the expectancy of the future does not necessarily indicate a teleological approach or the denial of determinism; it simply indicates the capacity for image drive, for ideation. When a perception, "A," has been followed several times in the past by a perception, "B," an image of "B" is generated in the animal perceiving "A." Hebb finds that the highest forms of animal behavior would necessarily include image drive, for instance, when a dog "asks" to get out of the room or a chimpanzee "begs" to be given an object which it cannot reach by himself. Hebb also considers two basic problems of the higher form of behavior: (1) the nature of ideas, images and concepts, and (2) the nature of the interconnection and the temporal organization of ideas. However, his analysis of the behavioral acts for the elucidation of these problems is limited to general considerations of the psychology of associations and has limited reference to contemporary knowledge of the brain structure.

Individual goal-reaching behavior does not have to be carried out only in the environment in which it was elicited originally. Experiments and observations show that the higher vertebrates, such as birds and mammals, may exhibit the same individual behavior, driven by images, in completely different environments. Thus, for instance, the animals escape certain stimuli and run away from their enemies when they are encountered in any situation. If, during the sounding of a metronome, a painful electrical stimulus has been applied to the skin of a dog, it will exhibit a defensive behavior at the subsequent sound of the metronome not only in the usual experimental room, but in a completely different environment. The sounding of the metronome will make the animal yelp, run away and hide behind the first encountered object just as it did in the original experimental situation (Beritoff *et al.*, 1934). This shows that the image-driven individual behavior is essentially directed by the neuropsychological process of image reproduction and not by the external environment in which the behavior takes place, although it may to a certain degree be related to that environment.

Automatized Individually Acquired Behavior

Any behavioral act elicited by the image of a food location may be reduced to a chain reflex if it is repeated several times in the same environment. At the onset of the formation of food-getting locomotor behavior, in response to a certain signal, the animal does not go to the foodbox immediately. Following the signal, he starts to move with some delay and a certain slowness. He remains a long time at the foodbox after finishing eating and only then returns to his cage by a zigzag route, not by the shortest possible path. It is clear that the animal's movements are not directed by the signal only. Characteristically, the animal may have already gone to the foodbox without waiting for the signal after the first feeding from this foodbox.

Figure 14 gives a schematic representation of the experimental room where the behavior experiments were usually carried out.

If the instrument generating the auditory signal for animal feeding is located at the foodbox, then its location becomes an integral part of the food image. This is why if this instrument is moved elsewhere, the animal goes at a signal to this new place and sniffs the instrument. Afterward, the animal will go to the foodbox itself. This happens at the beginning of the training period, during the very first trials. However, after a certain time, following many reinforcements and after several trials with the transfer of the audiometer to another place, the animal goes to the foodbox at the signal by the shortest possible route, and after finishing eating, returns to its cage also by the shortest possible path. This behavior may not change even when the sounding instrument, together with the foodbox, is transferred to another place while the animal is watching the transfer. At the sound, the animal still goes to that place where the foodbox and the sounding instrument were previously located. Only afterward does the animal go to the new location of food.

One may infer from this that initially the dog goes to the foodbox being driven only by the image of food location. However, afterward, with repetition of trials in the same experimental situation, the animal behavior becomes automatized by the transformation of one or another components of the environment into a conditional signal for one or another segment of behavioral activity. This behavior was called by us 30 years ago "individually acquired automatized behavior." Some of its characteristics are analogous to instinctive behavior, as each component of the automatized act depends exclusively upon contemporary or antecedent excitation of an unconditional or a condi-

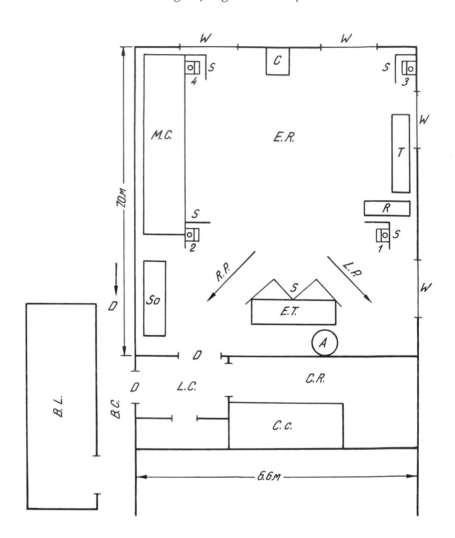

Fig. 14

Schematic representation of the experimental room. E.R., Experimental room for behavioral studies; D, door; W, window; So., sofa; M.C., large empty cage; E.T., experimenter's desk; T, table; R, cupboard; A, pump for pumping air into the Stern audio-oscillator; C, cage for experimental animal; 1, 2, 3 and 4, foodboxes which can be opened and closed by pulling string; S, wooden screens (1.5 by 1.5 meters). The foodboxes and desk are hidden by the screen; however, they may be moved around. R.P., right passage; L.P., left passage; C.R., conditioned reflexes room; C.c., cabin for the animal; L.C., short corridor; B.C., long corridor; B.L., biochemical laboratory.

tional character. Moreover, each conditioned behavioral component is activated through specific temporary connections according to the principle governing chain reflexes. Although during this behavior a representation of an image may arise, it does not play the major role, as the behavior is secured more rapidly and more economically by means of temporary connections activated one after the other. However, the presence of a spatial food image unquestionably facilitates the food-getting behavior, for this image serves to direct the animal to the same foodbox which he will reach as a result of automatized behavior (Beritoff, 1934a,b,c, 1935, 1947b).

Experimental studies prove that under certain conditions psycho-neural, image-driven behavior may be selectively affected, while automatized conditioned behavior is not significantly modified. We have studied the behavior of dogs, cats and pigeons after subjecting them to a brain concussion resulting from an explosion of trinitrotoluene. During this study, physiologic, biochemical and morphologic changes of the organism were investigated. Our observations showed that when a certain degree of brain trauma is caused by such an explosion, the animal loses the ability to move spontaneously. The dog lies motion-less as if it were shocked, and the pigeons remain without moving in the same place with ruffled feathers and retracted heads. For several days following the explosion, they are unable to make even an orienting movement. However, the animals can see and differentiate edible from inedible substances and react to alimentary conditioning signals by getting up and going toward the usual foodbox. These observations indicated that a concussion affected the psychoneural, image-driven processes while the inborn and individually acquired conditioned reflexes were spared.

Another specially conducted experiment seems to prove this point. Following an explosion-generated concussion, the dog cannot remember to differentiate the respective locations of bread and meat. Thus, if one shows a dog a box with bread and another box with meat, a normal animal after 1 to 5 minutes will run first to get the meat and then the bread. However, after experiencing trauma generated by explosion, it will not differentiate between these two boxes in the usual manner, and will always run in the same direction. After a rela-tively strong blast, the dogs and pigeons first would lose their general ability to find food by memory, in other words, to react adequately to a spatial image of food. Obviously, the psychoneural processes respon-sible for ideational projection of food into space suffer. However, if the animals have been trained to show an automatized reflex activity or conditioned reflexes to some specific visual or auditory signals, the latter remain effective after the blast without a significant change; even differentiation of stimuli remains unchanged (Bregadze, 1945, Beritoff, 1945). According to our neurophysiologic and neuropsychologic concepts to be developed below, the psychoneural functioning of stellate cells generating images are more affected by the blast than cortical functions involving the other cells. This is why we believe that image-driven behavior is affected more than conditioned reflexes.

Thus the highest vertebrates are characterized by two types of behavior. In behavior of the first type, each phase depends upon those internal and external stimuli which the animal experiences during the preceding phases of the behavioral act; while in behavior of the second type, each of these phases is determined not only by these stimuli, but also by an emergence of concrete images of vitally important goal-objects which originated this behavior. The behavior of the second type, if repeated many times in the same environment, is automatized and then becomes similar to the first behavioral type. It is then carried out according to the principles of chain reflexes.

Psychoneural activity of the animal as expressed by individually acquired acts of behavior which are image-driven not only qualitatively differ from the inborn or conditioned activity of the brain, but also are probably sustained by more highly organized neuronal complexes than those responsible for reflex activity.

There has been a tendency to consider each behavioral act of an animal or a man as a complex chain reflex (Pavlov and his pupils as well as American behavioralists). Years ago I also shared this view (Beritoff, 1929a). At that time we did not see any qualitative difference between the brain processes responsible for image-driven individual behavior and conditioned reflexes. Our more recent studies, reported above and below, make it clear that a qualitative difference between these two types of behavior undoubtedly exists.

Other Behavioral Experiments for Differentiation of the Brain Structures Involved in Conditioned Reflex and Psychoneural Behavior

We have further investigated the following problem, "Is the brain substrate sustaining conditioned reflex activity the same as that involved in psychoneural behavior?" Our experiments seem to confirm the conclusion that the psychoneural substrate of the brain differs from that of the conditioned reflexes. A series of such experiments was conducted in pigeons. It was assumed that the peculiar organization of the visual analyzer in these birds, i.e., the complete crossing of the optic pathways, would enable us to solve this problem.

We blindfolded one eye in a pigeon, for instance the left eye, by closing it with adhesive tape. Then we repeatedly brought the bird to a foodbox while simultaneously exposing it to a visual signal consisting of a certain pattern projected on a screen. Afterward, any projection on the screen and even any luminous signal in the cage would elicit approach behavior toward the foodbox and return of the pigeon to its cage. In this case, visual stimulation was perceived through the right eye by the left hemisphere for, as is well-known, in pigeons the optic nerves are crossed completely. Seemingly, this visual stimulation produced the food image projected into space, making the pigeon go directly to the foodbox. Let us assume that this approach behavior in response to any luminous stimulus was a conditioned reflex, in other words, was due to a formation of a temporary connection with the efferent pyramidal cortical neurons. With only the right eye opened, this connection would then be formed in the left hemisphere according to the usual concepts governing establishment of conditioned reflexes. Therefore, the described individual behavior should disappear if the right eye is now taped while the left remains open. In fact, the following takes place: After the transfer of the tape from the left eye to the right, the pigeon still goes to the foodbox in response to any visual stimulus (light), exactly in the same way as he did when the right eye was opened. Additional investigation proved that in pigeons the ipsilateral hemisphere becomes involved in psychoneural activity through the corpus callosum. Indeed, after section of the commissura supraoptica dorsalis, the individual reactions which were formed when only one eye was opened could not be reproduced in response to a stimulation of the other eye (Chichinadze, 1939, 1940). This fact, incidentally, favors the belief that the psychoneural complex responsible for the mental image of food and of the foodbox was formed in the opposite hemisphere when only one eye was opened. However, its reproduction could be elicited by stimulation of this eye or of the other via the commissural fibers.

Let us now repeat this behavior a great number of times, eliciting it by presenting the same optical stimulus to the right eye. Furthermore, let us establish a differentiation to the effect that only one particular pattern or color will elicit this behavior, while another pattern or color becomes ineffective. This signifies that temporary connections with efferent pyramids were established and reinforced to one pattern only. Transfer of the tape from one eye to the other then leads to an essential modification of the behavior; differentiation of the optic signals disappears. The pigeon goes to the foodbox no matter which pattern or color is produced, as at the very onset of the formation of his individual behavior.

Obviously, in a pigeon with the left eye closed, after numerous repetitions of the presentation of a particular pattern during food-getting behavior, temporary connections are formed with the motor efferent neurons in the left hemisphere which received peripheral volleys, originating from the right eye stimulated by this particular pattern. These differentiated temporary connections are not activated if the stimulation is applied to the other eye in spite of the presence of the commissural pathways. This favors the belief that the psycho-neural processes of image-driven behavior and those of conditioned reflexes are not the same. Although both take place in the same hemisphere, one of them is activated via the commissural fibers, while the other is not.

One should assume that from the time of the establishment of temporary connections with the efferent neurons of the brain, the impulses originating in the retina of the right eye, generated by the elements of a particular pattern, run within the cortex of the left hemisphere, mostly along the temporary connections. If another pattern or another color does not elicit the food-getting behavior, it is because there is a reproduction of the mental image of a lack of food in the foodbox, as these visual stimuli were presented to the bird several times without being associated with food. Moreover, these negative stimuli at the same time establish their own temporary connections with those efferent neurons of the brain which inhibit the food-getting behavior. We shall suggest later that this inhibitory process is probably carried out by the dendrites of the cortex and subcortex. Moreover, the activation of these "negative" connections may elicit a movement of the animal in the opposite direction, or its general pacification since the animal usually closes his eyes in response to these stimuli. We observed this negative effect in rabbits, dogs and cats when stimuli differentiated from the effective conditional signals were used.

After the transfer of the tape to the right eye, the differentiation of the optic stimuli is no longer possible, as the stimuli originated in the retina of the left eye are directed to the right hemisphere and therefore are not able to stimulate the temporary connections previously formed in the left hemisphere. But when these impulses travel via the commissural fibers into the right hemisphere, they probably activate the same system of stellate cells stimulated by the impulses

generated by the right eye, and by means of these mechanisms they elicit the food image projected into space.

One might consider another possibility, namely, that psychoneural activity expressed by mental images is not localized in the cortex, but in the lower divisions of the brain. This problem was attacked experimentally in the following way: In experimental pigeons, the right hemisphere was ablated. Then, after several weeks, the birds were trained to go at a visual signal to the foodbox and to return to the cage. If now one taped the right eye (projected upon the remaining left hemisphere), the visual signal did not elicit the usual approach behavior to the foodbox. The pigeon reacted with an orienting movement, which obviously originated from the mesencephalon. Therefore, the mesencephalon was activated, but did not produce the usual individual acquired behavior. If now, we taped the left eye, the behavior of the pigeon would not be modified in any way. It would continue to go to the foodbox at the visual signal (Chichinadze, 1940).

In conclusion, images of the outside world are formed independently in each hemisphere of the pigeon's brain, via pathways from the opposite eye. However, a reproduction of these images can be affected following perception with either eye. The "untrained" eye affects the "trained" hemisphere via the interhemispheric commissure. In contradistinction to this, temporary connections of a differentiated conditioned reflex, also formed in the opposite hemisphere to the trained eye, cannot be activated by the impulses running in the commissural fibers.

When the experiments are carried out in rabbits and puppies, the transfer of the tape from one eye to the other does not change the character of the individual reaction to the visual stimuli in the initial phase of generalized excitation or in the stage of differentiation which follows. The differentiation of the individual reactions was fully effective in these animals, even though the "untrained" eye was opened (Chichinadze, 1940). Obviously, this is because each eye anatomically and functionally is equally connected with both hemispheres, and therefore the temporal connections are formed in both hemispheres originally.

Psychoneural Activity and Planned Behavior in Man

EMERGENCE OF NORMAL PLANNED BEHAVIOR

Psychoneural activity of an adult during any industrial or other form of behavior, characterized by conscious planning and conscious goals,

constitutes the highest form of nervous activity. It represents the most important qualitative difference between an adult considered as a social being on the one hand and a child or an animal on the other. In our terminology, conscious psychoneural activity of man is not synonymous with psychological activity in general. The latter is proper not only to an adult, but also to an infant, and to animals which occupy a certain level on the phylogenetic scale. In our terminology the conscious psychoneural activity of a member of a community is rather a particular new form of psychological action emerging as a result of historical development of man's activities. Briefly, this aspect of psychoneural activity has from its inception a social implication which will remain as long as man exists.

Many outstanding psychologists, particularly animal psychologists, used the term "consciousness" as a synonym for psyche and applied it to animals as well as to man (Morgan, 1913). According to W. Wund, a differentiation of self from the outside world, through a cognizance of one's own ego, is the basic constituent of consciousness. We do not share the opinion of those psychologists according to whom consciousness defined as above is common, not only to man, but also to the whole animal world. However, in view of the semantic difficulties arising when one uses the term "consciousness," we shall call human conscious behavior "planned behavior."

In early infancy behavior is regulated by the same type of psychoneural activity as seen in higher vertebrates. In children 1 to 2 years of age, the individual acts of behavior are very easily formed and are elicited by images of the outside world. They also easily form automatized acts of behavior, conducted according to the type of chain reflexes. Nevertheless, they do not exhibit planned activity; they do not have a definite and conscious goal for actions. From the age of 2 years, the child starts to develop planned behavior. Individually acquired, image-driven behavior is gradually replaced by such behavior. However, of course, even in the mature period when planned behavior predominates, image-driven behavior may also take place. The emergence of planned behavior depends not only upon the everyday participation of man in the activity of his community, but it also depends on a progressive ontogenetic development of the brain. If for some reason the morphologic development of the brain is arrested, particularly if this arrest involves cerebral hemispheres, there will be a corresponding retardation in the emergence of planned psychoneural activity.

LACK OF PLANNED BEHAVIOR IN A MICROCEPHALIC GIRL

A striking example of such delay in emergence of mature behavior, due to retarded development of the brain, is exhibited in microcephalic individuals. We studied a microcephalic girl of 10 to 12 years of age (Beritoff and Dzidzishvili, 1934a). She was brought by a policeman to a Tbilisi psychiatric clinic at the age of approximately 8 to 10 years. As she could not speak, or understand verbal instructions, we could not find out where she was from or who her parents were. She remained in the hospital for 3 years. We called her Peta in view of her resemblance to a pithecanthrope. She reacted adequately to the stimulation of all sensory organs, displayed ordinary emotional manifestations, could produce movements with her hands and feet and vocalize a few sounds, like, dia-dia, or tia-tia, not making any sense. She did not dress herself and was unable to perform such simple duties as sweeping a room or starting a fire in a fireplace. She would imitate these actions, but would only throw things around or try to put the wood in the air vent, etc. She was very easily excited emotionally, would become aggressive, then scratch, bite and scream. However, no matter how unmanageable she became, she would calm down after very patient handling. At that time we started to carry out experiments with her as we would in our animal research. We would put her on a sofa while giving her a verbal order to "sit down" and when she would resist, we would seat her forcibly. She rapidly learned to go to the sofa and sit down at a verbal signal. Then, at the sound of a bell we would push her forward 3 or 4 meters, and then around a screen, where sugar would be given to her; then she would be taken back to the original place. A spontaneous, stable behavior to get food behind the screen in response to the sound of a bell appeared on the ninth day after 116 reinforcements. However, this difficulty in forming an alimentary behavior in response to a certain signal was experienced only at the beginning of our work with her. When Peta became accustomed to the experimental situation, she started to go after food much more quickly (after 3 to 4 reinforcements) in response to the word "go" or simply to a waving of the hand. The same may be observed in dogs. Each successive food-getting behavior was formed more rapidly than the initial one.

We carried out on Peta many different behavioral experiments, just as we would in our animal research. Thus, for instance, we would make a passage of only 25 cm. in width between two wooden screens blocking the way to food. At the sound of the bell, she would go after the food, but would stand helplessly in front of the screens, look first at them, then at the experimenter and finally would go back. However, when the passage was widened, Peta went through it to get her food. After several experiments, the passage was narrowed progressively to 25 cm., but now she would go through sidewise without helping herself by pushing the screens with her hands.

We would take her to different corners of the room and there, behind a screen, would show food and then bring her back to the sofa. After 3 minutes, at a signal "go," she would go alone to find the new location of food. If one placed food in front of her under a plate and then brought her back to the sofa, at the signal she would go to the plate, but would not look for food under the plate. We had to show her how to remove the plate to get the food.

We also conducted experiments testing her ability to use canes in order to obtain food located across a wire fence, just as Köhler did with monkeys (Köhler, 1925). At first we would place food a short distance behind a grating. Peta would then put her hand through and take the food. Then we would place the food further away and would put three canes in front of the fence, each cane of a different length. She would stop, completely helpless, in front of the fence and would not even try to put her hand through. This is exactly what a dog would do. If the food was near the fence, he would try to get it with his paw; if the food was beyond his reach inside the grating, he would not try to get it. Neither did Peta try to use the canes. When we put a cane in her hand, she simply waved the cane. Then she picked up one or the other canes and played with them. When the experimenter in front of Peta got the food with the help of the cane, she immediately grabbed the food. But afterward, Peta herself, still would not use the cane. After three demonstrations by the experimenter, Peta imitated the movement of putting the cane through the screen but again she simply waved the cane across the fence and did not try to get the food. The experimenter took her hand, with the cane in his hand, and helped her to move the food closer to the grating. After he repeated it once, Peta started to use the cane in order to get food. However, she was unable to judge the length of the cane. When the food was far away, she would take the short cane and would wave it persistently without reaching the food, although a longer cane with which she could get the food was on the floor nearer her (Beritoff and Dzidzishvili, 1934a).

Other behavioral experiments were conducted on Peta. It became absolutely clear from these experiments that the microcephalic girl was unable to carry out planned acts of behavior, but was able to perform behavior based either on a chain of conditioned reflexes, or driven by mental images.

POSTMORTEM EXAMINATION OF MICROCEPHALIC BRAIN

Peta died, and postmortem examination showed that the whole brain was extremely retarded in development. The cerebral hemispheres were particularly small. In general, they were similar in weight and configuration of the circumvolutions of the brain of a chimpanzee. The total weight of the brain was 410 Gm., just as in a chimpanzee, while the weight of the hemispheres was one fourth of the normal value for a 10-year-old child. Accordingly, the cortical surface of the hemispheres was one third of what it should have been at 10 to 11 years of age. Although there was the usual sixth layer, pyramidal cells were extremely rare, particularly in the temporal lobes (Figure 15) (Natishvili *et al.*, 1936).

The general size, weight and length of gyri and the surfaces of Peta's cerebral cortex were evaluated in the light of anthropologic and encephalometric studies of postembryonal development of the brain from birth to the age of 15 years (Tvaladze, 1936, 1939, 1942). Tvaladze compared these various parameters of Peta's brain with the average values found in a newborn baby and an 11-year-old child (Tvaladze, 1936). He showed that in Peta they were below those generally found in a newborn baby. This indicated that the delay in the development of her brain took place in utero. The total weight of both hemispheres, without the meninges, was in Peta 289 Gm., while in the newborn baby the average weight is 350 Gm. and in a child 10 to 11 years of age, 1160 Gm. The total length of all the gyri of three different orders in Peta was 2641 mm., while in a newborn baby it averages twice as long, 4590 mm. and in a child 10 to 11 years old, four times as long, 10,538 mm. There was the same considerable difference as far as the general surface of the cortex is concerned. In Peta, it was 44,041 mm^2, while in a newborn baby, it averages 59,954 mm^2 and in a child 10 to 11 years old, it averages 173,782 mm^2 (Tvaladze, 1939).

Obviously, the number of connections of cortical elements and their organization in our microcephalic child were perfectly sufficient for psychoneural activity characteristic of higher vertebrates; they were not sufficient for eliciting the human type of planned psychoneural behavior. It appears that for the latter it is necessary to have considerably more neuronal elements in the cortex and much more complex

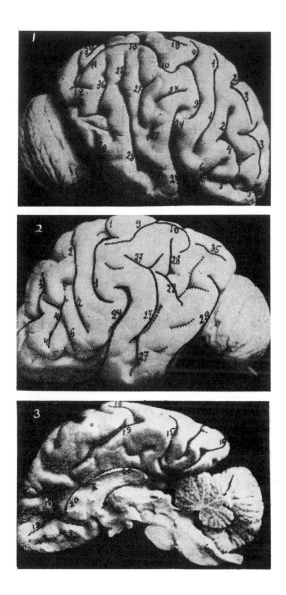

Fig. 15

Brain of microcephalic girl, Peta. *1*, Right hemisphere; *2*, left hemisphere; *3*, medial aspect of left hemisphere showing paucity of third order sulci. (Tvaladse, 1936.)

relationships between them. Such highly organized neuronal complexes were probably evolved in our monkey-like ancestors, as a result of progressive phylogenetic development of the cortex.

The above facts clearly show that in man the neuronal substrate of conditioned activity, as well as that of psychoneural activity, involving the reproduction of the images of the outside world, may be activated to the point of generating adequate behavior in the absence of planned activities with a measure of awareness which this term implies.

One must note that the brainstem of Peta was delayed in development only very slightly. According to Tvaladze, its weight (without cerebellum) was 13 Gm. In a newborn baby, the whole brainstem weighs about 5 Gm. on the average, and in a child 10 to 11 years old it averages 20 Gm. Thus, the development of the brainstem of Peta was only 7 Gm. below that of a normal child. According to Tvaladze (1939), in normal children the brainstem is about 13 Gm. in 2½ to 3 year olds, when definite, planned activity is already manifest. These data do not favor the hypothesis of Penfield, suggesting that the highest central nervous system level is located in the centrocephalic systems, namely, in the diencephalon. Rather, we should consider that the substrate of the awareness of the planned behavior is located in the widely developed associative fields of the cortex, particularly those from which Penfield could elicit by electrical stimulation complex memorizations and verbalizations related to past life experiences.

Experiments of Gershuni with Subsensory Stimulation

There are experiments and observations indicating that in man the substrate of conditioned activity is not the same as that of image-generating neural activity. This is the conclusion reached by Gershuni and his co-workers (Gershuni, 1947, 1949a, 1949b, Gershuni *et al.,* 1948). They compared thresholds of objective reactions with those of subjective perceptions (therefore, image-generating) elicited by a variety of stimuli. They found that when the skin was electrically stimulated in normal subjects, thresholds for subjective perception and for eliciting skin galvanic reactions were approximately the same. Also, auditory stimuli elicit a skin galvanic reflex at the threshold of hearing. However, this is no longer found in subjects having decreased perceptual abilities, as for instances, in the case of a concussion following a blast, or in drowsy states following administration of phenobarbital (Luminal). In such cases, there is a difference between the respective thresholds, the objective reaction occurring to a weaker stimulus than its subjective perception. Thus, auditory, olfactory, tactile and painful stimuli may affect the cortex without their actual subjective perception and without the occurrence of an orienting reaction; despite this absence, they may block the alpha rhythm in the occipital region (Gershuni, 1947).

Furthermore, Gershuni and associates found that in normal individuals conditioned skin galvanic reactions to sound obtained by pairing the latter with a strong electrical stimulation of the skin may be formed even though the sound is 8 to 12 decibels below the hearing threshold and, therefore, cannot be perceived subjectively (Gershuni *et al.*, 1948, Gershuni, 1949a, 1949b). It is remarkable that a sound 8 to 12 decibels below the threshold of hearing (subception, McCleary and Lazarus, 1949), paired with the electrical stimulation, establishes temporary connections following only a few associations.

Gershuni and associates also observed conditioned changes of the electrical activity of the cortex to the subceptual auditory stimuli after their association with electrical skin stimulation. However, this conditional sound did not elicit the psychogalvanic reflex, although the temporary connections were formed. The latter appears only when a more intense sound (3 to 6 decibels below the hearing threshold) is produced. Obviously, the temporary connections formed to the weak subceptual stimuli have functional characteristics such that in order to elicit external manifestations one must increase their strength. Analogous conditioned reactions could be formed to nonperceived visual stimuli (Gershuni, 1947, 1949a, 1949b).

Conditioned reactions to subceptual stimulation such as a sound of 100 c./sec. had all the characteristics of a conditioned reflex. They could be differentiated from a sound of 300 c./sec. They could be extinguished by nonreinforcement by the unconditional stimulus. They were, however, relatively unstable and more difficult to form; they manifested themselves after a longer latency time than the conditioned reactions established to perceived stimuli (Figure 16).

These facts indicate that the cortex may perceive peripheral stimuli and form temporal connections without subjective awareness of them and without orienting reactions. As we shall suggest later, this probably occurs without the participation of the stellate cells. Certain morphologic and psychophysiologic data led us to assume that peripheral stimuli, from the outside world in general, may affect the cortex and elicit observable reactions without participation of the stellate neurons, through the system of the internuncial pyramidal neurons.

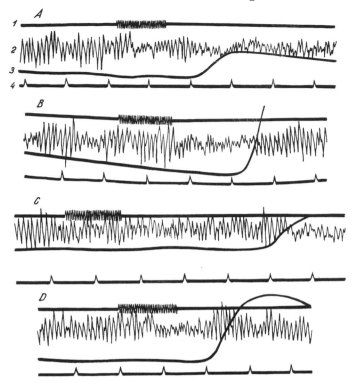

Fig. 16

EEG changes and skin galvanic reflex elicited by a conditional sound.
1, signal of the auditory stimulus; *2,* EEG; *3,* skin galvanic reflex recorded
by means of a DC amplifier; *4,* time in seconds; *A,* threshold of hearing
(sound of 1000 c./sec., 65 decibels above one bar); *B,* same intensity of
sound but below threshold of hearing; *C,* same auditory stimulus 4 decibels
below threshold of hearing; *D,* two decibels above threshold of hearing.
Note a more prolonged latency of the skin galvanic reflex and of alpha
depression when the signal is not perceived. (Gershuni, 1949a.)

Also the temporary connections in the cerebral cortex may be established through the internuncial and association neurons with and
without the participation of the stellate cells.

Neuropsychological Regulation of Individually Acquired Behavior

As suggested above, individual behavior may be directed by the
neuronal processes responsible for mental images, provided that it is

not repeated time and again in the same environment, and under the same conditions. When frequently repeated in the same environment, individual behavior becomes automatized and is reduced to a mere conditioned reflex.

One may easily illustrate how one or another part of the environment becomes a conditional signal to a certain segment of behavioral action. Five meters from the home cage in the middle of the path leading to the foodbox, we placed a metronome which was set in motion only when the animal reached it. After several such associations, the presence of the metronome was so linked with the movement of the dog toward the foodbox, that if the metronome was not started at the right time, the dog would stop at that spot and would not go any further. Obviously, the metronome became a conditional signal to the movement of the dog from the metronome to the box.

With the formation and reinforcement of temporary connections, the behavioral act is carried out according to the principle of a chain reflex. The movement from one point to another in a familiar environment is carried out according to the stimulus-reaction principle. Namely, conditional signals, leading the animal from one point to another during a certain behavioral phase, are formed at first by the visual stimuli arising from each point on the path followed by the animal from the cage to the foodbox; then by the proprioceptive and vestibular stimuli which are elicited during the movement; and finally, by the olfactory, the auditory and tactile stimuli from the objects found in the same environment. During the automatized movement of the animal, a psychoneural process subjectively expressed by the emergence of an image of the corresponding vitally important object must also take place. But such a movement is effected more quickly and economically by means of temporary connections rather than the emergence of the image-generating psychoneural process. The fact that such a process with the corresponding mental representation is present during automatized behavior is well exemplified when the environment is suddenly changed. In one experiment the foodbox was suddenly hidden by a set of screens without leaving any passage between them. In one place, however, the screen was relatively low, only 80 cm. high. At a conditional signal for food getting the dog went to the foodbox, stopped for just an instant before the obstacle, then went around the set of screens. When it saw the low screen, it jumped over it toward the foodbox. Obviously, before reaching the obstacle, the dog was behaving according to the conditioned type of behavior, but as soon as the obstacle was recognized, it started to act as if directed by the image of the foodbox, projecting it upon the other side of the screens. This dog was accustomed to jumping over low obstacles, but we might conjecture that this time he did it not simply because he saw a low screen, but because he had projected the image of the foodbox beyond the screen.

The presence of the image of the location of the foodbox is still better illustrated in the following example: A dog was taken out of the experimental room into another room and there given a signal for feeding. The dog at first would move forward 1 or 2 meters in the same direction as the one it would take in ordinary circumstances. But then it would turn around toward the door and would run through the corridor toward the experimental room, directly to the foodbox where it usually was fed following this signal. The character of this behavior could be explained in the following way. At first the conditional signal elicits the initial link of the usual automatized reaction; however, because of the change of environment, the ensuing segment of the automatized behavior cannot occur. At this moment, the psychoneural process, involving mental representation of the foodbox, emerges and projects the location of the box into the usual experimental room. The dog runs from the second room toward the room where the foodbox is located as if it actually saw the box.

From all this, one may infer that when the conditioned salivary and defensive reflexes are formed by the well-known methods of Pavlov and Bechterew, the original individually acquired reaction, in response to the conditional stimulation, should occur as a result of a neural process involving mental representation and is not directly elicited by the conditioned temporary connections. These emerge following frequently repeated reactions evoked under constant experimental conditions. One may state that the initial period of the generalization of individually acquired reactions to the exteroceptive stimulus is in reality the result of psychoneural activity. We studied the behavior of a dog located in an experimental cabin and attached to a stand during the initial period of the formation of an individual defensive reflex, which consisted of pairing an indifferent sound with electrical stimulation of the paw. We came to the conclusion that the initial motor reaction of the animal to the sound was sometimes much more violent than the reaction to the electrical stimulus itself. The sound was associated with yelping, increased respiration and attempts to run away from the stand. This behavior represents an individual act of escape from the stand, and in general the running away from the experimental cabin where the animal was subjected to the painful stimulus. At first the same violent escape reaction occurs in a dog soon after being placed in the stand as well as in the intervals between the conditional stimuli. Obviously, in all these cases, the violent reaction occurs as a result of a reproduction of the image of the "stimulating

cabin" and an associated emotional state perceived as a very unpleasant feeling. Only later on, when the shorter temporary connections
from the analyzer perceiving the conditional stimulus to the motor
analyzer are reinforced according to a mechanism to be considered in
detail below, will the more complex psychoneural reaction progressively disappear. Finally in response to the conditional signal, the dog
will lift only the stimulated paw, slightly turn his head toward the
stimulus and manifest very limited respiratory changes.

As was indicated above, one should not represent each individual
behavior of the animal as a chain reaction, consisting of a series of
natural conditioned reflexes established during the earlier life experiences of the animal. The behavior of the higher vertebrates, unless it
is automatized by repeated reoccurrence in the same environment,
does not have the character of an automatized chain reflex. When
some external stimulus elicits in the animal a behavioral act as a result
of a psychoneural process involving mental representation, the movement succeeds the preceding ones, not because of a preferential spread
of neuronal messages along specific temporary connections linking
together corresponding cortical elements, but in an entirely different
way. Namely, each time the psychoneural complex involving the mental representation of the environment including some vitally important objects emerges, the movements of the animal and all of his
reactions, as well as corresponding neuronal events in the cortex and
their spread toward the subcortical areas of the brain, are determined
essentially by the location and significance of the vitally important
object incorporated into the mental representation. It is true that during these behavioral acts, the animal makes use of natural conditioned
reflexes, for instance, opening a door by pushing it with its muzzle or
jumping over obstacles of a certain height when the image of a vitally
important object is projected beyond the door or to the other side of
the screen. But it would not use these mechanisms if they were not
necessary for these particular acts, i.e., if the images of vitally important objects were not projected beyond the obstacles.

Neuropsychological Process as a Whole

Psychoneural activity of the cortex during each behavioral act is integrated as a whole. At the same time that a certain neuronal complex
is activated reproducing images of some vitally important object so as
to elicit the corresponding behavioral act, all other neuronal complexes in the cortex are inhibited to a greater or lesser degree. Also,

this integrated activity of the cortex does not take place without participation of the other brain structures. In each behavioral act all the divisions of the cerebrum are integrated. During the activation of certain neuronal centers, there is inhibition of some others. However, in this section we will consider exclusively the integration of the cortical activity.

We believe that the following experiments demonstrate this integration of psychoneural activity. A dog was taken out of its cage and brought to a certain spot in the experimental room where it could see some food behind a screen. Then after approximately 1 minute it was taken to another place in the same room where it also could see food behind a screen. If after a minute the dog is released from its cage, it runs to the location in the room where it was shown food the last time. If the food is there, the animal eats it, but then always runs by the shortest possible path to the place where it was shown food previously. It does the same thing even if it does not find food in the first place.

In another experiment a dog was taken to the right for a distance of about 4 meters where it was shown food; then it was taken to the left for a distance of about 7 meters, shown food there and then taken back to the cage. If after 1 minute the dog is released, it will run first to the nearest location of food and then to the more distant location. If the food is shown in two places, equally distant from the cage, the dog will run first to one place and then to the other. It is obvious from these observations that the dog, while mentally reproducing several images of food location, is going first to a definite spot according to one image and then to another spot according to another image. One may assume that each time one image becomes dominant in the behavioral act, the food-getting behavior is directed by it. When this act is accomplished, driven by the first image, the other image becomes dominant and directs the food-getting behavior to another place.

The selective character of image-directed food-getting behavior is obvious if a dog is shown bread in one place and meat in another. The animal will always run first to the place where meat was shown and only after eating it, will it run to the place where the bread is located. We also made the following interesting observation. A dog was shown bread located nearby, and meat in the far corner of the room. It would first run to the bread and taking it in its mouth without eating it, would run toward the meat. There it would throw the bread on the floor and pick up the meat. Only afterward would it eat the bread. However, even more frequently, the dog would go first to the bread, look at it and then, without taking it, run to the meat. Only after having eaten the meat would it come back to the bread and eat it (Beritoff, 1934c).

These experiments clearly indicate that each time the images of food are projected to several different places, the behavior of the dogs is directed by one of these images, namely, the one which is the most effective either because it represents the preferred food or the closest location. The animal makes orienting movements with its muzzle and always goes to a definite location as if guided by the dominant image. Obviously, during this process, the psychoneural complex related to the other food image is inhibited. That during this type of experiment one deals with the process of inhibition can be inferred from the fact that the animal would not eat the bread, even if it is located in its mouth, as long as an image of meat is mentally projected to a place nearby. One may conclude from this that the complex neuronal process which reproduces the dominant food image elicits on the one hand the orienting reaction of the head followed by the behavior of approach to the projected food location; on the other hand, it elicits a general inhibition of those cortical regions which do not participate in this particular food-getting behavior.

When a dog goes to a place according to a given dominant image and eats food there, or when it does not find food there at all, one may assume that in both cases a mental representation of the absence of food is formed. Accordingly, the orienting reaction to this food location disappears. At the same time, the previously elicited general inhibition is suspended. Because of this, another image of food location may become dominant and elicit a new corresponding orienting reaction of the head followed by the approach reaction to another location of food.

Thus, one may state that the integrated reaction of the cortex in each individual image-driven behavioral act, just as during a response to a direct perception of food, is expressed by the predominance in certain neuronal complexes of excitation over inhibition and by the predominance of inhibition over excitation in other cortical areas.

The Significance of Psychoneural Activity in the Setting Action of the Environment Upon the Individual Behavior of Animals

At the very beginning of our studies of conditioned defensive reflexes, we came to the conclusion that the experimental situation, namely, the room itself in which the experiment was conducted, is significant in eliciting a dog's reactions to a conditional stimulus. Later on this same observation was made during a study of free movements in various animals (dogs, cats and pigeons). It was clearly seen that the introduction of the animal into the experimental room, in general its introduction into the experimental situation, predisposes it in a certain way toward the conditioned reaction which has been formed in this particular situation. In a paper published in 1930, we formulated, in the following way, this predisposition of the central nervous system toward the individually acquired reaction.

Everyone who has studied individual conditioned reflexes in animals knows very well the considerable significance which the usual experimental environment has on the elicitation of an individual reflex. During the initial trials, often during many days and weeks, the individual conditional signal produces the reflex only in this situation: in other words, only after the dog was introduced into the experimental room and put in the customary place. In other situations, even those well known to the animal, it does not exhibit this reflex. Obviously, the experimental room changes, in a certain way, the functional state of the central nervous system.

Therefore, the whole environmental situation under which the animal shows the reflex to a given signal becomes a "directive (instructive) stimulus," and we considered this predisposition to be "directive" in the physiologic sense of the word.

The nature of this phenomenon was understood in the following way:

Each of the components of this complex stimulus connects in the cortex with the motor centers of certain movements, as well as with the sensory fields related to these components. Each of the latter considered alone is able to activate all these connections but not to the degree necessary in order to elicit behavior. They only heighten the excitability of the whole complex of temporary connections and predispose the central nervous system to a certain activity; in other words, they play a sort of directive role (Beritoff, 1930).

Starting in 1945, we studied in more detail the phenomenon of the directing action of the environment in regard to the individual behavior of animals. We were interested in determining the physiologic role of this action of the environment, not only during the period of automatization of the individual behavior, but also in the initial period, when the behavior is being led by a mental representation. In our first brief communication, published in 1947, we termed this directing effect of the environment, a "setting effect."

Nature of the Setting Action of Environment

The nature of a "disposition" or "setting effect" of the environment was first considered with regard to the understanding of the conscious, purposeful behavior of man. Man satisfies his organic, intellectual and social needs under the influence of certain initial readiness, sets which are a product of either a given environmental situation or life-long individual and social experiences. This polarization of consciousness is referred to by psychologists as a determinant tendency or set, that is, a psychophysical state which exists between the awareness of a need and that behavior which serves for gratification of the need.

More than anybody else, Uznadze and his associates contributed to the experimental study of set (1930, 1939, 1949). They developed their teaching on the basis of the study of sensory illusions. They accumulated considerable factual material concerning visual, tactile, kinesthetic and auditory illusions, and disclosed a series of laws governing the onset and the extinction of these illusions. Uznadze found that sets are created continually as a result of interaction with the outside world and represent an integrated reaction of the personality to all integrated subjective reflections of reality. However, according to Uznadze, the set is not produced in the organism merely by the direct influence of the environment upon psychological and physiologic activities. On the contrary, he asserts that the whole mental activity, as well as individual behavioral acts, depends entirely upon an integrated reflection of reality, and this is what constitutes the set. In other words, the actual work of the psyche expresses a derivative phenomenon. With this understanding of the individual set, a belief is created that it originates independent of physiologic and psychological activity, seemingly without the participation of specific central nervous system structures; it is considered as some modification of an inner state of the organism as some kind of attuning of the psychophysical forces of the personality in order to activate them in a certain direction.

Very recently some pupils of Uznadze thought that the set, being the primary form of psychological reflection of a situation as a whole and a state of readiness of a subject to act accordingly, should therefore have its own physiology. This physiology of the set consists, according to the teaching of Pavlov concerning higher activity of the central nervous system, of the systematization of cortical functions. According to Pavlov, there is in the cortex a functional integration of aftereffects or traces of excitation and inhibition elicited by each pattern of stimulation ("stereotype") and that each component of the original stimulus pattern is able to activate the whole functionally united system. It follows that the course of a reaction is basically determined by this inner set of a patterned "stereotype" in the central nervous system and not by a specific configuration of external stimuli (Bjalava, 1953; Khojava, 1951). It is assumed that the set consists of a psychic counterpart of that physiologic activity which may be called systematization (Bjalava, 1953). In other words, Khojava and Bjalava see the physiologic basis of a set in the form of temporary connections relative to conditioned activity, just as I did in 1929 and in 1947.

Lately, the concept of the set has been transferred to the field of animal behavior. These attempts were made not only on a theoretical, but also on an experimental basis. Uznadze in 1941 and Voytonis in 1945 in our country, and Woodworth (1906, 1939) as well as others abroad, gave explanations of animal behavior in terms of a set.

Recently the setting action of external experimental conditions was studied by Asratyan and his associates (1941), by Laptev in the laboratory of Anokhin (1949), by Vatsuro (1947) in the laboratory of Orbelli and by Kupalov (1947, 1948). All of them are in agreement that a setting action is achieved by a form of conditioning mechanism. However, the explanation they give, as well as that formulated by Uznadze and associates, is not based on any experimental analysis of observed phenomena such as would allow one to penetrate deeper into the physiologic mechanism of the setting action of the environment. These authors are content to limit themselves to expressions which refer to an inner shift or psychophysical modification of the personality (Uznadze, 1941); to directionism, the mobilizing of the readiness of an organism for a certain action (Woodworth, 1906, 1936); to activation through a series of functional changes of a certain background tone (Asratyan, 1941); to occurrence in the central nervous system of certain functional structures or certain constellations of foci of excitation and inhibition (Vatsuro, 1947); or to a systematization of temporary connections (Bjalava, 1953). All these verbalizations do not give any physiologic explanation of the concrete phenomena underlying set, but only express, in diversified and more or less complex hypothetical ways, the general description of the phenomenon. In order to understand the set scientifically, it was necessary to analyze certain concrete situations in which it occurs and to disclose those inner processes of the neuronal or psychoneural character which are at the basis of these observations.

We noted the phenomenon of predisposition of the organism toward some particular reactions when we studied the neck and vestibular tonic reflexes; this was in 1915. As is known, Magnus (1909a, b, 1910a, b, 1924) found that changes of the position of the head in space, or in relation to the body, modify the tone of the extremities. We found, however, that if the head is turned very carefully, without eliciting strong stimuli, then the tone in the extremities may not change. And yet, if after that one applies a stimulus, for instance, pinching the tail, an extremity or the ear of the animal, then immediately the tonic reflex occurs, corresponding to the new position of the head. The analysis of this phenomenon led me to conclude that there is a predisposition in the organism consisting of an increase in the excitability of certain tonic centers of the central nervous system. This heightened excitability is due to the subliminal action of the peripheral impulses arising from the proprioceptors, those of the neck muscles which are distended during the turning of the neck and those vestibular receptors which are stimulated by the change of the position of the head in space (Beritoff, 1915). Because of the heightened excitability of these centers, they react very easily to all sorts of stimuli spreading within the central nervous system.

We studied the variability of other reflex reactions. In all cases, we found that each reflex of the animal is not elicited only by one or another component of the external situation or by the action of this or that stimulus applied by the experimenter for this purpose. The elicited response results from a complex made of all the present and preceding environmental, situational and experimental conditions which have created a particular functional state in the central nervous system. This state is expressed by an increase of excitability in certain nervous centers; it is this functional state which constitutes the very readiness, which in regard to the behavioral act, is called a set.

EXPERIMENTAL STUDIES ON SETTING ACTION OF ENVIRONMENT

Initial stage.   In order to clarify the role of this or that component of the environment in individual behavior, we conducted the following experiment by the open field method. In a large experimental room, one experimenter, *K*, elicited food approach behavior toward the right foodbox, while the other experimenter, *D*, elicited with the same signal an approach behavior toward another (left) foodbox; the signal consisted of ringing of a bell. Every day, the experiments were conducted by both experimenters. Each came a few minutes or a few hours after the other and several times fed the animals, after the signal, from the appropriate foodbox. Initially, the dog would run in the presence of one or the other experimenter to both foodboxes, not only when the bell was ringing but also spontaneously. However, later on, the dog reacted only to the signal and in the presence of one experimenter would run to one box, while in the presence of the other, it ran to the other box. We studied in detail these two stages of individual behavior and found the following differences between them. In the initial phase of the experiment, after the formation of an individual food-getting behavior, such behavior seems to occur only on the basis of the evoked image of the foodbox with its projection to a certain part of the experimental room. This image or the concrete mental representation seems to be created after only a single feeding. The reproduction of it is easy under the influence of the conditional signal, as well as under the influence of one or another component of the experimental situation. The reproduced mental representation seems to elicit in the dog the same behavioral act, an approach to food located in the box hidden behind the screen as if the animal actually saw it.

In our experiments the food in the experimental room was given by opening the foodbox only when a certain signal, in this case the bell ringing, was present. In all other instances when the dog approached the foodbox, the latter was not opened, and the food was not given. One may, therefore, assume that after a while the signal elicits the mental representation of an open foodbox and this is associated with the corresponding emotional excitation experienced subjectively as a feeling of gratification. The experimental situation alone without the alimentary signal could reproduce the mental representation of a closed foodbox, and this was probably not accompanied by this emotional alimentary excitation. Correspondingly, the experimental situation without the alimentary signal extinguished the approach behavior toward the foodbox or elicited it only very seldom, mostly when the animal was introduced into the experimental room and thus could see the box itself.

However, one may assume that stimuli in the experimental environment were always acting on the cortex, and they evoked not only the representation of a closed foodbox, but also that of the food in the box. Because of this, as long as the animal was located in the experimental room, the motor structures of the cortex must have been submitted to a certain subliminal excitation. It is possible that at this same time a certain emotional excitation also occurred, associated with an activation of the paleocortex and the reticular formation. One may further assume that as a result of this, the excitability of the motor structures of the cortex was all the more increased, and this probably occurred also in other motor centers of the brain. This created the readiness toward the food-getting behavior in a certain direction. This explains why the dog might suddenly leave its usual place and run to the foodbox, not only after the alimentary signal, but also at the occurrence of other stimuli which were incorporated into the experimental situation.

In other words, at the phase of the training when the outside environment ceased to stimulate the animal actively and direct it toward the foodbox, it still affected its behavior by creating a set, through a heightening of excitability of certain motor centers by reproducing the image of a closed foodbox and by certain emotional excitation.

Our experimental data indicate that in this initial stage of training, the feeding signal (bell) also elicits food-getting behavior when it is given by somebody else in the absence of the experimenters; even when it is given in a different room. At the feeding signal, the dog runs toward the experimental room and toward the foodboxes. The animal also behaves in the same way "spontaneously," i.e., without the occurrence of a signal. Then also, the animal goes from another room through the corridor into the experimental room, and runs toward the foodbox. These facts show convincingly that we may be dealing here with an expression of a dynamogenic behavior elicited by a mental representation of the food location. Obviously, an essential controlling role is played in these examples of an adaptive behavior in animals by the image of food projected to a certain foodbox located in the experimental room.

The same facts have another very important theoretical significance. They indicate also that after the stimuli in the environmental situation of the experiment start to exercise a setting action upon the food-getting behavior, the signal (bell) elicits the alimentary behavior not only in the presence of an initial set, but also without it. That is, the image of the food location may be reproduced directly at the ringing of the bell, and then is perfectly sufficient to elicit the onset, the direction and the expedient course of the food-getting behavior.

Second stage. In the second stage of training, when in the presence of one of the experimenters, the dog runs at the signal, without mistakes, to one of the foodboxes and in the presence of the other experimenter runs to the other foodbox, we are dealing with an automatized food-getting behavior occurring according to the principle of a conditioned chain reflex. In this period of training, the animal behaves in the same way even if there are no signals as soon as it is introduced into the experimental room, and also in the interval between the signals if this interval becomes too long. In the presence of the experimenter, *K*, the dog ran toward the right foodbox, while in the presence of the other experimenter, *D*, to the left. The animal was strongly affected by the very appearance of the experimenter; when *K* or *D* entered the room, the dog would suddenly leave its usual place and run to the appropriate foodbox.

We studied the character of this food-getting behavior and concluded that all the components of the intricate complex of stimuli experienced by the dog in the experimental room are in the nature of conditional stimuli. However, at any given moment some stimuli act on the dog by creating a set only. In other words, by themselves they do not elicit any movement either toward the place where the dog was usually resting or toward the foodbox, but they prepare the animal for such a movement. Other stimuli play the role of a starting stimulus; i.e., when they occur, the animal actually goes either toward its usual place of rest or toward the foodbox. Thus, when the dog entered the experimental room, the view of the experimenter getting ready to sit down at his desk usually became a starting stimulus sending the animal toward its usual couch; all other stimuli in the experimental room created a set favoring this movement. During the food approach behavior of the dog toward a certain foodbox, the feeding signal which initiates its movement constitutes a starting stimulus, while the whole remaining experimental situation, and particularly the presence of a certain experimenter, creates a set; the animal's pose expresses such a set. It looks toward the foodbox where it received food from the given experimenter.

The starting stimulus acts upon the dog, as does the setting stimuli, in the period of the automatization of the alimentary behavior through the established temporary connections. These connections, of course, are created as a result of a repeated occurrence of the same food-getting behavior in the same environment. Through some of these connections, an increase in excitability occurs in certain motor centers of the cortex and, because of this, the disposition of the animal toward a certain movement is created. Then, other stimuli act through the temporary connections upon the same centers and initiate the onset of a particular movement.

However, the experiments showed that even at the stage when the greatest automatization of the animal's behavior occurs, the feeding signals arouse the images of food location. This is obvious in cases when the experimental situation is changed and, therefore, an automatized behavior cannot be entirely realized. For instance, it occurs when the animal is transferred to another room and the bell is rung there in the presence of one of the experimenters. The dog at first turns around and then runs in the same direction as if it were in the usual room. Then quickly it changes direction, leaves the room it is in, runs into the corridor and from there goes without stopping into the experimental room, directly to the appropriate foodbox. This observation suggests that even after automatization of the individual behavior of the dog, the image of food location with its psychoneural content arises and may guide the behavior.

As we indicated above, during the phase of automatization of the animal's behavior, the approach of one or the other experimenter determines the orienting attitude of the dog. That is, the presence of a particular experimenter, his appearance, his voice and his smell creates in the animal a set for the movement of approach toward one of the foodboxes, including an orientation of the head toward this box; whereas, the presence of the other experimenter elicits an analogous set of responses toward the other foodbox. We studied in detail this setting effect of experimenters, and we found that the dog's approach toward a certain foodbox, during this automatized behavior, is determined by the appearance, the voice or the smell of the experimenter, and not by the feeding signal. If, for instance, before approaching the experimental desk the experimenter covers himself with a sheet, the dog will not go toward the foodbox at the feeding signal (bell). But either the sound of the experimenter's voice or his smell when he approaches the animal is sufficient to make the dog move to the appropriate foodbox at the same signal. This occurred because the appearance, the voice and the smell of a given experimenter always were associated with the movement of the dog toward one of the foodboxes, while the characteristics of the other assistant were similarly associated with the driving stimulus toward the other foodbox. The signal was associated with locomotion to either foodbox. Obviously, the appearance, the voice and the smell of each experimenter were associated through temporary connections to separate motor neuronal complexes, each eliciting movement toward the appropriate foodbox. The feeding signal (the bell) was connected by the temporary connections with both motor complexes. But, if this signal elicited a different movement in the presence of each experimenter, this must have been due to the effects of sets created preliminarily by the presence of each experimenter; sets resulting in differentially increased excitabilities in those integrating and motor elements of the cortex upon which movement toward one or the other of the two foodboxes depends.

Advanced automatization. After an advanced automatization of the food-getting behavior, during the presence of a stranger at the experimental desk, and in the absence of the usual experimenter, the dogs went to the foodbox at the signal only during the first trials. They were not fed during these trials; i.e., when the experimenter was a stranger. Because of this, later on in the presence in the room of the same stranger, as well as when other people sat at the experimental desk, the dogs would not even try to go to the foodboxes. It is noteworthy that the presence of the same stranger together with the experimenter did not influence the habitual behavior of the dog; at the signal, the dog ran immediately to that foodbox which corresponded to the experimenter who was present. This seems to indicate that after the automatization of the behavioral act, when the presence of a particular experimenter at an experimental desk constitutes the major factor determining the set for approach behavior to a certain foodbox, the whole remaining situation, either habitual or changed to some degree, does not have any significant influence upon the food-getting behavior in response to the signal. Obviously the fact that the dog did not go to the foodbox in the absence of the experimenters from the experimental desk, shows this to be the most important differentiating sign of all the other conditions of the experiment. Such a differentiation must have been established because in the absence of the experimenter the image of the opened foodbox would not arise, and the temporary connections of the chain reflex would not be activated due to the absence of the setting action, initiated by the experimenter sitting at the experimental desk.

In general, after automatization of the behavior, the sequence of behavior may run from beginning to end, according to the principle of a chain reflex, provided that all the habitual conditions of the experiment are present. If the situation and conditions are changed, then at the feeding signal, only the first link in the chain reflex makes its appearance directly in response to the signal. Later on, the behavior is entirely determined by the reproduction of the mental representation of food location.

Effect of changing experimental conditions. The setting action of the external attributes of the experimenter is very easily upset by each change of the experimental conditions. For example, after the establishment of setting influences of the experimenters, the shortening of the intervals of the trials from 4 hours to 5 minutes, or even to 30 minutes, disturbed this setting effect. Despite the fact that one of the experimenters replaced the other, the dog continued to go at the signal to the same foodbox as if the previous experimenter were present. It was necessary to carry out a certain number of appropriately reinforced experiments with this decreased interval in order to reestablish the differential effects of the experimenters. Also, we found that these disturbances of the differential setting effects of each experimenter depended upon the eating act itself, but this negative influence of the feeding upon the set lasts longer if it occurs in the beginning of the automatization of the individual behavior, than it does later on. In the later period of training, after several hundred associations of the signal with eating, the duration of this negative effect of the feeding decreased to one minute. If, however, the signal was given by the experimenter without reinforcement by feeding, the differential effects of the experimenters were not disturbed even if they succeeded each other within 6 to 16 seconds. The dog went, at the signal, toward that foodbox which corresponded to the experimenter who was present at that time.

All these data clearly indicate that this disturbance of the set is due to the interaction of the conditioned reflex activity of running, and psychoneural processes of the mental representation of food which the animal just ate, when the previous experimenter was present. The feeding signal elicits *this* reflex activity and at the same time induces *that* mental representation. The behavior of the dog is determined more or less by the intensity of either cortical process. The more the temporary connections of the chain reflex are reinforced, the weaker must be the negative influence upon this reflex of the mental representation of the food located in the incorrect foodbox. On the other hand, the more recent the after effects of the psychoneural processes of the incorrect foodbox, the more intense was the negative effect upon a given reflex activity (Beritoff, 1947a).

The negative action of a given mental representation of food located in one of the foodboxes upon the automatized food-getting behavior toward the other foodbox, seems to be carried out through the presence of a general inhibition exercised by the psychoneural process of mental representation. Such a psychoneural process implies an excitation of a great number of neuronal circuits which we believe to be constituted by the stellate cells and pyramidal neurons of the cortex, as well as the corticothalamic loops. The stimulation of these neuronal loops through the collaterals of the participating neurons will activate the dendrites of the neighboring neurons and, as we will see below, by these mechanisms produce a general inhibition of all the cortical and subcortical neuronal circuits in which these neurons take part. It is probably because of this that the automatized food-getting behavior was inhibited under the conditions of these experiments.

When, however, the change of experimenters was done without feeding the dogs in the corresponding foodboxes, the setting action of the experimenters was not disturbed, even when the interval was shortened to 6 or 16 seconds between the experiments led by each of them. Apparently this occurs because of the fact that, after the feeding of the dog from a given foodbox by one experimenter, the excitability of the psychoneural complex, responsible for the representation of this foodbox, is significantly increased. This is why, after a rapid change of experimenters, the conditioned signal still activates this complex, and therefore, walking to the other foodbox is inhibited.

The setting effect of the experimenter is disturbed also in the absence of the reinforcement in consecutive experiments. When the automatized individual behavior was repeated several times without reinforcement, the dog at first ran at the signal to the corresponding foodbox and if this foodbox would not open, it immediately ran to the other foodbox. Later on, however, the dog might at the signal run to the second foodbox and then to the first; in other words, the set disappeared.

This disturbance of the setting effect must have resulted from the occasional arising, at the signal, of the image of food in a wrong foodbox; that is, the directing force of the psychoneural process of experiencing mental representations apparently shifted to the other foodbox.

The setting effect of the experimenter is preserved even after a prolonged interruption in training; except that after an interruption of training for as long as 2 months, the presence of the experimenter ceased to play the role of a setting stimulus. This was probably due to a weakening of the temporary connections, in particular, connections with the additional integrating elements formerly elicited by the whole complex of the stimulating situation, including the external attributes of the experimenters, the appearance of the experimental desk and the nature of the signal. Despite this there must have been a reproduction of the mental representation of the food in the foodboxes. The dog would go to one or the other foodbox, probably according to the representation that happened to be more active at the time. If, for instance, the preceding feeding was from the left foodbox, then in the following experiment the psychoneural processes related to the left foodbox were reproduced more intensely and, therefore, the dog would go to the left foodbox no matter which experimenter was present.

In another condition of the experiment, after a stronger automatization of the alimentary behavior, the dog went to the foodboxes, at the signal, even when it was satiated. In this condition, the setting influence of the experimenter was preserved. In the case of experimenter K, the dog would go to the right foodbox; in the presence of experimenter D, to the left one. This food-getting behavior was due exclusively to conditioned reflexes. It reflects the predominant excitation of those temporary connections which were formed in the presence of a given experimenter. While a psychoneural process related to the mental representation of the food was also present, it could hardly play any significant role in this behavior because the satiation of the animal would prevent the corresponding emotional excitation. It follows that after the automatization of food-getting behavior, the latter may occur in the habitual situation even though the animal is not hungry.

The setting influence of the experimenter would also be disturbed when the food was changed. In the experiments conducted by one experimenter, for example, by K, meat was given two or three times instead of bread in the right foodbox; later, when experimenter D was present, the dog would first go to the right foodbox. This could be explained easily by the assumption that in the presence of D the mental representation of both foodboxes was reproduced at the signal but with meat in the right one only. Obviously, the meat component of the mental representation was associated with greater emotional excitation as the dog would bark and run to that foodbox, would sniff about and would not leave it for a relatively long time. According to a theory which we will develop below, we believe that a very intense activation of the dendrites of a great number of pyramidal neurons takes place at that time, activation arising from the neuronal circuits responsible for the animal's behavior. Slow biopotentials may arise there, as we will see below, and, thus, inhibit the neuronal elements of the cortex which participate in the formation of the reflex pathways responsible for the movement of approach toward the left foodbox.

The setting effect of the experimenter is also disturbed when bread is replaced by an inedible object. For instance, if bread was mixed with quinine and put in one of the foodboxes, the set was disturbed and all the behavior of the dog in the presence of experimenter K, who was responsible for these experiments, was changed. The dog went to the foodbox containing inedible food with considerable delay or ran to the other foodbox or even toward the door, and it was very difficult to get it away from the door and make it go back to its usual place. When the other experimenter came, the dog behaved perfectly normally, went at the signal directly to the left foodbox and after eating bread went back immediately to its usual place on the couch. These observations clearly indicate the psychoneural nature of the described changes in the behavior of the animal. It suggests that in the presence of K the dog has a mental representation of inedible food in the right foodbox, and a simultaneous emotional excitation of an unpleasant nature. The dog escapes this foodbox, tries to leave the experimental room and behaves in the same way it would if it met an enemy in its path, with the associated negative emotional excitation. Such behavior implies, of course, the inhibition of temporary connections, particularly those which are formed in the presence of a given experimenter, and which determine the automatic approach of the dog to the right foodbox. In the presence of experimenter *D* the behavior followed its normal course for, along with the excitation of temporary connections eliciting reflex movement of the dog toward the left foodbox, mental representation of pleasing food in that box was reproduced.

4 CONDITIONED BEHAVIOR WITHOUT THE PARTICIPATION OF THE NEOCORTEX

Historical Background and Recent Studies

The ability to manifest conditioned activity after removal of the entire cortex was studied by several investigators. As early as 1892, Goltz, the first investigator of reflex activity in decorticate dogs who survived for several months after the operation, showed that these dogs were unable to have individually acquired reactions. They could not recognize food by its smell or sight and could not recognize their master by his voice or appearance. They would run into obstacles without getting around them, whereas normal dogs go around obstacles, even when their eyes are closed (Chapter 6), with the help of conditioned reflexes to tactile and vestibular stimuli (Beritoff, 1953). These individually acquired reflexes were called natural conditioned reflexes by Pavlov.

Goltz claimed, on the basis of these observations, that decorticate dogs are deprived of all the aptitudes which would require the presence of intelligence, memory and cleverness and stated that these dogs cannot learn anything because they are unable to memorize.

Afterward, several investigators using decorticate dogs tried to form conditioned salivary or defensive reflexes in an experimental chamber. The method of Pavlov was used. Despite hundreds of reinforcements, the conditioned salivary or defensive reflexes could not be established to the indifferent stimuli associated with painful excitation of the paw. In Pavlov's laboratory Zeliony (1911, 1929, 1930) had one such dog which survived the operation for more than a year. He tried to form a salivary conditioned reflex to a sound strong enough to elicit a movement of the head and ears of the animal. He associated this sound with the introduction of an acid into the mouth of the animal which elicited an intense salivation. These associations were repeated 324 times, but the sound did not become a conditional signal; in other words, when presented separately, it did not elicit the salivation.

Later on, however, in another decorticate dog, Zeliony (1929, 1930) was able to establish a defensive reflex to a very strong stimulus (a whistle). He ablated the entire cortex with the exception of a very small area over the corpus striatum and a very limited sector of the temporal lobe at the base of the brain on the left side. The dog behaved in a way characteristic of decorticate animals. It could not orient itself in space; it would not evade objects; it would eat only if the food was introduced far back in its mouth; if its paw happened to be in cold water, it would not withdraw it. Despite this, it was possible in this dog to form a defensive reflex to a whistle by association of the latter with an electrical stimulation of the paw. At the whistle, the dog would withdraw the leg that had been stimulated. This reflex was formed after 104 associations. It was immediately generalized; in other words, other sounds would elicit the same reflex. However, after extinction of the effects of extraneous sounds, the conditioned stimulus was still effective. One could not form a defensive reflex to stimuli of another kind, such as smell, light or tactile stimulation. Also, one could not form a salivary reflex to any type of stimuli.

In decorticate dogs one could establish a defensive conditioned reflex to intense sound even when the diencephalon was markedly injured. Popov attempted (1950) to form a conditioned reflex in a dog after a decortication with the partial exception of some allocortical and paleocortical formations. Histologic investigations showed that these preserved parts of the cortex were degenerated to a certain degree, as there was a marked disturbance of the architectonics of the cellular elements and a rarification of the tissue. This is why, according to Popov, they must have been almost completely nonfunctional. The authors found considerable degenerative changes in the basal ganglia, in the diencephalon and particularly in the thalamus and the metathalamus. This is why these investigators believe that after a complete decortication, one should not consider these animals as "thalamic dogs." According to them, they probably were hypothalamic animals or even bulbar animals.

However, in such an animal which survived the operation for more than 3 years, Popov (1950) succeeded in eliciting a conditioned defensive reflex to the sounding of a metronome after 200 associations of these sounds with electrical stimulation of the paw. But this reflex did not occur in the form of an isolated leg withdrawal. Lifting of the paw usually was associated with prolonged emotional excitation of the dog and with a disorganized movement of all the other extremities, as well as the whole body. This reflex action was very stable, but it could not be differentiated and could not be extinguished. The same was found in another decorticate dog. The author was not inclined to call this reflex a typical conditioned reflex.

Inasmuch as in the decorticate dogs of Zeliony and Popov no defensive reflexes could be elicited by visual, olfactory or tactile stimuli, and no alimentary reflex could be established, it would seem to me that these decorticate animals were not capable of conditioned activity. The explanation of why, after a considerable number of painful electrical stimulations of the paw, one could elicit defensive reflexes to an intense auditory stimulation, could be quite simple. Certain neuronal complexes of the brain may undergo structural change under the influence of multiple excitations of painful stimulations; i.e., their excitability may be increased. By this mechanism, a constant focus of heightened excitability is created, a focus which could be activated by an intense sound through the process of the general spread of excitation originating from the neuronal structures activated by the sound and not because of a formation of conditioned connections.

One may ask oneself why sounds alone could be effective and not other extraneous stimuli? The main reason for this, according to Popova's data from dogs (1960), is that the brainstem relay nuclei for acoustic afferent stimuli are developed more intensively than those for visual and possibly for other stimuli. It follows that the acoustic relays must exert more intense influence than other afferent systems upon the motor centers in the brain stem which are activated by the nociceptive stimulation.

However, the experiments of Ten Cate (1934) and Belenkov (1950, 1957), as well as others, show that conditioned activity is preserved in cats without a neocortex. Individually acquired behavior of the animals after the ablation of the neocortex, according to the experiments of Ordzhonikidze and Nutsubidze (1959a) conducted in our laboratories on cats, can be described as follows. The neocortex was ablated in several cats, but a prolonged observation over several months was done in five animals. In these animals, the paleocortex with the limbic system (gyrus cinguli, gyrus limbicus, gyrus hippocampus and the amygdala) as well as the basal ganglia and all the diencephalon were not involved during the operation.

Cats without neocortex, as is known, can react to any stimuli affecting any receptor; that is, they exhibit an adequate orienting reaction. Obviously, the starting mechanism of the orienting reaction exists also in the paleocortex. Ordzhonikidze and Nutsubidze, using such cats, established food approach behavior, such as going to a foodbox which was located 1 or 2 meters from the cage where the animals were kept. The animals were taken to the foodbox and fed simultaneously with the occurrence of either a sound or light, such as turning on of an electrical bulb.

One must mention, first of all, that cats without the neocortex do not acquire an approach reaction to the foodbox after only one feeding. Normal cats do it routinely, and this occurs spontaneously as well, without any artificial signal, seemingly through the reproduction of the image of the food location. Such an image is formed in a normal cat after only one feeding.

The cats without neocortex learned to get to the foodbox after a dozen reinforcements. They might go there after the opening of the cage, not only at the corresponding auditory or optic signal but also without it. In this instance, the cage opening became a feeding signal. But this individually acquired behavior was not stable. The source of the sound or light was located near the corresponding foodbox, and this favored the approach of the appropriate box. In spite of this, after many scores of reinforcements, these cats very often would deviate from the correct path and would go around the room without reaching the foodbox. Moreover, one could not differentiate the approach behavior to different foodboxes by giving different signals. They usually went at the signal to that foodbox from which they ate the last time. Furthermore, when the experimental situation was changed (such as increasing the distance between cage and foodbox, or hiding the foodboxes behind a screen or cessation of the conditional stimulus after the animal had left the cage), the operated cats were not able to reach the foodbox, while normal cats could do so easily.

Generally if the cats were trained to have feeding reflexes to sound or to light prior to the ablation of the neocortex, these reflexes would completely disappear after the operation, and one had to give scores of reinforcements in order to retrain them. But in cats without neocortex, it was very easy to form temporary connections by which painful stimuli elicited emotional anxiety reactions or fear reactions. Ordzhonikidze and Nutsubidze (1959b) observed that if cats without neocortex were presented with a painful electrical stimulus during feeding at the foodbox, they would afterward cease to go to the foodbox at the food signal. This avoidance reaction of a given foodbox persisted for several days. Normal cats would show the same reaction under analogous conditions, but the avoidance response would then last for several months.

These observations suggest that in normal cats temporary connections which determined spontaneous or voluntary approach reactions through the mental representation of the image of the foodbox location, as well as the automatized alimentary behavior in response to certain signals, are necessarily formed in the neocortex. The paleocortex may participate in automatization of the alimentary behavior to a given foodbox only after a prolonged consistent reinforcement.

These observations also suggest that the temporary connections are established as a result of emotional reactions elicited by painful electrical stimulation originating entirely in the paleocortex. Evidently the neural elements of the paleocortex responsible for emotional experiences may form temporary connections as rapidly as psychoneural elements in the neocortex do in regard to the perception of the outside world.

An oscillographic investigation of the limbic system recently revealed characteristic changes of electrical activity during the formation of a conditioned reflex. Thus, Lissak *et al.* (1957), while recording hippocampal activities under such conditions, found the following changes in the electrograms. A completely unusual sound produces a desynchronization in the neocortex as well as in the hippocampus. However, after a series of pairings of this sound with the electrical stimulation of the leg, the sound produces slow potentials at a rhythm of 5 per second in the hippocampus. At the same time, one could observe an increased tonic orienting reaction to the sound. The appearance of the slow potentials was considered by the authors to reflect the establishment of the temporary connections and the emotional conditioned reactions in response to the sound. Later on when the sound started to elicit defensive movements of the leg, the slow potentials ceased to occur, and the orienting reaction disappeared at the same time. The conditioned sound afterward elicited desynchronization just as the electrical stimulation did.

It follows from these observations that the hippocampus participates in a certain way in the formation of the conditioned reflex. However, as regards the formation of the temporary connections for the conditioned reaction, the authors considered this to be related to the activity of the ascending activating system. Yet, it is more probable that the temporary connections determining the orienting reaction originate primarily in the neocortex. That is, the sound is reinforced by the electrical stimulation of the leg, and it is likely that the conditioned orienting reflex is elicited through the somesthetic analyzer where the starting mechanism of the orienting reaction is also located. Also, since the temporary connections with the emotional reactions elicited by the painful stimulation are formed in the limbic system, it is probable that the slow potentials in the hippocampus occurring at the conditional signal are related to the onset of the conditioned emotional reaction and not to the conditioned orienting reflex.

Paleocortex and Reticular Formation

In the animals without neocortex, behavioral reactions occur with the participation of the basal ganglia, diencephalon and other divisions of the brain. What is the role of these different structures in psychoneural and conditioned activity?

At the present time, with the role of the reticular formation of the brainstem in the waking brain being studied, many investigators (Yoshii *et al.*, 1958, Gastaut *et al.*, 1957, 1958) claim that the temporary connections sustaining the formation of conditioned reflexes involve the collaterals of afferent paths to the intralaminar and reticular nuclei of the thalamus. According to these authors, the diencephalic regions constitute a site of the closure of connections during conditional activity. Later on, the same authors broadened this area of closure. They concluded from their investigations that the closure of reflexes responsible for conditioning takes place in essence in the nonspecific formations of the brain, particularly in the nonspecific structures of the brainstem. Moreover, they find that in conditioned reactions the cortex is secondarily involved by the system of nonspecific projections responsible for the reactions of surprise and, particularly, of attention. It is assumed that the cortex is affected by a stream of excitatory processes spread from the focus of conditional stimulation arising in the reticular formation of the brainstem.

Gastaut and others based their hypotheses upon oscillographic recordings of electrical activity arising in different nonspecific nuclei of the brainstem. Yoshii *et al.* (1958) studied the electrical activity of subcortical structures during the formation of temporary connections, for instance during the association of the flicker with the sound. They found that the sound became able, through conditioning, to elicit electrographic effects usually evoked by light in the reticular formation of the diencephalon. Incidentally, this conditioned response occurred much earlier, much more intensely and persisted much longer than in the neocortex. Later on, Yoshii demonstrated that the conditioned reactions expressed by these repetitive specific effects disappeared after production of a bilateral lesion of the thalamus.

Lissak *et al.* (1957) came to the conclusion that the temporary connections are primarily established in the reticular formation. They assumed, as was indicated above, that the first indication of the formation of a temporary connection in the form of a conditioned orienting reaction appeared in the ascending activating system. In this they have reference to the same orienting reaction which permits the conditional stimulus to establish a more intimate association with the unconditional stimulus.

Yet it is known that the typical orienting reaction of the head appears phylogenetically only in those animals which acquired a cerebral cortex. Thus both cerebral cortex and orienting reactions occur for the first time in reptiles.

We will discuss below some special starting mechanisms for carrying out the orienting reaction in area 17 of the visual analyzer, as well as in the somesthetic and auditory analyzers. It is natural to think that these mechanisms are able to act more quickly in the different analyzers of the cortex and by this elicit a conditioned orienting reaction. Since the coordinating apparatus of the orienting reaction is located in the mesencephalon, then the reaction may be directly elicited by stimulation of this structure or those afferent pathways arising from the thalamus which terminate there; but this does not imply necessarily that the starting mechanisms, the original point of the temporary connections of the orienting reaction, are not located in the cerebral cortex.

The most important basis for the hypothesis that the temporary connections between the conditional and unconditional stimuli may be formed in the diencephalon and mesencephalon is an observation that during the formation of the conditioned reflexes, the nonspecific nuclei of the brainstem give rise to the same type of electrical effects during the conditional stimulation as those seen during the unconditioned reactions. Moreover, during the conditional signal while recording from different nuclei in either the diencephalon or the mesencephalon, one may find a special type of enhanced electrical response in some specific nuclei of the subcortex only when the conditioned reflexes are elicited. This is in no way evidence for the contention that it is only there, in these nuclei, that the conditioned closure takes place and that the conditional signal is connected directly with these particular nuclei. If these nuclei are a coordinating or motor center of one of many somatovegetative components of emotional behavior, then they should react each time during the occurrence of a conditioned reflex, even if the latter is established by closure of the conditioned and unconditioned connections in the highest division of the brain, the cerebral cortex.

We believe, therefore, that in mammals the temporary connections for typical conditioned reflexes are formed exclusively in the highest divisions of the brain, in the neocortex and the paleocortex. This is in agreement with the oscillographic data obtained most recently and reported in the papers of Yoshii and Matsumoto at the Moscow Colloquium of 1958. These authors asserted that the amygdalohippocampal system is responsible for the temporary connections between the "representations of conditional and unconditional stimuli." The alleged proof is that during the action of the conditional stimulation, either alimentary or defensive, simultaneously with the cortical desynchronization, slow waves at a frequency of 4 to 5 per second appear in certain structures of the paleocortex, basal ganglia, diencephalon and mesencephalon. At the same time, the authors found that the paleocortex, "the amygdalohippocampal" system, plays the leading role. Therefore, they assumed that all the other structures were activated under the influence of this system. In other words, during the formation of a conditioned reflex, the temporary connection would be established in this system and only from there would activate the neocortex, through the reticular formation, as well as all the other somatovegatative centers of emotional behavior.

However, on the basis of the above discussed particulars of cortical activity, one may assert that the amygdalohippocampal system has a leading role only in regard to emotional reactions, either inborn or individually acquired (pp. 91–104).*

Role of basal ganglia. We came to the conclusion during a fore-

---

*One of the early examples of the participation of the hippocampus in the "individually acquired behavior of mammals" was disclosed by Liberson and Cadilhac (Confinia Neurologica *13*: 277–281, 1953) and Liberson and Akert (EEG Clin. Neurophysiol. 7: 211–222, 1955). In their experiments, the dorsal hippocampus of the guinea pig exhibited a rhythm of 5 to 8 c./sec. each time an experimenter approached the cage containing the animal. This was called by these writers the manifestation of the guinea pig's "social intercourse." Later Liberson and Ellen (in *Recent Advances in Biological Psychiatry*, Grune & Stratton, Inc., pp. 158–171, 1960) succeeded in recording a progressively developing (see p. 161) resting 3 c./sec. hippocampal rhythm when a 3 c./sec. flicker was used to condition an avoidance reaction of a rat. The same authors also succeeded in conditioning an alimentary behavior to the electrical stimulation applied to the hippocampus of one side, as differentiated from the effects of the hippocampal stimulation of the opposite side. (Editor.)

going discussion that conditioned activity disappears after a full decortication associated with a destruction of basal ganglia, but is preserved after the ablation of only the neocortex with the preservation of the paleocortex and basal ganglia. We also suggested a role for the paleocortical limbic system in conditioned activity. It remains now to ask to what degree the basal ganglia, consisting of the nucleus caudatus, putamen and the globus pallidus, participate in the accomplishment of different types of inborn and individually acquired behavioral acts.

The study of the anatomic connections of basal ganglia with the rest of the brain has been the object of investigations by many authors. Ramon Cajal has shown that the fibers of the internal capsule give up collaterals running toward the basal ganglia. Then Spiegel (1919) found in the nucleus caudatus many fibers of small diameter running into the internal capsule. Many neuronal connections are found between the basal ganglia and the specific as well as nonspecific diencephalic nuclei (Glees and Wall, 1946, McLardy, 1948, Cowan and Powell, 1955).

Neuronal connections between the cortex and the basal ganglia were also the object of investigations by many anatomists. Glees, who conducted the most thorough investigation, came to the conclusion that the suppression areas 2S, 3S and 8S in cats are connected to the nucleus caudatus by the nonmyelinated fibers originating as collaterals of the corticofugal pathways. These fibers branch between the cells of the nucleus caudatus and participate in the formation of the pericellular plexuses. The degeneration of these fibers after cortical ablation may be revealed in the silver stained preparations with typical preterminal and terminal degenerative changes.

Connections between different divisions of the brain were found in some recent physiologic investigations. Spiegel *et al.* (1956, 1957) found marked changes in the electrical activity of the caudatus and the globus pallidus during the stimulation of specific thalamic nuclei, as well as during the stimulation of nonspecific formations.

Oscillographic investigations have pointed up the connections between the cortex and the basal ganglia. Dusser de Barenne and McCulloch (1941a, b) found that the suppression strips of the cortex 4S, 8 and 24, project to the nucleus caudatus, area 6 to the putamen and the lateral part of the globus pallidus and areas 4_q and 4_r to the putamen only. Therefore, according to these investigators, the inhibiting action of these suppression areas upon the thalamus is carried out through the basal ganglia.

The functional significance of the basal ganglia was investigated by many authors in the last century. (See the review of Gottschik, 1955.) At the very beginning of this century for many years, Bechterew (1905) and associates studied these ganglia using all the methods of their predecessors. In addition, they applied electrical stimulation only after the degeneration of pyramidal fibers in the internal capsule following the ablation of the sigmoid gyrus or a section of the pyramidal tract, in order to avoid the spread of current over those fibers. They could not elicit any motor reactions by stimulating the nucleus caudatus, but excitation of the nucleus lenticularis elicited tonic convulsions of the facial muscles and in the opposite extremities. From this they concluded that the caudatus does not have the motor function which they found in the nucleus lenticularis or possibly only specifically the globus pallidus.

The most recent investigations have repeatedly confirmed the facts established by Bechterew. However, it has also been shown that stimulation of the nucleus caudatus elicits inhibition of the cortical motor effects and, for this reason, cannot elicit motor reactions (Mettler, Ades, Lipman and Culler, 1939). The stimulation of the globus pallidus produces, in general, an inactivation of the animal, progressively transforming his behavior from an active state to a state of immobility and finally to sleep occurring after a latency of from several seconds to 2 or 3 minutes (Akert and Anderson, 1951).

However, still more recently, the stimulation of the nucleus caudatus through implanted electrodes in the nonanesthetized cat (Forman and Ward, 1957) was reported to elicit simple isolated movements, just as if the fibers of the internal capsule were stimulated. These movements were stereotyped and were observed on the opposite side. However, the authors claim that these effects do not involve the internal capsule by a spread of current. They did not observe the inhibitory effect which other authors did while dealing with anesthetized animals. They found a tranquilization of the animal after repetition of brief stimuli, but sleep did not occur. According to Forman and Ward, the basal ganglia function as a transmitting station from the cortex to the diencephalon, and in general participate in the integrating activity together with other divisions of the forebrain.

The foregoing conclusion was also arrived at on the basis of an oscillographic study of the basal ganglia. Kogan (1949) investigating the electrical activity of the caudatus found that the same electrical effects could occur to various stimuli, even though these stimuli might have an opposite significance for the animal, as for instance, alimentary and painful stimuli. He concluded that this subcortical formation does not contain integrating mechanisms for complex behavioral reactions.

Instead, he feels that they are transmitting stations in the centripetal pathways to the integrating mechanisms of such reactions; these mechanisms, according to him, are located in the hypothalamus.

Many authors attempted to understand the function of the caudatus by ablating it bilaterally. Such experiments had been done in the last century, with the resulting observation of disturbances in the motor sphere, followed by a return of functions after several weeks. The most extensive investigations were done by Margaret Kennard in 1944 using monkeys. The substance of the caudatus was sucked out. Motor distrubances were then observed, such as involuntary tremor at the beginning of movements, particularly when there was an intense muscle contraction.

The most interesting results were those of Klosovsky and Volgina (1956) following the ablation of the caudatus of puppies on both sides. These dogs survived after the operation for 2 to 3 years. During the first postoperative days, the experimental animals showed a considerable decrease of reflex activity in response to external stimuli. They did not react even to most intense visual and auditory stimuli, such as a bright light, the sounding of an organ, ringing of a bell or the experimenter's voice. Sleep in these dogs was at first very prolonged and so deep that external stimuli could barely produce their awakening. They did not take food spontaneously; their muzzles had to be put into the plate.

However, after several weeks, these postsurgical disturbances disappeared to a considerable degree. Some of the animals became very mobile, ran very well and jumped over obstacles; others were, on the contrary, inhibited, passive and fearful. In general, all of the animals' movements were well coordinated. They would go around obstacles; sexual and maternal instincts were fully preserved; there were no disturbances in the vegetative system; there were no trophic disturbances.

Despite this apparent normalization of behavior, conditioned activity was affected. It was found by the open field method that most of the experimental dogs could not be trained to approach the foodbox at an auditory signal and return to their resting place despite a great number of associations (from 320 to 1225). In only two experimental dogs, an unstable alimentary behavior was formed to sound after 300 associations, but no differentiation could be established. However, the experimental dogs could recognize the foodbox and its location. They ran from the experimenter to the foodbox and back, although without any association to the conditional signal. They would stand on their hindlegs in order to get a piece of meat. All of this indicated that the dogs had some temporary connections for conditioned reflexes to the visual stimuli. Many of the animals reacted to being called by the experimenters; that is, they were able to form some conditioning to sound.

Generally, the major alterations in conditioned activity to sound were also found after a unilateral ablation of the caudatus. A conditioned approach to the foodbox at the sound was established much slower, after many scores of associations; differentiation was not achieved until 150 to 200 associations.

The same results were obtained by Klosovsky and Volgina in experimental dogs after the separation of the thalamus from the internal capsule, in that area where the fibers from the thalamus run to and from the corpus striatum, without destroying the caudatus and the whole striate system. This led them to conclude that the changes in conditioned activity after the bilateral ablation of the nucleus caudatus depends upon the suspension of transmission through the thalamus of impulses which contribute to the normalization of the processes of excitation and inhibition in the cerebral cortex.

Obviously, the basal ganglia in general play the same role in regard to the cortex as does the reticular formation; namely, they act upon it through the thalamus with both facilitating and inhibiting action. One may assume that the suppression strips in the cortex produce inhibition of cortical activity through the caudatus. The general inhibition of the cortical motor effects must take place in this way, just as does the general decrease of cortical excitability to electrical stimulation. The fact that this inhibition is general, is indicated by the occurrence of sleep. Putamen and globus pallidus may produce facilitating effects upon the motor system since this stimulation elicits various movements that are tonic in character. Serkov and Palamarchuk (1958) studied electrical activity of the head of the caudatus and of the occipital and central cortical areas. In the "resting state" the electrical activity of the caudate is characterized by a variety of electrical potentials, with a higher frequency than in the cortex, but of a lower amplitude (10 to 80 microvolts). Relatively slower potentials, on the order of 10 to 12 per second, are occasionally recorded. The indifferent stimuli (light or sound) did not influence the activity of the caudate nucleus; however, in the occiptal cortex the light elicited depression at first, and then an increase of electrical activity.

But when the stimuli eliciting alimentary behavior were applied (such as showing food, or even giving food), the electrical activity of the cortex and particularly that of the caudate nucleus changed significantly. In the cortex, the amplitude of the brain waves was somewhat increased and the rhythm became more regular; while in the caudate, regular spiking potentials appeared with a frequency of 15 to 18 per second, each spike being preceded by a slower wave. After such stimulation, this effect persisted for several minutes.

An alimentary conditioned reflex was established to the light from a 15-watt bulb, located 40 cm. from a dog's eyes, using meat and bread powder as reinforcements. After 10 associations, the light produced a conditioned effect in the caudatum; after 32 associations, it produced considerable changes in the electrical activity of the cerebral cortex and in the subcortex. At first there was an increase of electrical activity in the cerebral cortex and then a progressive increase of activity in the caudatus. The degree of change was almost the same as during feeding.

The fact that the light produces in the occipital cortex a different electrical effect than before its association with food, namely, a rapid increase in background electrical activity instead of an initial depression followed by an increase, clearly indicates that the cerebral cortex entered into interaction with the alimentary stimulus. Furthermore, the fact that these effects in response to light started earlier in the tracing from the cortex than from the caudatum, indicates that the cortex manifests a conditioned reaction earlier than the caudatum. And finally the fact that the conditioned effect of the caudate was the same as in the case of an unconditional stimulus and lasted significantly longer than the conditioned effect in the cortex, suggests that this effect depends upon activation of the subcortical regions driven by the conditioned excitation of the visual cortex.

On the basis of all these observations there is no reason to believe that the basal ganglia in mammals participates directly in the formation of conditioned temporary connections. Obviously, when temporary connections are formed in the neocortex, the caudate is involved secondarily, either through direct connections with the cortex or by more complex pathways through the thalamic nuclei.

Integration of the Neocortex and the Paleocortex

This monograph presents the arguments which in our judgment are in favor of the neocortex as the main site for the formation of images of the outside world. The presence in the primary areas of the neocortex of sensory stellate cells with their histological characteristics makes this conclusion all the more certain.

The basic meaning of the phylogenetic development of sensory stellate neurons, with their pericellular net and the entire mechanisms for their integration, seems to consist in the formation of images of the outside world. Because of this particular neuronal substrate, men and animals may regulate their behavior in a given environment without the necessity of being further activated by this environment. In other words, the image of the environment replaces the real environment to the extent that these images are projected to points corresponding with those in the real environment.

The main characteristic of neuronal connections of receiving stellate neurons is that they are formed after only one simultaneous or consecutive activation of these cells, and that in these connections is included a "starter" for the mechanism producing a reaction of orientation in space. Because of this, with each reproduction of a food image projected to a definite place in a given environment, the animal goes to this place; or during the reproduction of the image of an enemy, or of any undesirable object at a certain place in the environment, the animal escapes or avoids it. This goal-directed adaptive behavior reflects an aptitude of the highly organized nervous system which has developed phylogenetically in the animal world.

Each of us knows very well that perception of the external characteristics of a musical instrument does not occasion the reproduction of those auditory perceptions which we have experienced from it in the past; nor does the perception of an object from a previously perceived environment necessarily result in a reproduction of the visual image of the total environment. One must conclude, therefore, that the perception of an object does not necessarily lead to the activation of all the connections which have been formed in the cortex during the perception of this object. In the waking state it seems that the whole subjective effect is limited by the presence of a given image so that ensuing neuronal processes run along certain temporary connections between the internuncial and associative neurons. However, the presence of dreams and hallucinations clearly suggests that under certain conditions an active re-excitation occurs, which spreads along temporary connections from one system of stellate neurons to another, and results in the consecutive reproduction of images as they occur in dreams or hallucinations. In general it is characteristic of neuronal connections of sensory stellate neurons to be formed after only one simultaneous or consecutive activation of these cells, and that included in these connections is a "starter" for the mechanism producing a reaction of orientation in space.

However, for the emergence of one or another behavior, it is not enough to have the occurrence of an image of the outside world; there must also be a certain emotional excitation. For instance, during the reproduction of the image of food one must also have a feeling of hunger and of the expected pleasant emotional satisfaction with corresponding autonomic reactions in order for food-getting behavior to emerge coincident with an image of the location of food. Characteristically, when a dog has an image of bread in one place and meat in another, it will go first to the place where meat is located, and then to the location of the bread. It appears that the images of different foods are associated with different degrees of emotional excitation, and the behavior of the dog is directed by that image which is associated with the greatest emotional excitation.

Naturally, a question arises as to the mechanism controlling the simultaneous reproduction of an image and a corresponding emotional excitation. Briefly, one may answer this question in the following way: The structure which controls the emotional excitation is the paleocortex. The image of the outside world emerges in the neocortex. As is known, environmental stimuli may activate the paleocortex, as well as the neocortex. During the process of eating at a certain place in a certain environment, for example, a spatial image is formed with regard to the food, along with the emotional excitation of the enjoyment of food. The temporary connections are formed between the receptive elements of the neocortex and paleocortex, exactly as they occur between the receptive elements of different regions in the neocortex. Obviously somewhere in the cortex or the subcortex there is a neuronal substrate which integrates the activity of the paleocortex and the neocortex. One must assume that activation of this integrating substrate generates both the image of food and a corresponding emotional excitation. In other words, it seems that when some component of the environment activates the neocortex, eliciting the spatial image of food, the corresponding psychonervous complex of this image acts upon this integrating center and through it elicits from the paleocortex a corresponding emotional excitation. We shall now study these processes of integration of emotion.

5 MODERN CONCEPTS OF THE NERVOUS MECHANISM OF EMOTIONS

Our study is related to the role of emotions in animal behavior aimed at satisfying the needs for food and self defense.

When one considers an emotional state, one should differentiate between its two aspects: emotional *perception* (of hunger, satiety, thirst, fear, rage, etc.) and emotional *expression* of these needs (such as a voracious swallowing of food or its avoidance; escape from an enemy or nociceptive agents; change of respiration, pulse, blood pressure, perspiration, etc.).

Thalamus and Emotional States

Expression or Reactions

Cannon (1929) suggested the following explanation of the nervous mechanism of emotional reactions. Afferent stimuli activate the thalamus, and are then switched to different structures of the interbrain. As a result of their activity, nerve impulses are generated running downstream (activation of the visceral and somatic structures), as well as upstream to the cortex (conditioning the "perceptual tone" of the emotions). Cannon also suggested that the impulses running upstream decrease the cortical inhibiting influence upon the thalamus and hypothalamus and thus favor the emergence of an emotional reaction.

According to Cannon, the influence of the interbrain upon the visceral organs consists mainly in the activation of the sympathetico-adrenal systems. However, Gellhorn (1953) and his associates showed that during this process the vago-insulin system is also activated. Normally during an emotional state, sympathetic activity predominates, and therefore, the blood sugar content increases. However, if one removes the adrenals, i.e., if one disturbs the sympathetico-adrenal systems, then the same emotional reaction leads to a decrease in the blood sugar content which reveals the activation of the vago-insulin system.

Moreover, it is assumed that autonomic endocrine activity conditions the different types of external manifestations. For instance during rage there is activation of the skeletal muscles; whereas during fear, they are inhibited.

On the basis of more recent investigations (Hess, 1956, Gellhorn, 1953, Kaada, 1951, Kogan, 1949) it has been established that the centers of emotional expression responsible for the coordination of somatic and autonomic reactions are located mostly in the hypothalamus. For example, on the basis of study of the electrical activity recorded in the hypothalamus, as well as taking into consideration the results of local stimulation of different nuclei of this structure, Kogan came to the following conclusions: In the anterior division of the hypothalamus, in the area of the subthalamic nucleus of Luys, and the neighboring reticular formation, a mechanism of central coordination of defensive behavior is located, whereas the mechanisms of alimentary behavior are located in the posterior part of the lateral hypothalamic nucleus. These neural mechanisms elicit all the somatic and autonomic reactions of defensive and feeding behavior.

EMOTIONAL FEELINGS

When an emotional expression arises, consisting of a certain somatic and autonomic reaction, it is associated with a certain feeling. It is assumed that this emotional feeling is due to the activity of certain cellular systems of the cerebrum. But in contradistinction to the specific perceptions of the outside world, this emotional feeling is not localized by the subject in a certain region of the organism, nor is it projected outside of the body. All the external and internal stimuli are able to activate these central systems and elicit corresponding emotional feelings. There is no special inborn connection between the central structures perceiving external or internal stimuli and those which generate both the objective emotional expression and the subjective emotional state. Even pain associated with a nociceptive skin perception elicited predominantly by specialized afferent structures is not localized by itself. The subjective localization of pain in a certain body segment is conditioned by a simultaneous stimulation of tactile receptors of this segment of the body. Moreover, although pain receptors are present in the skin or in the blood vessels being represented by bare nerve endings, pain is also elicited by other receptors, auditory or visual, etc. One may further assert that each form of emotional feeling together with corresponding emotional expressions may be generated by an external or internal stimulus provided that the related central systems reach a sufficient level of excitability. Thus, for the feeling of hunger, the corresponding cellular structures should be in a definite receptive state; the same can be said about the sexual feeling or fear, rage and pain.

It is known that the feeling of hunger depends upon the chemical state of the blood. Obviously, in an animal deprived of food, some chemical substances disappear or their content decreases in the blood; thus, the metabolism in certain cells of the alimentary center changes in such a way as to lead to a considerable increase in the excitability of this center. During the state of satiety, the opposite situation occurs. The role of the metabolic processes is well expressed in relation to other emotional states, fear for instance. It is known that extraordinary events in the environment may arouse fear. During certain encephalo-pathies, for instance following intoxication with nicotinic acid, fear arises also under circumstances which normally would not elicit it. Obviously, nicotinic acid exerts an influence upon the metabolism of specific neuronal elements responsible for the subjective feeling of fear (Hebb, 1946).

It seems that all types of emotional reactions may be elicited through the reticular formation of the brain stem. It is known that all afferent pathways have collaterals running into the reticular formation, and therefore, nerve impulses orginating from peripheral stimulation may reach through this formation those cellular structures which generate an emotional state.

The origin of emotional feelings is still a matter of debate. Sometime ago it was thought that all emotional feelings, as well as emotional expressions, were localized in the hypothalamus (Gellhorn, 1953, Hess, 1956, and others). Lashley, in 1938, critically discussed this hypothesis and came to the conclusion on the basis of some clinical observations that the hypothalamic centers that are responsible for the origin of emotional *manifestations* do not constitute the source of corticopetal impulses which determine the character of the subjective *feelings*.

Lashley also criticized the concept postulating the presence of par-ticular diencephalic centers for emotional feelings. For example, it is known that the compulsive laughter or crying which can be observed in some patients is not associated with the corresponding emotional feeling. Such dissociation of emotional expressions and feelings suggests that these two aspects of an emotional reaction may be localized in different neuronal structures, in other words, are not related to the same hypothalamic or other centers.

Furthermore, Lashley showed that certain affective disturbances associated with lesions of the thalamus may also be observed in patients with lesions of any other segment of the afferent pathway; for instance, hyperalgesia is observed in all the cases of involvement of the afferent pathways at the level of peripheral nerves or at the level of the spinal cord.

The experiment of Masserman (1943) showed still more convincingly that the emotional effects elicited in cats by a direct stimulation of the hypothalamus do not express the full emotional experience even if such a stimulation is applied to this structure in a normal animal. The resulting emotional effects are not directed toward a certain definitive object of the environment; they disappear immediately following the end of the stimulation without any after effects (such as meowing, tremor, escape, etc.) which are observed following a true emotional reaction. Moreover, when the animal was stimulated while it carried out normal behavioral acts of feeding, grooming, etc., these emotionally expressed behavioral acts were not changed by the activation of the hypothalamus unless the latter elicited strong motor effects which would interrupt the behavior. Characteristically, the data of Roberts (1958) showed that the aggressive reaction elicited by stimulating the hypothalamus usually cannot be conditioned. Obviously, the integration of the full emotional reaction does not take place in the hypothalamus.

One may, therefore, ask where the neuronal substrate originates emotional feelings and integrates the whole emotional reaction with both its subjective and objective manifestations? More specifically, is it in the neocortex or in the paleocortex?

Neocortex and Emotional States

Experiments carried out in animals without the neocortex showed that these animals may experience emotional reactions. The experiments of Ordzhonikidze and Nutsubidze revealed after ablation of the neocortex the presence in cats of a feeling of hunger and satiety. In the fasting stage, the animals became restless, meowing and screeching; after feeding they calm down and stop meowing. These cats show a preference for meat compared to bread. When they are offered meat and bread simultaneously, they eat meat first as a rule. If one sticks a piece of beeswax onto a piece of bread and gives it to the animals, they swallow only the bread. These cats easily manifest rage following skin stimulation. They also show an exaggerated defensive reaction in response to minimal stimuli. When one tries to put them on one's knee, they always try to escape; if one prevents it, they manifest a rage reaction.

However, cats without the neocortex do not manifest a reaction of pleasure, such as purring, lifting the tail up, rubbing the head or trunk against objects, moving the forelegs rhythmically, showing claws and abducting the toes. Such a reaction of pleasure does not occur for many months following the ablation of the neocortex. According to Olds (1958), stimulation of the amygdala or of the septum, the preoptic region as well as other segments of the paleocortex, and even of the interbrain, elicits a very intense feeling of pleasure. Obviously, the neocortex plays an important role in the activation of that neuronal substrate located in the paleocortex which may generate the feeling of pleasure.

However, the neocortex plays an important role in relation to other emotional reactions also. This is revealed first by the fact that the reactions of fear and rage may be elicited by electrical stimulation of the occipitotemporal regions. During the stimulation in cats of the posterior and inferior regions of gyri sylvius, ectosylvius and supra-sylvius, Kaada and his associates observed a reaction of fear, the cats first pricking up their ears, becoming restless and making escape movements followed by searching movements (Kaada *et al.*, 1954, Ursin and Kaada, 1960a, b). A reaction of fear was observed in patients with epileptic foci in the temporal lobe as well when these areas were electrically stimulated during an operation (Penfield and Jasper, 1954). During stimulation of the gyrus marginalis in its most posterior occipital area, Gedevani (1947) observed a rage reaction in cats, meowing, snarling, characteristic tail movements, showing of claws and characteristic mimic expressions.

The participation of the neocortex in eliciting various emotional states related to behavior is revealed by comparison of a normal animal with the one without the neocortex. It is known that in a normal animal the fear reaction is preserved for many months (Beritoff, 1959c) in an environment in which a strong electrical stimulation was applied even only once, while in a decorticate cat it lasts for only a few weeks (Ordzhonikidze and Nutsubidze, 1959a, b, c). The neocortex also influences the reaction of rage. In a normal cat the rage reaction to repeated pinching of the tail by tweezers is progressively increased and in the intervals between the stimuli the cat shows readiness to avoid the stimulus. When it sees the tweezers, it reacts with an appropriate movement of the paw, tries to escape and to hide itself.

The cat without the neocortex reacts to the repeated stimuli in the same excited way; yet, such an animal does not try to face the tweezers and does not try to escape. It just screams and moves away for only a short distance (Ordzhonikidze and Nutsubidze, 1959a, b, c). All this suggests that in a normal cat the emotional reactions of fear and rage are integrated organically by the neocortex with the behavioral act of the animal; this integration promotes in a definite way the goal-directed adjustment to the conditions of the environment. In the cat without the neocortex, on the contrary, these emotional reactions occur as if they were isolated, without a goal-directed defensive behavioral experience.

With regard to the alimentary emotional reaction, one may assert that its emergence in connection with food-getting behavior is essentially independent from the neocortex; searching for food, finding it, feeding to satiety and the ensuing resting state may take place with participation of the rhinencephalon alone.

We showed above that the interbrain, just as the hypothalamus, cannot be considered as a structure responsible for a complete emotional reaction. It contains only somatic and autonomic centers of emotional expression. Therefore, one may assume that it is the paleocortex which contains the neuronal substrate responsible for emotional feelings and for the integration of the activities of somatic and autonomic centers into some kind of a complex full-fledged emotional reaction.

Paleocortex and Emotional States

Recently there has been an increased investigating effort aimed at the elucidation of the functions of the paleocortex. It is now firmly established that the rhinencephalic structures associated with the hypothalamus and the paleocortex in general—the gyrus limbicus (cinguli), lobus pyriformis, corpora mammillaria, fornix and amygdala—are the site of emotional feelings. The same paleocortical structures are considered as the substrate of a neuronal mechanism which integrates the coordinating centers of the hypothalamus for different emotional behavior (Kaada, 1951, Magoun, 1963).

AMYGDALA. The amygdala is affected by peripheral stimuli. Certain investigators came to the conclusion that this structure contains the projection of certain afferent systems and that the stimulation of the amygdala affects the activity of some somatic and visceral organs

(Kaada, 1951). It is directly connected with the reticular formation, with the nuclei of the interbrain and in general with the whole subcortex including the caudate nucleus and the tegmentum.

Using threshold stimuli one may elicit from the amygdala some typical behavior reactions with an emotional coloring. With certain threshold stimuli, one can observe an alerting reaction which is followed, after an increase in the intensity of the stimulation applied to the anterior division of the lateral nucleus, by a reaction of fear, whereas during the stimulation of the basal nucleus, a rage reaction is elicited. In the amygdala, one also finds functionally differentiated areas which during a liminal stimulation may determine somatomotor reactions (sniffing, licking, chewing, contraction of the facial muscles) as well as autonomic reactions (changes in respiration, salivation, urination, defecation) (Ursin and Kaada, 1960a, b). Obviously, the amygdala is one of the central formations participating in the integration of emotional reactions of somatic and autonomic structures.

LOBUS PYRIFORMIS. Important data concerning the role of the paleocortex in emotional functions were published by Ordzhonikidze and Nutsubidze (1959a, b, c). They produced partial bilateral lesions of various structures of the paleocortex for the purpose of studying emotional reactions. They showed that after bilateral lesions of the lobus pyriformis, the rage reaction (snorting, snarling and aggressive movements), which prior to the operation usually occurred in response to pinching the tail, was significantly decreased afterward. Also, a well-established rage reaction to a conditional auditory signal was decreased. However, after ablation of both the lobus pyriformis and the posterior part of the orbital area, the emotional reaction of rage was considerably increased. Such an animal would react violently, not only to pinching of the tail, but also to a slight touch. On the basis of these data, one may assume that the lobus pyriformis and the posterior orbital area are the basic structures controlling the emotional rage reaction. Here is also located, probably, a subjective feeling of rage.

The same authors found, following partial bilateral lesions of the uncus in the vicinity of the hippocampus, a negative reaction of the animal to food. The cat would not take food spontaneously and would react violently to artificial feeding. It would fight, snarl and spit the food out. This experiment suggests that the feeling of hunger and integration of the corresponding somatic and autonomic reactions are associated with an activation of neuronal elements of the uncus.

GYRUS CINGULI. Characteristic effects upon the emotional reactions resulted also from bilateral lesions of different areas of the gyrus cinguli. After a bilateral ablation of the middle part of this gyrus, the animal became very agile and manifested quick orienting reactions. Conditioned food-getting reflexes were formed and strengthened very rapidly. However, the ability to manifest an aggressive reaction decreased. For instance, the animal would not respond to the attack of other cats. Following the ablation of the anterior segment of the gyrus cinguli, the previously determined fear reaction became more prolonged and intense. The ablation of the posterior splenial segment of the gyrus cinguli was followed by a suppression of fear reaction. For example, the cat would not react to the appearance of a dog. Even when it was attacked, it would not snarl or escape (Ordzhonikidze and Nutsubidze, 1959a, b, c).

The cat shows a typical reaction of fear during the electrical stimulation of the mid cingular gyrus through implanted electrodes. On the basis of this reaction, one may form a conditioned reflex to outside stimuli, for instance, by illuminating from above the stand where the animal is located. The cat shrivels and turns away from the light. It is characteristic that the stimulation of the cingular gyrus inhibits feeding reactions; the cat stops or does not start eating during such a stimulation. The same can be observed following turning on of the light after the latter became a conditional signal to the fear reaction (Nutsubidze, 1960). These observations prove that the gyrus cinguli contains that neuronal substrate which integrates the corresponding motor and autonomic centers during the emergence of fear. This substrate seemingly produces at the same time a general inhibition of other emotional reactions, in particular those of alimentary behavior.

HIPPOCAMPUS.   Under the influence of cholinergic substances applied to the hippocampus and limbic structures, an alert cat shows an extremely intense emotional reaction (hissing, snarling, fighting) in response to skin stimuli (pinching). This reaction is followed by a general violent excitement. At the same time, the structures submitted to the action of the drug show epileptic discharges without participation of the neocortex. In a normal cat, the same stimulation of the tail would elicit only meowing (MacLean, 1948). These observations suggest that this aggressive reaction is due to an increased activation by the drug of the areas of the paleocortex which are responsible for emotional feelings and for integration of the whole emotional expression of aggressive behavior.

During the stimulation of certain regions of the hippocampus there is a general inhibition of various movements, the spontaneous ones as well as those which are elicited by stimulation of the cortex or of the afferent systems; also inhibited are the defensive and food-getting conditioned reflexes.* Stimulation of certain regions of the hippocampus inhibits one type of conditioned reflex while another type is facilitated. Also, sometimes during such stimulation, the animal becomes restless or shows a rage reaction while the cortex exhibits, at the same time, desynchronization of electrical activity. Often at the end of the stimulation, the animal wakes up and escapes (Lissak *et al.*, 1957). The recent experiments of Olds (1958) also constitute a good illustration of the presence in the paleocortex of the neuronal substrate for emotional feelings. This investigator implanted electrodes in rats in the rhinencephalon and in the ventral region of the brainstem. The rat was placed in a box containing a lever. If the rat fortuitively pressed the lever with its paw, the current would stimulate a brain structure corresponding to the implanted electrode for a short period of time (0.5 seconds). Most rats, following chance manipulations of the lever, begin purposely to press the lever rhythmically hundreds and thousands of times per hour. Sometimes after an occasional lever pressing, the rat would try to escape and would not press the lever again. This behavior can be explained by assuming that during the first type of experiment the rat experienced some kind of pleasure of either an alimentary or sexual nature, while in the second experiment, it experienced an unpleasant feeling.

It is true that such effects could be obtained also following the implantation of electrodes in the region of the hypothalamus and in the anterior nucleus of the thalamus. However, this does not mean that the neuronal cells responsible for the integration of the feeling of such pleasure are located in these structures. It is more probable that these areas of the brain are connected with the rhinencephalon and participate with the latter in the formation of corresponding neuronal circuits. Stimulation of these circuits in the hypothalamus may elicit an activation of the emotion generating structures of the rhinencephalon, just as if the latter were stimulated directly.

*Inhibiting function of the paleocortex has been revealed by electrical stimulation of the periamygdaloid cortex (uncus) during neurosurgical operations in man (Liberson, W. T., Scoville, W. B., and Dunsmore, R. H., EEG Clin. Neurophysiol. 3: 1–8, 1951). Such stimulation was applied as the patient, under local anesthesia, was given a word-association test. During the stimulation of the uncus, the patient stopped talking and showed a prolonged apnea. This effect could not be obtained by stimulating the convexity of the prefrontal lobes, the posterior orbital surface, or the anterior cingulate gyrus. (Editor.)

When one assumes that the paleocortex (rhinencephalon) is the neuronal substrate of emotional feelings and of integrated emotional manifestations, one also assumes that the paleocortex may be activated by some receptors to generate an external reaction independently from the neocortex. In reality, it is well known that the hippocampus reacts to the stimulation of almost all the receptors and that in this structure the electrical potentials may be recorded in response to the visual, tactile and acoustic stimuli; while in the mammillary bodies they are elicited also by proprioceptive stimuli (Kaada, 1951). According to the most recent investigations, the hippocampal response to the stimulation of somatic and visceral receptors is expressed by slow potentials up to 500 msec. duration and a prolonged latency time (Dunlop, 1958). The same slow waves are also recorded following stimulation of the afferent pathways and of the reticular formation of the brainstem. It was assumed that the hippocampal effects are generated through the connections originating in the ascending activating system and transmitted via the dorsal fornix to the hippocampus. It is also assumed that the activity of the hippocampus affects the hypothalamus and thalamus through the fornix (Green and Arduini, 1954).

Therefore, an important role is played by the hippocampus in the genesis of emotional reactions. After production of bilateral lesions of the hippocampus, there is a marked increase of the emotional reactions of pleasure to positive stimuli; the cats rubbed their heads against the object, purred, rolled on the floor. One of the cats showed this reaction so well that it tried very often to force the experimenter to hold his hand on its head or back (Nutsubidze, 1960).

In contrast, following an ablation of the entire orbital cortex, Nutsubidze observed a disappearance of the active manifestation of the pleasure reaction to caressing of the animal. Following the operation, the cat would not rub its head against an object, manifest the characteristic posture of making a round back or hold its tail in a vertical position. One could assume that the basic substrate of this emotion was the oribital cortex, while the hippocampus seemingly regulates in some way the activity of this structure. The increase of the reaction of pleasure following injury to the hippocampus may be interpreted as the release of the oribital cortex from the inhibiting influence of the hippocampus. The disappearance of this reaction following ablation of the neocortex is seemingly due to the fact that normally this emotion is generated through the skin analyzer.

Following ablation of the hippocampus, the cats also show an increased emotional reaction of hunger. They overeat and, following the feeding, remain near the foodbox for a long period of time; they resist when one attempts to get them away from the foodbox. It seems probable that regulation of the activity of somatic and autonomic centers of an alimentary reaction for which the uncus is responsible is transmitted to these centers through the hippocampus. One may assume that the hippocampus exercises upon these centers an inhibiting tonic effect while the uncus during the fasting state suppresses this tonic effect. The same is observed following a lesion of the hippocampus.

A marked increase of the emotional reaction of rage is also observed following injury of the hippocampus. For instance, each attempt to prevent feeding in such an animal elicits a rage reaction. This violent reaction of rage also is elicited during any painful stmulation, for instance, pinching the tail, as well as during the appearance of another cat near the foodbox or during an approach of a dog. The cat always fights, screams, snarls, bites and shows its claws (Nutsubidze, 1960). The normal cat in all these cases will run away from the stimulating agent, be it pinching of the tail or the appearance of a dog or another cat near the foodbox.

Following a bilateral ablation of the hippocampus the fear reaction disappears. The fear reaction cannot be elicited even by electrical stimulation. If the latter is applied during feeding the cat does not stop eating, does not run away from the foodbox and does not stop coming back to the foodbox as do normal cats (Nutsubidze, 1960).

The above-mentioned experimental data make us conclude that the feeling of fear and the integration of its external expression are the combined responsibility of the gyrus cinguli and the hippocampus. This conclusion is a result of the finding that a lesion of the gyrus cinguli, as well as of the hippocampus, leads to the disappearance of a fear reaction. Also, a bilateral destruction of the amygdala and of the neighboring areas of the gyrus pyriformis leads to a considerable and lasting decrease of emotional reactions. Thus, pricking up of the animal's ears, fear and rage could be elicited in such animals only by intense stimulation. These animals became tamer than is usual (Ursin and Kaada, 1960a, b).

Therefore, one may assert that the paleocortex plays an essential role in the genesis of subjective feelings of hunger, satiety, rage, fear and pleasure and that it integrates the activity of somatic and autonomic centers of the hypothalamus and other structures of the interbrain responsible for the genesis of the external manifestation of the hunger, satiety, fear and rage. These observations show that some specific parts of the paleocortex facilitate the activity of certain nuclei of the hypothalamus while others exercise a continuous inhibiting action. Furthermore, these effects may be observed to a different degree at different times. As a result of these mechanisms, the animal presents either alimentary or defensive behavior.

Structure of Paleocortex

One finds in the paleocortex a great number of stellate cells with short axons and other analogous small cells. These cells, just as the stellate cells of the third and fourth layers of the neocortex, must probably have a sensory function. The neuronal structure of the paleocortex which integrates the emotional behavior of the animal probably basically involves pyramidal neurons of different sizes. The axons of these neurons partly present their arborizations near the cell bodies and partly run to the other neuronal formations, in particular into the hypothalamus and even the thalamus. These connections must be inborn. The nerve impulses originating in the limbic system and in the paleocortex in general and running through the above-mentioned pathways probably generate excitation in different somatic and autonomic centers of the hypothalamus eliciting a certain behavior reaction and at the same time inhibiting other somatic and autonomic centers of the hypothalamus and of the interbrain in general. It is probable that the same relationships prevail here as those found in the spinal cord, where each time, during a stimulation of the receptive field of a certain reflex, there is a general inhibition of the other reflexes.

Sager (1960) showed that the activation of the rhinencephalon by a stimulation of different receptors is probably mediated through the reticular formation. From there the nerve impulses run to the hypothalamus, then to the dorsal medial nucleus of the thalamus, then through the internal capsule into the hippocampus, the amygdala and the rhinencephalon in general. However, that the nerve impulses are certainly also transmitted to the rhinencephalon through the neocortex was shown by the oscillographic investigation of Sager and Butkhusi (unpublished observations). They demonstrated that these connections run in both directions and seemingly form closed circuits. Therefore, these intercentral connections of the paleocortex and of the interbrain permit the occurrence of all the emotional behavioral reactions. The same two-way connections exist obviously between the gyrus cinguli and the thalamus. According to Papez, the impulses originating in the gyrus cinguli run through the hippocampus and the fornix to the mammillary bodies and from there to the anterior nuclei of the thalamus to the original locus in the gyrus cinguli. The interaction of these nervous circuits according to Papex is one of the most important factors in emotional excitation.

The neocortex is connected by two-way connections with the paleocortex, and it is therefore understandable that the activation of the latter is mediated through the neocortex also. Thus, all the receptors affecting the neocortex through the direct specific system must also influence the paleocortex via the neocortex and activate there the integrating mechanisms of emotional states securing different needs of the organism.

The presence of complex connections between the different parts of the paleocortex and between them and other divisions of the cerebrum makes it understandable that different emotional reactions are elicited from many areas of the brain and may be disturbed as a result of the injury of a great number of neuronal structures. Thus, for instance, the reactions of alerting and of fear can be elicited from the amygdala, the gyrus cinguli, the hippocampus and the neocortex.

Complete Decortication — Effect on Emotional States

For a better understanding of the function of the emotion-generating excitation of the rhinencephalon, one should consider the behavior of an animal after a complete decortication (the ablation of both neocortex and paleocortex). As is known, fasting dogs, following a complete decerebration including the paleocortex and the basal ganglia, cannot search for food and feed themselves spontaneously. According to Popov (1950), such decorticate dogs spit out food put in their mouths, and this behavior is associated with a definite defensive reaction. In order to feed such a dog, one had to place pieces of bread and meat very deep in the buccal cavity. After a certain time, the dog would start to accept food from a cup, but only when its muzzle was plunged into the cup. Characteristically, if the cup is taken away, then the dog repeatedly makes movements toward the food and if it does not find it, manifests a rage reaction.

The alimentary behavior of a decorticate satiated dog manifests itself by the fact that the animal stops taking the food, lies down and very quickly falls asleep. In the fasting state, it wakes up and walks around incessantly in the cage. However, the decorticate dog may calm down when out in the sun and may even exhibit a playful behavior.

A decorticate dog responds to outside stimuli by stereotyped reactions which, with increased stimulation, are usually associated with emotional manifestations. An intense visual (light from an electric lamp operated at over-voltage) or auditory stimulation elicits marked motor reactions which may be followed by rage. The dog reacts to the electrical stimulation by withdrawal of the stimulated paw and by emotional manifestations expressed by some disorganized movements (Popov, 1950). Thus, on the basis of the observations on decorticate dogs, it becomes clear that all kinds of external stimuli, if sufficiently intense and prolonged, elicit the same type of emotional reaction of rage. This type of reaction must be due to the excitation of the corresponding somatic and autonomic centers in the hypothalamus. In the normal animals these centers are probably inhibited all the time by the action of the cortex, particularly the paleocortex. Only after the release of cortical inhibition which may occur when the life of the animal is endangered, only then may the paleocortex normally manifest its function of integrating reactions of rage. Since in a decorticate animal, this integrating and inhibiting effect of the paleocortex is lacking, the excitability of the hypothalamus is considerably increased. In view of this, even those outside stimuli which offer no danger to the organism activate, in the hypothalamus, the somatic and autonomic centers of rage.

The decorticate animals are not able to form typical alimentary or defensive conditioned reflexes. As it was already mentioned, Popov (1950) succeeded in forming a defensive reflex to a metronome after 200 associations with an electrical stimulus applied to the paw. However, this reflex was manifested as a disorganized movement of the extremities and was not differentiated. Because of this, it cannot be considered as conditioned behavior or behavior appropriately adapted to the environment.

It follows from the foregoing discussion that the decorticate animals (dogs and cats), in whom the neocortex, the paleocortex and the basal ganglia are ablated, are unable to generate behavioral reactions with the appropriate emotional feelings and expressions.

PART II ORIENTATION IN SPACE

6 CHARACTER AND ORIGIN OF SPATIAL ORIENTATION

In the foregoing discussion of image-driven behavior, the ability of higher vertebrates to orient themselves correctly in space played an important role. For this reason we have devoted a great number of our investigations to this question. Spatial orientation in higher vertebrates is reflected in the ability of the animal to project into space or to localize the position of objects in relation to itself or to one another, to approach these objects, or to go from one to the other, even if the animal neither sees them nor perceives them subjectively by any other sense.

The investigations which we have conducted show that in higher vertebrates (cats and dogs) all the receptors may play important roles, under certain specific conditions, relative to orientation in space. However, the optic receptor and the vestibular semicircular canals, utricle and saccule, play a most significant part, since if they are suppressed, normal orientation in space becomes impossible (Beritoff, 1956b, 1959a, b).

Optic and Vestibular Receptors in Spatial Orientation

Spatial orientation is accomplished first by visual perception if the eyes are uncovered. For example, if a dog is shown a plate with meat, and then the plate is moved 4 to 7 meters and placed behind a screen, the dog will run directly there not only immediately, but even several minutes afterward, though it does not see the plate. If a plate with meat is shown first and is placed behind a screen in one corner of the experimental room, and then immediately or after several minutes a plate with bread is shown and is also placed behind a screen in another corner of the room, the dog will run first to the meat plate, i.e. to the preferable food, and then to the bread, or it may not go there

107

at all. The dog behaves in this manner not only immediately after being shown the food, but after several minutes as well. Finally, if a plate full of meat is shown, and placed behind a screen in a corner and a few minutes later a plate with only two pieces of meat is shown and placed behind a screen in another corner, the dog will run to the place where the full plate is located, and then it will go to the other plate.

On the basis of these observations, it is evident that the dog not only perceives external objects visually, i.e., by a visual analyzer, but it also projects the images of these objects into the environment. Therefore, the dog can perform correctly oriented movements toward either object in accordance with these images.

Spatial Orientation Without Vision

Orientation in space with eyes closed may take place more or less normally through the vestibular receptors only; in other words, with the participation of the vestibular analyzer only and, therefore, without a direct participation of the olfactory, auditory, somesthetic or motor analyzers.

Let us consider for example a blindfolded animal, dog or cat, placed in its cage in a certain area of the room. If one carries the cage for a distance of several meters to the other corner of the room, feeds the animal in that place and then takes it back by the same path, the animal may retrace this path not only with its eyes open but also blindfolded several minutes later, the only condition being that the animal has had, prior to the experiment, sufficient training to remain blindfolded (Figure 17). During these experiments we definitely established that the active locomotion of a blindfolded animal to the foodbox is due exclusively to the vestibular receptors. This was evident not only from the fact that in these experiments the animal was blindfolded, but also from the fact that during the transfer of the animal it remained motionless in the cage, so that there was no possibility of kinesthetic stimulation of the extremities, such as are, of course, present during ordinary locomotion. The influence of olfactory stimuli was also excluded, either by wiping the floor with gasoline or by sectioning of the olfactory nerves. If the blindfolded animal first is carried to the corner where it is fed and then to the other corner without being fed, the animal, after being released several minutes later, will go directly to the corner where it was fed but not to the other corner. It happens, at times, that a blindfolded animal finds

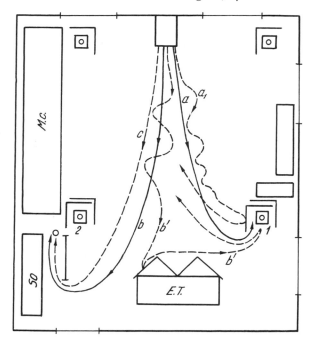

Fig. 17

Orienting food-seeking behavior after a single transportation to the place of feeding. Dog "Gilda" blindfolded. On this figure the solid lines indicate the path of the transportation of the animal in a cage, while the broken lines indicate the path of free movement. Path *a* indicates the transport of the cage to foodbox *1* where the animal was fed. The usual approach to this foodbox was barricaded. Released 2 minutes afterward, the animal followed path *a₁*, with small zigzags, but because of the obstacle returned to the original place; *b*, the path of the transfer of the animal to foodbox *2* where it was fed; *b₁*, 1 minute later the animal went in the same direction, found the screen at the experimental desk and from there went to foodbox *1*; *c*, after removal of blindfold, the animal went directly to foodbox *2*. (Beritoff, 1953.)

an obstacle in his path and then completely loses his orientation. However, if after this the blindfold is taken off, the animal will immediately run to the place where it was fed. It is therefore evident that in the transporting of the animal in a cage and with its eyes closed to a new place of feeding, an image is created of the path made by the experimenter (Beritoff, 1953).

In addition, as shown in Figure 18, if the blindfolded animal is taken first to the left for a distance of 3 to 4 meters without being fed, and is then taken to the right and fed there before being taken back

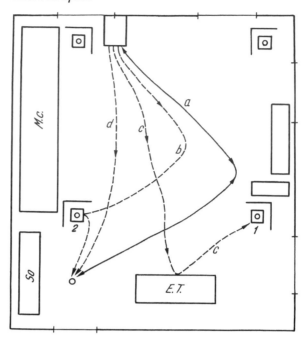

Fig. 18

Orienting food-seeking behavior along a new path. Dog "Gilda" blindfolded. *a*, Transport of the cage along the unbroken line in the direction of the sofa where the animal was fed and then returned to her cage along the same path; *b*, released a few minutes later, the dog ran to the feeding place along a shorter pathway, *b*. After being fed, it was taken back along path *a; c*, released again 2 minutes later the dog ran directly toward the experimental desk, encountered a screen which was in front of the desk, and then turned around to the left. From there, she was taken back to the cage from which the dog was transported again on path *a; d*, 1 minute later she was again released from the cage and then went directly to the feeding place. (Beritoff, 1953.)

through the same path to its cage, the animal after a certain time will be able to go directly to the feeding place and not along the path which was used by the experimenter. From this series of experiments, it is obvious that the blindfolded animal can precisely localize the feeding place to which it was transported in the cage, and this must be accomplished on the basis of vestibular perception (Beritoff, 1953).

Not only can the path toward a certain feeding place be perceived through the vestibular function, but also that place can be precisely localized in the room. Because of this, if the animal is at first carried or taken in the cage to a different place in the room, it may go from

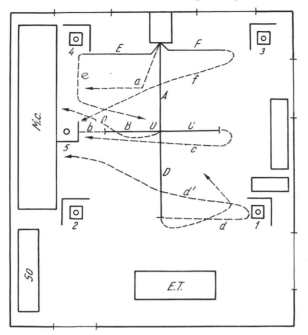

Fig. 19

Orienting movement toward a new feeding place. Cat "Belogrudka" blind-folded. The cat was forced to go 2 meters and then was turned 90° to the right, moved 1.5 meters further and there fed from foodbox 5. After being fed, the cat was returned along the same path. Then, the cat was taken to several other places from which, each time, she went by herself back to the foodbox. On this figure, the paths of the cat's forced movements are represented by solid lines and the spontaneously followed paths by broken lines. The cat chose path *a* when the cage was opened at its usual place; path *b* after first being forced along *AB*; path *o* after being forced toward *O*; path *e* after being forced from the cage immediately to the right along path *E*; path *f*, after being forced to the left immediately from the cage along path *F*; path *c* after a forced turn to the left along path *AC*; path *d* after being forced 4 to 5 meters directly forward from the cage along path *AD*; path *d′*, same. In these last two cases, the cat at first went to the left to the site of foodbox *1* because she ate very often from this foodbox and presumably had the image of its location, but since she did not find food there, she went directly to foodbox 5. (Beritoff, 1957b.)

this place directly to the feeding place, correctly performing all the necessary turns. Figure 19 shows one of these experiments conducted on a cat which was forcibly led to the feeding place, and Figure 20 shows the same kind of experiment on a dog transported in a cage toward the location of food (Beritoff, 1957b.).

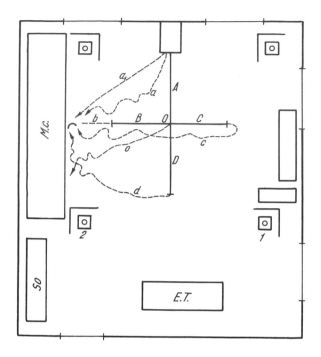

Fig. 20

Dog "Dica" blindfolded. The dog was transported in the cage nine times along path *AB* and was fed each time after being taken out of the cage. Then, it was transported to other locations in the room without feeding. Each time the dog was released it went directly to the location of food. *a* and *a₁*, free locomotion after release from cage at usual location; *b*, after transfer along usual path *AB*; *c*, after an unusual transfer to the left along *AC*; *d*, after an unusual transfer along path *AD*; *o*, after transfer along *A* to point *O*. (Beritoff, 1957b.)

We also established that the vestibular analyzer in the cerebral cortex reacts to stimulation of the vestibular receptors in a very precise manner and with fine differentiation. It is capable of analyzing the slightest changes in the pattern of stimulated vestibular receptors as well as changes in the duration and intensity of stimulation. This conclusion can be made from the observation that the vestibular analyzer very easily forms temporary connections with efferent projectional pyramids in response to different kinds of vestibular stimulation. In other words, this observation indicates that it is easy for an animal to form a conditioned food-getting reflex, consisting of leaving the cage for food, after being transported in a cage for a certain distance, for instance, 2 meters. The animal can also learn to differentiate this distance; it remains in the cage after being transported 1 or 4 meters, but leaves the cage after being transported for 2 meters. Also, its behavior may be conditioned so that it leaves the cage after the cage is turned 90° to the right, as opposed to remaining in the cage after it is turned 90° to the left, or even after a turn of 125° to the right. One may also form a "conditioned exit" to the lifting of the cage to a height of 80 cm., as differentiated from remaining in the cage when the latter is lifted 40 or 120 cm. (Beritoff, 1959a, b).

Also it is very easy to form a food-getting exit from the cage, conditioned to a certain speed of transfer. For instance, if after being transported a distance of 2.5 meters in 5 seconds, the animal is fed, whereas it is not fed after being transported the same distance in only 2 seconds or in 10 seconds, the animal at first would get out of the cage, but later would stop leaving the cage (Beritoff, 1956b). Therefore, vestibular stimuli arising during movement or the transport in the horizontal or vertical planes or during turns in one or another direction serve not only for the formation of the images of a given path, or a given turn, but can also become a conditional differential signal for starting certain behavioral acts.

When a blindfolded cat or dog moves from one object to another, perceiving them by various receptor organs, these objects are localized in the environment because of the ability of the animal to perceive the accomplished path by means of the vestibular receptors.

The localization of the objects on the basis of vestibulary stimuli is so precise, and their images are so effective, that a blindfolded animal is able to reach them over the shortest possible path and, if need be, correctly go around any obstacles on its way. Guided by the same vestibular stimuli, the animal is capable of going around the obstacles without touching them, or turning away from them at a certain distance, on the basis of only a single contact with these obstacles. The image of the object's location is projected to a certain part of the environment, by means of vestibular perception, and this enables the animal to avoid encountering them (Beritoff, 1953, 1959a, b).

Thus we established that the activities of vestibular receptors during the movement of an animal are a very important factor for its spatial orientation in the environment. It follows from this that blind animals, normal blindfolded animals or animals moving in absolute darkness, are able to orient themselves in space with the aid of vestibular perception.

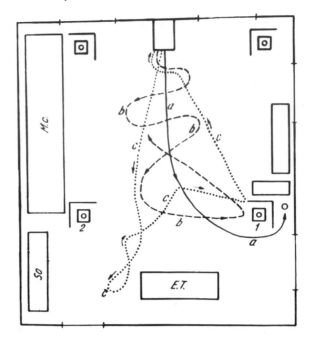

Fig. 21

Dog "Zabla" (without labyrinths), blindfolded, 13 months after vestibular ablation. The animal was taken along solid line, *a*, behind foodbox *1* and fed from a ball. Broken line, *b*, shows free movement of the dog 1 minute later. The blindfolded dog was taken again along path *a*. One minute after, it was brought back and the blindfold removed. The dotted line, *c*, indicates free movement following removal of the blindfold. (Beritoff, 1953.)

SPATIAL ORIENTATION WITHOUT LABYRINTHS

An animal with destroyed labyrinths was incapable of orienting itself in space in the absence of vision. It could not locate the place to which it had been taken for feeding once before; in fact, it was not able to locate it even when it had been fed at that place scores of times (Figure 21). This also showed that during such food-getting behavior the olfactory stimuli do not play a significant role.

Vestibular perceptions participate most actively in spatial orientation even when the eyes are open. This is inferred from the fact that animals without labyrinths, and with eyes open, behave significantly differently in experiments of the type described above. For example, if an animal without labyrinths is taken to a certain place in the experimental room or to a neighboring room where it sees food, and is then taken back to the initial place, the animal does not go to the location of food along the shortest pathway. Instead, even though its eyes are open, it goes from one place where it has previously been fed to another, finally reaching the desired foodbox (Figure 22). Thus, the orienting movement of the animal to the alimentary goal being driven by its image depends significantly upon vestibular receptors. A normal animal that goes to a newly experienced place to get food by the shortest possible path must have an image of this path, acquired on the basis of vestibular perception, which guides it in its approach toward the goal (Beritoff, 1953, 1956b, 1959a, b).

If a normal animal goes over the same path several times to the location of food, this food-getting behavior becomes automatized and then is carried out in accordance with the principle of a chain condi-

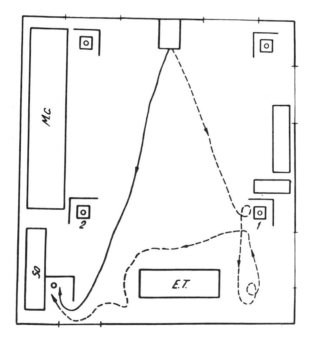

Fig. 22

Dog "Zabla" a half year after labyrinth destruction. The animal, with eyes open, was taken (solid line) to a new place of feeding, *So,* at the sofa, behind a screen. Released 1 minute later, she went spontaneously (broken line) to foodbox *1,* then to the left corner where she had been fed some time ago and only then to the present food location. The dog went first to all the places where she had been fed previously. (Beritoff, 1953.)

tioned reflex, with each segment of behavior depending upon the antecedent segment of behavior. Each of these segments of behavior is elicited through temporary connections formed in response to stimulations of the skin, muscle, auditory and vestibular receptors which occur during the antecedent segment of behavior. In this automatized behavior, optic perceptions, visual images, vestibular perceptions and spatial images, all play an important role. This can be inferred from the fact that if a feeding signal is given, eliciting a particular food-getting behavior, an animal with its eyes closed can go directly and precisely to the desired food location. If, however, the labyrinths are destroyed and then a conditional signal is given, for instance shaking the cage, a blindfolded dog will leave its cage and will execute all sorts of searching movements in the room, but it will not go directly to the location of the foodbox. However, if its eyes are open, the animal may go to this place directly, without any searching movements, just as a normal animal would do. Thus, an automatized alimentary behavior toward the foodbox in normal animals is carried out principally through the activity of the temporary connections formed to visual as well as vestibular stimuli.

Auditory, Olfactory, Skin and Muscle Receptors in Spatial Orientation

AUDITORY RECEPTORS

The remaining receptors, namely, auditory, olfactory, skin and muscle, each considered separately, may play a significant role in spatial orientation under certain conditions. Thus, for instance, the auditory receptors stimulated by a sound will accomplish not only the perception of the sound, but may also project the direction of the sound so that its source will be localized in a certain point of the environment. Then, on the basis of the projection of the image of this sound, the animal can travel for many meters along a strictly straight line toward the source of the sound; it may also avoid obstacles encountered in its path. The animals can do this not only at the time the sound is perceived, but also after a certain time has elapsed following the perception.

The precise localization of the direction of the sound and the location of its source is, under normal conditions, based upon its perception by both ears. However, after the destruction of the organ of Corti on one side, the animal only temporarily loses the ability to localize precisely the source of the sound and make correct orienting movements toward it. Such an animal then begins, after a certain time, to orient itself correctly by turning its head toward the origin of the sound, projecting the location of its source and then correctly moving toward this location.

When the source of the conditional sound is located at the foodbox itself, this circumstance strongly favors the projection of the foodbox location because the projected image is accomplished on the basis of both auditory and vestibular perceptions. Also, the orienting reaction of the head is a function of both these perceptions. This situation facilitates the rapid formation of a conditioned chain reflex to the given foodbox.

When the source of sound is not at the foodbox, it is then projected to a point in space other than the location of the foodbox. In this case, the orienting reactions of the head are directed either toward the source of the sound or toward the location of the foodbox. This does not prevent the formation of the image of the foodbox location, and the animal goes toward it on the basis of its image. However, this situation makes it more difficult to establish the conditioned chain reflex to the foodbox along the shortest pathway. Usually in the first stage of the formation of conditioned food-getting behavior, a blindfolded animal moves first toward the source of the sound toward which its head turns at the onset of the conditional signal, but, not being fed at that place, it turns its head toward the projected image of the foodbox and then goes toward the food. Only after several scores of reinforcing trials does the animal go directly to the foodbox. Thus, there is an extinction in the effectiveness of the image of the source of the sound, because the animal is not fed at that place.

If the source of the sound is located at a blindfolded dog's cage, formation of the food-getting approach behavior toward the foodbox is very much delayed. It seems obvious that the animal has an image of the food location, for in its spontaneous runs even during the first day of training, it takes the shortest possible path. However, the dog does not leave the cage at the conditional sound, but only sticks its head out toward the sound. It is necessary to force the animal to go to the foodbox scores of times in order to establish a conditioned behavior to the foodbox at the given signal.

In the first stage of the formation of food-getting behavior toward a foodbox at an auditory signal, a change in the location of the source of the sound does not influence the course of the food-getting behavior to any appreciable degree. The animal will still run to the foodbox over the shortest possible path. It may turn its head toward the sound, but immediately afterward it will turn it toward the location of the foodbox and run directly there. This too is evidence that food-getting behavior is directed by the image of food location.

But when auditory stimulation has already become a conditional signal for the automatized behavior toward a certain foodbox, a transfer of the source of the sound exerts an important influence upon its course. At the conditional sound the dog goes to the source of the sound, where he looks for food and only after a few searching movements turns its head toward the location of the food and goes there by the shortest possible path. This behavior reflects some integration of the projections of the source of sound and of the location of food. That is, the transfer of the source of sound now determines not only the orienting reaction toward the sound, but also the chain conditioned reflex which leads the animal toward the source of sound. During unsuccessful searches for the foodbox, the image of its real location must be reproduced and accordingly the orienting reaction toward the foodbox appears followed by the animal's successful attainment of the goal. This occurs not only in a blindfolded animal but also in one with its eyes open. After the source of the sound was transferred, the animal, even if it saw the foodbox, would still go to the source of the sound. Presumably under the influence of the sound, the image of the foodbox is also transferred, and the driving power of the image orients the animal in its direction.

Because the animal was not fed at the place to which the source of sound was newly transferred, a state was very rapidly reached when the dog would, at the sound signal, go directly to the location of food. Thus, the orienting reaction toward the sound became extinguished, and because of this the animal turned its head to the site of the foodbox immediately or after only a brief turning toward the sound. The conditioned chain reflex then leads the animal toward the foodbox again.

In the absence of vision, the auditory receptors play an important role in spatial orientation. They permit perception of solid objects at a distance by a reflection of sound waves. This was inferred from the observation that blindfolded cats and dogs do not always run into obstacles, and seem actually to avoid some of them. However, they always run into a net placed in their path. They also always run into the legs of chairs or tables or into any objects which do not reach as high as their heads, but will often avoid solid objects, such as a screen or a wall. Usually such objects will be avoided if the animal is moving slowly; it will then stop within a distance of 22 to 25 cm., and go around the object. However, when animals move rapidly they run into

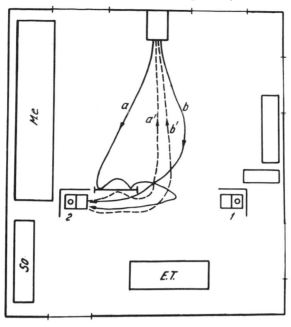

Fig. 23

An unusual obstacle in front of the foodbox. Dog "Trezor" blindfolded. The animal had an automatized alimentary response to foodbox *2* at a signal (tone of 600 c./sec.). The path was blocked by a screen. *a,* The first trial of the conditioned tone after blocking the path to the foodbox; the animal ran into the screen twice during locomotion toward the box, and once on the way back, *a'; b,* during the second presentation of the tone, the dog ran to the foodbox, making a large detour and reaching it without running into the obstacle; *b',* the animal returned making a large detour again. (Beritoff, 1958a.)

obstacles to which they are not accustomed, that is, ones which they have previously encountered only once or twice. With repeated experience in running over the same path, they go around and begin to anticipate the obstacles at a relatively great distance, that is, well before they reach the object. When they reach this stage of accuracy, blindfolded cats and dogs run rapidly from the cage along the path to the foodbox with their heads raised and without any delay. If one then places an obstacle in this path, the animal usually runs into it at least once. However, the next time the animal will go around it, starting to avoid it at a distance of 30 to 50 cm. On its return trip in the first trial, the animal will go in most cases around the obstacle without touching it (Figure 23) (Beritoff, 1958a).

However, sometimes a blindfolded dog avoids a completely new obstacle without ever having touched it. This occurs when the obstacle is a large solid object located at the level of the head and in front of it. This is an example of the role of auditory receptors in the perception of objects at a distance, which we will discuss later on.

It seems that an avoidance reaction by a blindfolded animal, occurring at a distance from the obstacle, must be primarily conditioned by vestibular perception. Obviously, even at the time of the first avoidance of an obstacle after having run into it, a normal animal must form, on the basis of vestibular perception, an image of the location of the screen along with the image of the foodbox and the path from the cage to the obstacle. Directed by this image, the dog goes to the foodbox, accomplishing necessary detours in the approach to the foodbox or even immediately after leaving the cage. Blindfolded animals without labyrinths are not capable of projecting the pathway into the environment and therefore cannot avoid the obstacles without touching them (Beritoff, 1958a).

OLFACTORY RECEPTORS

Olfactory receptors, perceiving the smell of food, also create images which are projected and the animal may move toward them along the shortest possible path. But cats and dogs, under the conditions of our experiments, were able to perceive the smell of bread or meat at a distance of only a score of centimeters; therefore, the orienting movements were guided by olfactory images only when the foodbox was located nearby. Accordingly, if the olfactory traces are located without interruption for a distance of several meters, then the dogs and cats may move long distances following these traces. If the scent emanates from the entire path leading to the goal, the movement of the animal has an orienting character and may be effective. At each moment this orienting movement of the animal will be determined by the scent originating only in the vicinity. However, if the traces are washed out, at a distance of even half a meter, the animal is not able to orient itself, and it begins to show zigzag, searching movements. Only when it again perceives the scent does it renew its orienting movements (Beritoff, 1953).

We convinced ourselves that if the animal acquired a recent image of the food location, it can approach it with its head raised and without olfactory-guided searching movements, even though there may be traces of scent on the floor. The animals, either blindfolded or with eyes open, usually manifest sniffing in their searching movements, but only after they are near the foodbox which they have approached on the basis of the image of the projected location of food. However, when an animal deviated from the correct path and lost its orientation, it started to make zigzag-like searching movements over the whole room, with intermittent sniffing behavior (Beritoff, 1953, 1050b).

MUSCLE RECEPTORS

Muscle receptors activated during locomotion do not participate in the arising of images of the path toward the box and therefore do not have any direct significance for spatial orientation. This became obvious from the fact that in the absence of visual and vestibular perception in cats and dogs, it was not possible for the animals to reach the foodbox after they had been walked there. They could not accomplish that task, even if they had been walked there with their eyes open, prior to having them blindfolded. However, normal animals after only one or a few times of just being carried in a cage to the foodbox, even if they were blindfolded and were given no opportunity to walk, could reach the goal with their eyes closed.

It follows from this that the stimulation of the muscle receptors does not significantly participate in the formation of an image of the accomplished path or in the projection of the image of the objects among which the animal was passing.

However, after being passively led several scores of times over the same pathway toward the foodbox, a blindfolded animal without labyrinths learns to go along this pathway with the aid of olfactory, skin and muscle receptors. But such food-getting behavior is carried out automatically, according to the principle of a chain reflex.

Thus, the stimuli momentarily arising in the olfactory and somesthetic receptors, and in the proprioceptors of the walking extremities, become conditional stimuli for the succeeding segments of behavior.

SKIN RECEPTORS

Tactile receptors by themselves do not play a significant role in spatial orientation. However, if one places an object in the pathway which the blindfolded animal systematically touches on his way toward the foodbox, then these tactile stimuli become conditional signals in the movement toward the foodbox. Therefore, tactile stimuli can cause orienting movements toward the foodbox in this manner.

Since, in the movement of the animal back to his cage, contact with the same objects directs the animal on his return path, the same tactile stimuli can apparently, in one case, direct the animal toward the food-box, and in another toward the cage. In other words, when a blind-folded animal touches familiar objects, the image of these objects must be projected to a certain place in the room and must relate it spatially to the foodbox and the cage. On perceiving the conditional alimen-tary signal, an image of the foodbox location arises; then, coming into contact with a familiar object, the animal starts its orienting movement toward the foodbox. However, after being fed, the animal heads back toward the cage, the image of the cage location must arise and this, along with getting into contact with the same object, orients the dog straight toward the cage.

An animal without labyrinths can acquire an automatic food-getting behavior toward a certain foodbox on the basis of tactile stim-uli, if one builds a corridor from the cage to the foodbox. Then the animal, blindfolded and without labyrinths, may very easily establish an automatized conditioned locomotion from the cage to the foodbox and back by touching the walls of the corridor with its body. This is possible because the tactile stimuli become conditional signals for the movement. If the corridor is removed, the animal soon deviates from the straight path, moves about in zigzag fashion through the room and in the vicinity of the cage or the foodbox and finds the latter by coming into contact with it (Beritoff, 1956b, 1959b).

Skin and muscle, as well as interoceptive stimuli arising during the transport of the cage to the location of food, that is, from the shifting movement of the animal's body and its internal organs, can play some role in spatial orientation. This is most obvious in animals deprived of the labyrinths, when the feeding occurs in front of the cage or follow-ing certain transports of the cage. During feeding immediately after turning the cage to the right, the animal spatially relates the food to the right of the cage. During feeding following lifting the animal in the cage to a certain height, the food is spatially related to an upper level. When the animal is let out of the cage to look for food, there is a reproduction of the food image projected to the front of the cage or to the right or above the cage, whichever is appropriate. But if an ani-mal deprived of labyrinths is repeatedly transported in the same man-ner and fed in the same place, temporary connections are established in the cortex of the brain between the neuronal elements perceiving stimuli arising in the skin and muscle, on the one hand, and certain efferent neurons permitting the animal to leave the cage and get its food, on the other. Because of this, a conditioned orienting movement for food is established.

Hence, all the receptors take part in spatial orientation, but only visual and vestibular stimuli, and in some way auditory stimuli, also permit the animal to locate mentally external objects in the environment in their mutual relationship in space, as well as to relate its own body to them spatially. All these stimuli are partly inborn and partly individually acquired signals for certain movements necessary to carry out food-getting behavior directed toward the projected images of food location.

7 ROLES OF THE CEREBRAL CORTEX AND CEREBELLUM IN SPATIAL ORIENTATION

Role of the Cerebral Cortex in Spatial Orientation

After establishing the fact that the images of spatial relationships of objects in the environment, and the orienting movements toward these objects, are performed mostly through visual, vestibular and auditory perception, we asked ourselves which central brain structure is responsible for these important characteristics of behavior.

We know that stimulation of the vestibular nerve or the labyrinth receptors affect, in a certain way, the electrical activity of the cortex in the area of the sylvian fissure. Some investigators have found this predominantly in the upper corner of the posterior ectosylvian gyrus (Gerebtzoff, 1940, Spiegel, 1932, Khechinashvili, 1958). Others note evoked electrical potentials predominantly at the anterior end of ectosylvian and suprasylvian gyri (Kempinsky, 1951, Walzl and Mountcastle, 1949, Mickle and Ades, 1954). But some observations have also been made to the effect that evoked potentials following stimulation of the vestibular nerve were present all over the ectosylvian gyrus (Anderson and Gernandt, 1954). Because of this, one could assume that conditioned reflex activities in response to vestibular stimulation, as well as the projection of objects into the environment and the orienting movements toward these objects guided by the labyrinth receptors, occur as a result of the activity of the cerebral cortex in the sylvian gyri. Consequently, one had to assume that an ablation of these gyri would bring about certain disturbances in spatial orientation.

ABLATION OF VARIOUS AREAS OF SYLVIAN AND ECTOSYLVIAN GYRI

We ablated the temporal lobe cortex in areas of and around the sylvian gyri (sylvius, ectosylvius, and suprasylvius). Observations were then made over a period of many months, the animal being allowed free movements. When the injury involved a limited area in the middle part of the ectosylvian and suprasylvian gyri, as in the case of two dogs, one could not find any defect in spatial orientation. In other words, we did not note any changes in their ability to form food approach behavior toward certain foodboxes at certain signals when they were blindfolded. They could project the images of perceived objects in the environment and then perform orienting movements toward these objects.

ABLATION OF POSTERIOR SYLVIAN GYRI. However, when the posterior half of the sylvian gyri was destroyed, definite changes were observed in orienting movements. In two such dogs, Zjak and Rosa, the operation was done in two stages; at first the sylvian gyri in one hemisphere were operated upon and then after 3 or 4 weeks, the other.

In these cases, the cortex was ablated predominately in the upper and the posterior parts of the sylvian gyri. Following this operation, performed on one side, all behavior became normal just one week after the operation. The animals could spatially relate the new locations of food after only being transported to these places and could then find them by themselves after only one transportation. Conditioned activity to vestibular stimuli was also undisturbed. For example, a blindfolded dog learned to leave the cage and look for food, after being taken in the cage, which involved either turning it to the right or taking it along a straight line for a distance of 4 meters; also, it could differentiate its behavior and would not leave the cage after being turned to the left or after being transported a distance of only 2 meters along a straight line. These food-getting reflexes had been established before the operation, and the behavior was correct at the first trial, 6 to 7 days following the operation.

However, after the second operation, on the temporal lobe of the other hemisphere, spatial orientation was significantly disturbed. In this case, if the blindfolded dog was taken to a new place in the same room, or to a neighboring room, and fed without removal of the blindfold, it was not able to reach this place again whether its eyes were open or shut. The dog would make searching movements near the cage or in the middle of the room without any definite indication of ability to orient itself correctly. However, when it was taken, still blindfolded, to the divan or to the next room and was given food there with its eyes open, then again blindfolded and brought back to the original location, it was able to find its way to the food over the shortest possible path. This suggests that an animal with a lesion in the temporal lobes can very well project the location of food with the aid of vision and may go there by the shortest possible way, but it is not able to do so on the basis of vestibular perception; that is, it could not project the food location into space or make effective orienting movements.

However, in many instances, we observed a definite improvement in behavioral reactions 3 to 4 months following this operation. After being taken blindfolded to a new place, the dog could not find the site with its eyes closed, but could reach the place with its eyes open. For instance the dog, Rosa, after being taken or transported to the new place blindfolded could not go there alone wearing the blindfold, but could reach it with its eyes open via the shortest possible path. Therefore, the dog can project in space the food location perceived vestibularly, but it is not able on the basis of this perception alone to locate the food, as is done by normal dogs.

In another experimental situation, we would transport the blindfolded dog along complex zigzag pathways to some hidden place in the room, in order to make vestibular perception difficult. We would then uncover its eyes, display some food, and blindfolding the animal again, would transfer it back over the same complex pathway to the original place. The animal could reach food by the shortest possible path, but only with its eyes open. If the eyes remain closed it would perform searching movements, looking for food near the cage or going to the foodboxes where it had been fed many times in the past.

All these observations suggest that the animals had intact their ability to project new food locations into space on the basis of restored labyrinthic perceptions, but they failed to recover their ability to move in an oriented manner toward these locations. This loss of ability to perceive movement over a pathway on the basis of vestibular stimulation, must be related to a decrease in the activity of the injured vestibular analyzer in response to labyrinthic stimuli as a result of the operation.

In cases where there is a disturbance of spatial orientation when the animal is blindfolded, it is still easy to establish an automatized locomotion to the foodbox. This occurs as a chain conditioned reflex, each link of which is activated by labyrinthic and kinesthetic stimuli arising during the preceding segment of behavior. These stimuli constitute natural conditioned signals for moving forward according to the direction of the orienting movements of the head.

Several weeks following the second operation, the blindfolded dog, Zjook, would go out for food after being transported along a broken path to the right, where it was usually fed. However, the animal would not leave the cage if transported in other directions. But in 3 or 4 months, the dog, after being transported to a new place blindfolded, would leave the cage and turn toward the foodbox or even attempt to get there. It was sufficient to take the animal from a new place to the foodbox only several times in order to obtain spontaneous behavior toward the foodbox.

The other dog, Rosa, had an operation producing a more extensive lesion of the sylvian gyri than Zjook. She also showed a temporary loss in ability to project the perception of objects in the environment and to orient her movements toward these objects. In this dog this ability was also restored during the following months although to a lesser degree. Rosa could not find new places after being carried only once blindfolded even several months after the operation.

In these dogs with lesions in the posterior half of both sylvian gyri, disturbance in the ability to project the source of a sound into space was also noted. In Rosa, we conditioned food approach behavior toward foodbox 1 to the sounding a bell, the bell being located at the same place as the foodbox. Then food-getting behavior was formed toward foodbox 2 to a tone of 800 c./sec., the source of the sound being located near foodbox 2 at a distance of 1 meter. We failed to establish a consistent discrimination despite hundreds of reinforcement sessions. Immediately following the triggering of the tone and ensuing reinforcement from box 2, at the sounding of the bell the animal would run to the same box and only afterward would go to the correct foodbox 1. Also, after being fed from foodbox 1, she would run at the triggering of the tone to that foodbox, and only afterwards to the correct foodbox 2. Since in these experiments the bell was located at foodbox 1, while the source of the tone not too far from foodbox 2, the experimental situation, favored differential behavior toward the foodboxes. As this did not develop, we assume that in these blindfolded dogs the projection of food location into space is very difficult on the basis of vestibular and auditory perceptions.

ABLATION OF ECTOSYLVIAN GYRI. In two dogs we ablated the ectosylvian gyri in both hemispheres. In one dog, Sharik, we ablated the whole cortex in one hemisphere and only the ectosylvian gyrus in the other hemisphere. In the other dog, Nisha, we ablated only the ectosylvian gyri in both hemispheres. After the operation, these dogs manifested a significant defect in spatial orientation, much more so than the preceding dogs, Zjook and Rosa. They were unable to retrace the path along which they had been transported for feeding while blindfolded after one or even several times. The animals could not retrace this route even without blindfolds as long as 8 months after the operation.

With Nisha, we tried to establish conditioned reflexes to vestibular cues. In one series of experiments we took the blindfolded dog sitting in a cage 2 meters along a straight path, then turned the cage to the right at a right angle and carried it 1 more meter; after this we fed the dog. In another trial we took the cage straight ahead, again for 2 meters, but then turned it to the left at a right angle; under such conditions the dog was not fed. The resulting behavior was that the dog would come out of the cage and look for food after being turned to the right. If it had been turned to the left, it would still during the initial phase of training leave the cage and make searching movements; afterward however, it stopped leaving the cage under that condition. The dog also stopped leaving the cage after being carried for 2 meters, but not turned. Obviously, a conditioned food-getting reflex was formed on the basis of vestibular stimuli arising when the animal was turned to the right at a right angle.

In another series of experiments, the dog Nisha was transported forward 4 meters in a straight line, then fed; whereas, if she was transported over a distance of only 2 meters or less, she was not fed. The food-getting reflex to the labyrinthine stimulation from a forward movement of 4 meters became stable during the very first days of training; while when the animal was moved for only 2 meters, she would at first leave the cage and search for food but then stopped doing even this.

Therefore, the formation of conditioned reflexes on the basis of labyrinthine stimulation in dogs without ectosylvian gyri could be produced very quickly; whereas with these same animals such stimulation was apparently not effective in producing an image of the pathway which could enable a correctly oriented locomotion toward food while blindfolded.

We also studied the ability of the animal to orient itself in space following a sound. Whereas a normal dog, as was indicated above, not only hears the sound but also projects it into the environment and can locate the source of the sound even 1 minute after it occurrence, the dogs Nisha and Sharik were not capable of doing so after the ablation of ectosylvian gyri.

The ability to orient oneself in space according to the direction of a sound was studied in the following way. We made a noise, usually behind a screen, by tapping the plate from which the animals were fed in these experiments. This noise was an extremely effective food signal. Normal dogs, even when blindfolded, would run to this noise no matter where it was produced and would reach the plate, avoiding all the obstacles in their path. Even if the noise was produced outside of the experimental room, they would run through the door and make necessary turns in order to reach the source of the noise; whether the eyes were opened or closed was not important in this case. The dogs Nisha and Sharik lost this ability to orient themselves in space and locate the foodbox on the basis of sound after ablation of ectosylvian gyri. They would turn their heads toward the source of noise and take a few steps in that direction; however, if the noise was continuous, they could follow it to its source. As soon as the noise was discontinued, the animals ceased moving toward the sound source and executed some disoriented searching movements. They behaved in this way regardless of whether or not they were blindfolded; if their eyes were open, it was necessary for the experimenter to be located behind a screen so that the animal would not see him or the plate.

The experiments were conducted in the following way. The dog would sit in a locked cage while the noise would be made with the plate, behind a screen located several meters from the cage; then 2 to 60 seconds later the cage would be opened. A normal dog would run directly toward the plate, making the necessary turn around the screen. The dogs without ectosylvian gyri, Nisha and Sharik, would remain in the vicinity of the cage and would exhibit intense searching movements there or in the middle of the room, only at times approaching the foodboxes where they were previously fed. However, if during these searching movements they saw the plate, they would of course immediately approach it.

Thus, the dog without ectosylvian gyri loses the ability to project sounds into space, that is, to generate a spatial image of a sound. Because of this, they are unable to orient their movements toward the source of the sound after a lapse of time following its perception.

Yet the dog without ectosylvian gyri would react with well-oriented movements to the calling of its name. At an order (go back!) it would go to the cage; or given certain auditory feeding signals, it could reach certain foodboxes. In other words, conditioned activity to sound is not disturbed by lesions of the ectosylvian gyri.

These observations clearly indicate that the creation in higher animals of an image of a traversed pathway, and the projection of it into space on the basis of labyrinthine perceptions, as well as the ability to project the image of perceived sounds into the environment, constituted behavior which is entirely determined by the activity in circumscribed areas of the neocortex, namely, the ectosylvian gyri.

ABLATION OF ANTERIOR SUPRASYLVIAN AND ECTOSYLVIAN GYRI. As was indicated above, according to the observations of several authors, the anterior part of the suprasylvian and ectosylvian gyri produces high-amplitude primary potentials when the vestibular nerves are stimulated. In the light of these experiments, using another dog, Jack, we ablated the anterior half of the suprasylvian gyrus, together with the anterior half of the ectosylvian gyrus. This operation was done in two stages, first in the left and 7 weeks later in the right hemisphere. After the first operation, spatial orientation was normal. The dog could orient itself toward new locations of food exactly as it did prior to the operation. Even when the blindfolded animal was brought to the place of feeding along a complex path and taken back the same way, 1 minute later it could go directly to the food location, by the shortest possible route. Then the blindfolded animal was taken to the next room, fed there and taken back to its cage. One minute later it went to the place where it had been fed prior to this experiment, then went to the door, making searching movements, and stopped near the experimenter's desk. It was taken again to the other room, fed and returned to its cage. One minute later, with the blindfold removed, it again went to the place in the same room where it was usually fed, then went out through the corridor and from there went to the next room and directly to the food plate. These observations show that the dog was still well able to orient itself in space on the basis of vestibular cues.

Following the first operation, the blindfolded dog, Jack, could orient itself toward the sound. Thus, for instance, when the noise with the plate was made to the left of the foodbox 1, the dog went directly to this spot 40 seconds after the sound was produced. It went to the source of the sound, starting intense searching movements while still half a meter from the place.

Observations on Jack were made for more than 8 months following the second operation; the behavior of the animal was impaired. It was completely deprived of the ability to orient toward the sound and to locate the foodbox. Each time it was apparent that spatial orientation on the basis of labyrinthine and auditory perceptions was lacking. When this experiment was last attempted, 8 months had elapsed since the operation; yet the animal was still unable to locate a new feeding place after having been transported there, nor could it find the plate with which noise had been made even a few seconds following the sound.

However, after the operation, the dog still retained an ability to orient itself to the right or left. Thus, if it was taken to the left and fed or if one made a noise with the plate on the left side, most of the dog's searching behavior would be oriented to the left. Because of this he might finally reach the plate, but usually he would by-pass it because of the lack of capacity for spatial projection.

In this same animal, conditioned reflexes could be established, such as an automatized locomotion to the foodboxes in response to auditory stimuli, or leaving the cage to look for food after being transported along a certain route blindfolded. In other words, it was responding to labyrinthine cues.

Observations on all these operated dogs led us to conclude that orientation in space on the basis of labyrinthine and auditory perceptions, and the projection of perceived objects, is mostly a function of the activity of the anterior half of the sylvian gyri. We must assume that while perception of sound and vestibular stimuli occurs throughout the ectosylvian gyrus and, to a certain degree, in other sylvian gyri, the highest form of integration of these perceptions, that which enables orientation in space, occurs in the anterior half of the sylvian gyri, predominantly in the anterior part of the ectosylvian gyrus.

ABLATION OF SIGMOID GYRI

The question arises as to whether the disturbance of spatial orientation after ablation of the temporal cortex is due to the malfunction of these lobes *per se* or whether it is due to a general disturbance in the activity of the cortex as a whole. In order to solve this problem we ablated the sigmoid gyri in three dogs. In one dog we ablated the entire anterior part of the cerebral cortex in front of the transverse sigmoid fissure; in another the frontal lobes were entirely ablated; and in the third the parietal lobes were somewhat injured. These dogs were submitted to the same type of investigation as the above-discussed animals after the temporal lobe operations. We found that the dogs without frontal lobes, deprived of somesthetic and motor analyzers, were capable of exhibiting automatized locomotion to the foodboxes while blindfolded, returning to their cage after eating; also they were capable of forming food-getting reflexes to labyrinthine stimuli.

In these dogs locomotion was disturbed. The static muscle tone was weakened and the legs tended to move sideways; the animal would fall on its belly. There was a disappearance of a great number of reflexes conditioned to skin stimuli. Thus, for instance, when blindfolded the animal could not avoid obstacles after running into them, and after finishing eating, it would not leave the foodbox but would continue endlessly to lick the food receptacle. In addition, it was unable to enter its cage even after touching it. All the latter effects stem from an inability to perceive tactile stimuli and from the resulting inability to form, on the basis of somesthetic perception, images of objects which would serve to localize them in the environment.

In general, however, these observations show that the defects obtained did not significantly influence spatial orientation. For instance, the animals could go to the location of food, both with the eyes open and after being blindfolded a minute or more after they had seen the food and had heard the sound of the foodbox opening (Beritoff, 1959b).

Similar results were reported by Bregadze (1950) in cats after ablation of frontal lobes (sigmoid area). After such operations and even after larger ablations of the cortex, no disturbances of spatial orientation on the basis of labyrinthine and auditory stimuli could be noticed.

Incidentally, an important conclusion follows from these data, one which we discussed above. An automatized alimentary behavior, such as locomotion toward the foodbox and returning to the cage, may take place without participation of the motor analyzers. In other words, an animal without motor cortex may have individually acquired food-getting behavior in the form of a chain motor conditioned reflex carried out exclusively on the basis of labyrinthine stimuli, without the participation of kinesthetic stimuli from locomoting extremities. This means that temporary connections may be established between the cortical elements perceiving the vestibular stimuli and those efferent pyramidal neurons which connect the vestibular analyzer with the motor centers of the diencephalon and mesencephalon.

Role of the Cerebellum in Spatial Orientation

As is known, some of the afferent pathways from the vestibular receptors run to the cerebellum. Here they terminate in the posterior lobes of the cerebellum, in nodulus, flocculi and uvula, and also in the most anterior lobe, lingula. It is also known that stimulation of these areas of the cerebellum will elicit in the temporal lobes, mostly in the posterior half of the ectosylvian gyri, electric potentials similar to those which appear in response to direct stimulation of the labyrinthine receptors (Ruwaldt and Snider, 1956).

Therefore, we decided to study the role of the cerebellum in spatial orientation by removing tissue from various areas of the cerebellum in a number of cats and dogs.

Ablation of Nodulus, Uvula and Flocculi

In one dog, Sylva, we ablated only nodulus, uvula and flocculi. Various experiments during the 2 months following the operation convinced us that this region does not significantly influence spatial orientation, nor does it influence automatized food-getting behavior.

We did observe, however, that this relatively small lesion in the posterior lobes of the cerebellum leads to a temporary decrease in conditioned responses to vestibular stimuli and produces a significant weakening in the ability of an animal to project food images into space on the basis of labyrinthine perception or to effectuate orienting movements toward the foodboxes.

However, in from 1 to 2 months following the operation, these deficiencies progressively disappeared. The behavior of the animal became perfectly normal; that is, when blindfolded, spatial orientation on the basis of vestibular perception was as good as that observed in normal animals.

Even fewer disturbances were observed when only nodulus and uvula were ablated, and these disturbances disappeared 3 weeks after the operation. The dog in this case, Palma, was studied in detail before the operation and for 20 days afterward, when its entire behavior was found to be normal; in particular, conditioned differential reflexes to labyrinthine stimuli elicited when the animal was transported in its cage and its orientation in space on the basis of labyrinthine perception, remained unaffected.

Ablation of Lingula

In another dog, Matros, the injury affected not only the posterior lobes of the cerebellum but also the most anterior part of it, lingula, where the afferent pathways from the labyrinthine receptors also terminate. Following the operation, observations were conducted over a period of many months. It was found that conditioned activity dependent on labyrinthine stimuli was significantly decreased and that there was a very marked decrease in ability to project food images into space and to effectuate orienting movements toward foodboxes on the basis of labyrinthine perception. Three months after the operation this dog, when blindfolded, was still incapable of projecting food images into space, so as to effectuate orienting movements toward the foodboxes, even after several scores of trials in which it was forcibly led to these foodboxes. However, with its eyes open, the animal was able to project food images into space after only one experience of approaching the foodbox.

Because of these deficiencies in the ability of spatial projection, it was very difficult to automatize food approach behavior toward the foodboxes when the animal was blindfolded. After several days of training and several scores of forced transports toward the foodbox, the blindfolded dog was still unable to reach the foodbox regularly after receiving the alimentary signal. However, if the blindfold was taken off, the dog would immediately go directly to the foodbox from which it had previously been fed while it was wearing the blindfold.

Therefore, it can be concluded that lesions located in those regions of the cerebellum where afferent impulses from the labyrinthine receptors end, lead to a significant disturbance in vestibular perception. Furthermore, during the initial postoperative stage, there is a significant decrease in conditioned activity responsive to labryinthine cues.

ABLATION OF ENTIRE CEREBELLUM

We also ablated the entire cerebellum in three dogs, Mertzhal, Tetra and Pivka. Their behavior was studied over a period of several months following the operation. During the first postoperative month, all of them showed a loss of the vestibular type of orientation in space. When the dogs were taken blindfolded to an unfamiliar part of the room, they were not able to find their way to the same spot 1 minute later, either blindfolded or with eyes open. Also at the beginning they could not orient themselves toward the source of sounds. If at a distance a noise was made with their food plate, they would correctly orient their heads and leave their cages, but would not be able to find the source of the sound. They would make searching movements near the cage and later in the middle of the room. Even with their eyes open, they could not locate the place where the noise had been made with the foodplate or run to the call of the experimenter, if these sounds originated behind a screen and the animal could not see them being produced.

Therefore, in these dogs we observed the same disturbance of vestibular orientation that we had found following the ablation of the nodulus, flocculi, uvula and lingula.

In all these dogs, food-getting reflexes could be conditioned to vestibular stimuli, to the extent of their being able to differentiate moving the cage a certain distance, or lifting to a certain level, or turning at a certain angle, just as in normal dogs.

Several months after the operation in Tetra and Pivka vestibular orientation was signficantly improved. Thus, if they were taken or transported blindfolded, along a short route (several meters) to the place of food, they could later, still blindfolded, find the place directly and by the shortest pathway. However, if they were transported a further distance beyond the foodbox and in the process were turned in one direction or another, they could not find the path directly; they would show searching movements and sometimes, but not always, could reach the food.

Following ablation of the cerebellum in Tetra and Pivka, orientation on the basis of auditory stimuli was also disturbed. At first, blindfolded or not, they could not go directly to the place where the noise had been made with the plate. The noise was, of course, produced behind a screen so that the animal could not see the plate or the experimenter. The dog made orienting movements toward the source of the noise and even a few steps toward it. However, if the noise was stopped, the dog was not able to find the plate, but only made zigzaglike movements in various directions, starting from the place where it was located when the noise ceased. If the noise was continued, the dog without cerebellum could go directly to its source, probably as a result of its head and body being correctly oriented toward the sound. This disturbance in ability to orient on the basis of auditory cues lessened several months after the operation, at first in Tetra and then in Pivka.

However, Mertzhal showed a disturbance in space orientation on the basis of labyrinthine and auditory perceptions for 2 years following the operation, and auditory orientation was still somewhat disturbed at the end of this period.

The brain was then examined, at first oscillographically, during the application of auditory and vestibular stimuli. Using sound stimuli, primary potentials were observed in the middle part of the ectosylvian gyrus; while with stimulation of the vestibular fibers in the eighth nerve, effects were recorded in the anterior part of the ectosylvian gyrus. When the dog Mertzhal was sacrificed, it was found that there was neither vermis nor the cerebellar hemispheres, only degenerated tissue of the peduncles.

We suspect that in Tetra and Pivka some of the cerebellum remained uninjured. For this reason we decided to re-operate on these animals and ablate the remaining cerebellum. In Tetra we found that limited areas in the cerebellar hemisphere and the most posterior part of the vermis were preserved. These remnants were ablated, but the dog died several days later. In Pivka too, we found that some parts of the cerebellar hemispheres and vermis were not completely destroyed, and we completed the ablation. The dog survived this operation and was observed during the following 8 months. After this last operation, the ability to orient in space on the basis of labyrinthic perception was never restored. Orientation to sound, that is, the delayed approach reaction toward the source of a noise made with a plate, also disappeared; only when the noise persisted would Pivka reach food.

Eight months following the operation, Pivka was sacrificed. It was found that the right hemisphere and vermis were entirely ablated. The left hemisphere was also almost entirely destroyed with the exception of a small area of about 4 to 5 mm.

Relation of Cerebellum to Cerebral Cortex in Spatial Orientation

As shown above, the cerebellum contributes to the spatial function of the cerebral cortex, that is, its capacity for projecting perceived objects into space and generating orienting movements toward these objects. The cerebellum appears to produce a continuous facilitating action upon the cortex of the temporal gyri in the spatial function referred to above.

It is known that stimulation of the cerebellar hemispheres increases the excitability of the motor cortex. This is expressed by the increase of the amplitude and frequency of spontaneous cortical activity in the motor area (Walker, 1938, Rossi, 1912, Moruzzi, 1950) as well as in the sensory areas (Henneman and Snider, 1949) of cats. Furthermore, as was indicated above, the stimulation of the cerebellum may elicit primary potentials in the anterior half of the ectosylvian and suprasylvian gyri. These facts permit us to assume that a continuous bombardment of the cortex by the cerebellum, sustained by a flow of afferent stimuli, increases the excitability of the anterior half of ectosylvian and suprasylvian gyri and of the motor analyzer. By this means the functional activity of the cortex is increased to such a degree that labyrinthine and auditory perceptions result in spatial images of the route traversed by the animal and of the direction and the location of the sources of perceived sound. These images serve to effectuate oriented locomotion leading to the goal object.

8 SPATIAL ORIENTATION IN MAN

We will consider here that type of spatial orientation in man which directly depends upon the functional activity of receptors, and has to do with projection of perceived objects into space. We and our associates studied the space orientation of children 6 to 14 years of age. Three groups of children took part in the experiment; one group was normal in speech, hearing and vision, one group was deaf and mute; one group was blind.

Spatial Orientation in Normal Children

It is well known that spatial orientation in man is effected through receptors which perceive the outside world at a distance, these receptors being visual, auditory and olfactory. Man is able, with the help of these receptors, not only to perceive outside objects, but also to project them into space; in other words, he can localize objects as being at definite points in the environment. Because of this projecting and localizing ability, he can move toward these objects, not only at the time of their perception, but also later on when the image of these objects may be recalled.

Since the time of Setchenov, an important role has been given to the proprioceptors of skeletal muscles in the perception of spatial relationships. It was assumed that stimulation of the proprioceptors, so-called kinesthetic stimulation, determines the perception of a traversed space as well as the experience of making turns or other impressions from a route just taken. The experiments with animals proved to us that the kinesthetic stimulation from locomoting extremities does not play an important role in achieving orientation in space.

While rechecking this observation in normal children, we established the fact that if a child 10 to 12 years of age is blindfolded and taken to some corner of the room or even to the next room, then taken back over the same route to the original place, the child is able

137

to retrace the same route by himself. Moreover, if the blindfolded child is led through a circular or rectangular route, he can, even after one trial, retrace approximately the same pathway with his eyes closed (Beritoff and Khechinashvili, 1958).

In the above experiments, the blindfolded children were led over a certain route on foot, and therefore kinesthetic stimuli were involved. In later experiments such proprioceptive stimulation was excluded by placing the blindfolded children in a chair and moving them in a sitting position from one spot to another.

Experiments which we conducted with Kherkheulidze (Beritoff and Kherkheulidze, 1958a) showed that normal children, between the ages of 6 and 12, were capable of retracing the route along which they had been transported once in a chair while blindfolded. Some of them did it with greater precision than others, but the deviations were relatively small. There was no significant difference between children 6 and those 12 years old, when the child was transported along a distance of a few meters and in a pathway that formed a figure; 6-year-old children could repeat the same figure precisely, just as easily as did the 12 year olds (Figures 24 and 25). Furthermore, if the blindfolded child was led on foot along a path representing a more or less complex design, he could retrace this design with deviations of the same order as in experiments in which he had been taken along this design while seated in a chair (Figures 24 and 25).

These children, particularly the younger ones, sometimes made very marked deviations from the path they experienced when transported. For example, a child turned at a right angle toward the right during his transportation, might turn at a right angle to the left, or he might make the turn sooner or later than it occurred during the preceding passive movement. Mistakes were also occasionally made in cases where the passive transportation occurred along a straight line. However, the mistakes made were usually corrected after repeated transportations along the same path. Thus, for instance, Figure 24 shows that at the first trial the child did not go to the end of the straight line or the half circle (2 and 4), but the second time he did it correctly (3 and 5).

When the child deviated from the experimental path, he was not told about it. The children corrected their mistakes spontaneously on the basis of new perceptions of the route experienced during the repeated transportations along the same design.

Occasionally, one finds children who can retrace the route without

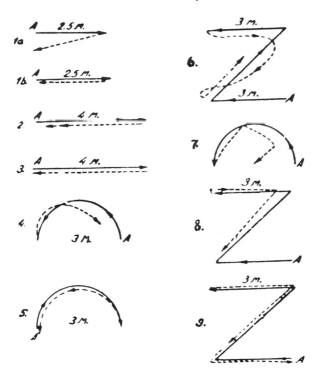

Fig. 24

A 7-year-old normal girl (KB) blindfolded. Solid lines on all the figures signify the paths along which the child was transferred in a chair or was led; broken lines, the paths taken by the child herself. *A*, Starting place; *1, 2, 3*, transfer along a straight line; *4* and *5*, along a semicircle; *6*, along the letter Z; *7* and *8*, along a semicircle and the letter Z while led; *9*, after being shown the figure Z on the floor. (Beritoff and Kherkheulidze, 1958a.)

any noticeable deviation on the first test trial, following the same figures along which they were transported in a chair or were passively taken on foot (Figure 25). Since a blindfolded child will retrace a route with the same precision whether he was taken along this route in a chair or on foot, it is perfectly clear that spatial orientation in man, in the absence of vision, is accomplished basically with the help of vestibular receptors. The normal blindfolded child not only correctly repeats the figure along which he was transported, but he precisely localizes the end point of the transfer and can go there by the shortest possible route.

If the child is shown a letter drawn on the floor, then blindfolded

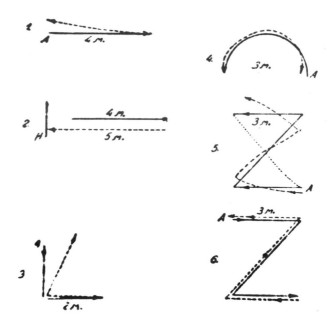

Fig. 25

Normal 12-year-old boy, DB, blindfolded. *A*, Starting place; *H*, obstacles into which child will run; *1* and *2*, when transferred along a straight line; *3*, when transferred at an angle; *4*, along semicircle; *5*, along letter Z; (after this, the boy said that he went along the Russian letter **И**); *6*, after showing letter Z on the floor. (Beritoff and Kherkheulidze, 1958a.)

and asked to walk along this letter, he will usually move more or less according to the lines of the letter, being more accurate than if he had first been taken over these lines blindfolded (Figure 24: 8 and 9; Figure 25: 5 and 6). Clearly, a visual projection based on visual perception is more precise than one which is made on the basis of labyrinthine perception.

Therefore, normal children orient themselves in space on the basis of both visual and labyrinthine perceptions, whereas kinesthetic stimuli, arising from moving extremities, do not play any important role. On the basis of the labyrinthine stimuli generated by movements of the body during the passive transportations afoot or in a chair, the child acquires a spatial image of the route which is conserved for a long time; this permits his future locomotion along the exact same path.

Spatial Orientation in Deaf-Mutes

We studied children who were deaf-mutes, in some of whom the labyrinths were nonfunctional (Beritoff and Khechinashvili, 1958, Beritoff and Kherkheulidze, 1958a). The absence of a functioning labyrinth was determined by the Bárány test. Included in this first category were those deaf-mute children in whom there was no evidence of nystagmus or other vestibular reflexes after 10 or 20 rotations during 20 seconds. For comparison, another group of deaf-mute children was selected in whom nystagmus was elicited as a result of being rotated, indicating the persistence of labyrinthine perception.

Deaf-Mute Children with Nonfunctioning Labyrinths

The children, between 10 and 12 years of age, with nonfunctioning laybrinths could not, when blindfolded, retrace the route along which they had been taken, even after several trials. This was true despite the fact that the child received a great deal of skin and proprioceptive stimuli arising during the course of going through the experimental pathway. Obviously, these stimuli did not cause a formation of spatial relationships on the basis of which the subject could determine the dimensions of the path just passed, or of the angles or the turns made during the movement (Figure 26: 6–9; Figure 27: 6–8).

Nor could such children, with nonfunctioning labyrinths, perceive a spatial image of the route over which they had been taken in a chair when blindfolded. They were even unable to perceive the route when it followed a given straight line, but would instead usually retrace another straight or inclined line (Figure 26: 1–5; Figure 27: 1–5).

If the deaf-mutes are shown a design on the floor and then blindfolded, they are able to retrace this design by walking over the corresponding path. Many times in later experiments, when they were blindfolded and taken over the path of a complex design, they would, in attempting to retrace the path, repeat a design which had been shown to them in a previous experiment (Figure 26: 10–11; Figure 27).

We may conclude that a deaf-mute cannot retrace the route along which he was taken with his eyes closed, and this fact is due not to any deficiency in the central coordination of movements, but to the lack of a spatial image of the trajectory.

Usually the deaf-mute with nonfunctional labyrinths, after being

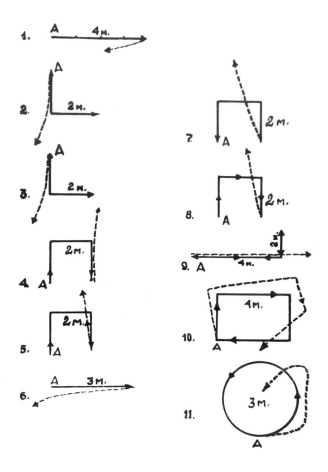

Fig. 26

Deaf-mute boy, D, 10 years of age, with nonfunctioning labyrinths, blind-folded. *1,* When carried in a chair along a straight line; *2* and *3,* at an angle; *4,* along Russian letter Π ; *5,* after third transfer according to same letter; *6,* after being led afoot along a straight line; *7,* during first trial of being led along Russian letter Π ; *8,* at second trial of being led along same letter; *9,* being led, afoot, forward, then turned at a right angle and then led back along the same route (solid line); the child spontaneously went along a straight line and ran into a wall (broken line); *10,* after being shown the design of a rectangle on the floor; *11,* when carried, blindfolded, in a circle; the child repeated approximately the same figure as in the preceding experiment. (Beritoff and Kherkheulidze, 1958a.)

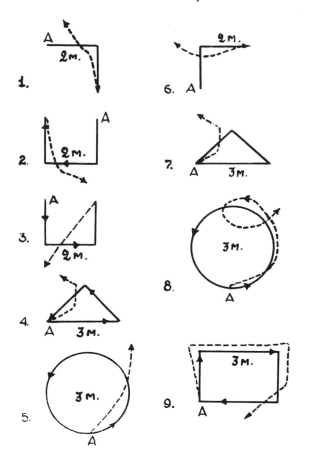

Fig. 27

Deaf-mute girl, 8 years old, with nonfunctioning labyrinths, blindfolded. *1*, During a transfer at an angle; *2*, carried along the figure U; *3*, after being carried along the same figure but asked to go to the original place the shortest way possible; *4*, being carried along a triangle; *5*, being carried along a circle; *6*, being led afoot at an angle; *7*, being led along a triangle; *8*, being led along a circle; *9*, after being shown a rectangle. (Beritoff and Kherkheulidze, 1958a.)

transported in a chair or being taken afoot along complex designs, follows a straight line, or a line inclined to the left or right. However, there was evidence in repeated experiments that these children can perceive movement along a circle and, to some extent, the angles at the turning points; this was particularly evident when the turns were very sharp. In the latter instances, the child would effect somewhat rounded movements, without exactly reproducing the figure (Figure 27: 2 and 4).

The deaf-mute children with nonfunctioning labyrinths very often would be mistaken as to the direction of movement. For instance, if after transporting them along a semicircle from left to right, they were asked to go in the opposite direction, they might instead go again from left to right. However, after repeated transportations over the same figure, they usually could go in the required direction. Earlier rotation experiments have shown that deaf-mutes can differentiate a rotation to the right from a rotation to the left (Beritoff and Khechinashvili, 1958).

It is thus possible to perceive the direction of movement during transportation in a chair or during rotation, without the cues based on labyrinthine and visual stimulation. We must then acknowledge the role in such perception of the receptors of the skin, skeletal muscle and viscera. Their stimulation is probably produced by the shifting of viscera and tissues, due to their inertia and the centrifugal forces elicited during rotation, for example. However, such perception is not sufficient for the purpose of retracing a route or forming an image concrete enough so that the path can be retraced when the child is blindfolded.

Improvement was observed in some deaf-mute children after they were transported passively, in a chair or on foot, for a number of times along the same design. In one case, a girl 10 years of age was transported along a semicircle 12 times without any significant improvement during her free trials along this figure. However, when she was led afoot over the same semicircle several times, her free movement approached the figure of a semicircle, and at the seventh and eighth trials she accomplished three fourths of the semicircle without mistakes (Figure 28).

The motor habit in children established after several passive repetitions of leading them on foot persisted for a long time. In one case it persisted for five days. All these observations showed that relatively simple motor habits may be established in deaf-mutes without participation of visual and labyrinthine stimuli, i.e., on the basis of kinesthetic stimulation only. One must assume that these habits emerge according to the principle of the chain conditioned reflex, in which each segment constitutes an elemental conditioned reflex. That is, a movement forward or a turn to the left or to the right occurs in response to the proprioceptive stimuli originated during the preceding segments of behavior.

In deaf-mute blindfolded children, establishment of movements

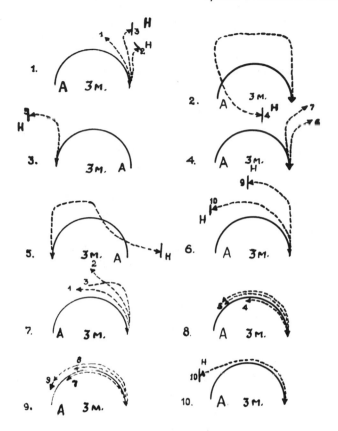

Fig. 28

Deaf-mute girl, CA, 10 years old, nonfunctioning labyrinths, blindfolded. *1,* After each of three transfers along a semicircle (*1, 2, 3*); *2,* after fourth transfer (*4*); *3,* after fifth transfer (*5*); *4,* after sixth and seventh transfers (*6, 7*); *5,* after eighth transfer (*8*); *6,* after ninth and tenth transfers (*9, 10*). In the majority of cases, the child went along an oblique line and stopped after running into an obstacle, *H. 7,* After each of three trials of being led along a semicircle (*1, 2, 3*); *8,* after fourth to sixth trials (*4, 5, 6*); *9,* after seventh to ninth trials (*7, 8, 9*); *10,* after tenth trial (*10*). (Beritoff and Kherkheulidze, 1958a.)

oriented along a limited path occurs after 10 to 15 repetitions; while in the previous studies with labyrinthless cats and dogs, this could be achieved, in the absence of vision, only after several scores or even hundreds of repetitions (Beritoff, 1957b). Furthermore, the deaf-mute children with eyes closed may easily retrace the path which they traversed with eyes open and even the path which was shown to them previously; while animals with ablated labyrinths were unable to repeat a movement immediately after it was performed with open eyes.

DEAF-MUTE CHILDREN WITH FUNCTIONING LABYRINTHS

Children who are deaf-mutes, but have functioning labyrinths showed that with eyes closed they are able to orient themselves in space just as normal children do. After being led on foot, as well as after being carried in a chair along a certain figure, they could retrace the same route with great precision. In addition they could go from the original point of the design to the end point, or the other way around, using the shortest possible path (Figure 29). This means that the deaf-mutes who cannot hear but who still retain labyrinthine perception are able to perceive an image of the spatial characteristics of a pathway, including its initial and end points, and to project these into space. Thus, they can direct themselves in space on the basis of vestibular cues just as normal children do.

Spatial Orientation of the Blind

Blind persons who have lost their vision in early childhood or who are born blind orient themselves very well in their usual environment. They can move about freely in their room, garden or even in the street without running into objects or people. Even in a completely new environment they may move about with some orientation, generally without running into obstacles and usually avoiding them. The orientation of a blind person in space is usually ascribed to his ability to perceive obstacles at a distance.

We studied spatial orientation in children who were born blind or who lost their vision no later than at the age of 2 years (Beritoff and Kherkheulidze, 1958b).

These experiments show that a blind child, just as a normal child who is blindfolded, can perceive a straight path along which he is asked to walk and can retrace, with considerable precision after only one trial, all the turns made within the limits of a given room. Thus, one blind child who was led only once over a pathway that extended from one end of the room to the other, involving a turn at an angle of 120° toward the divan and a return to the original starting place, could retrace this path not only the same day but even after one week.

A blind person can walk to a certain point in a room or follow a certain pathway even if there are no objects present which would

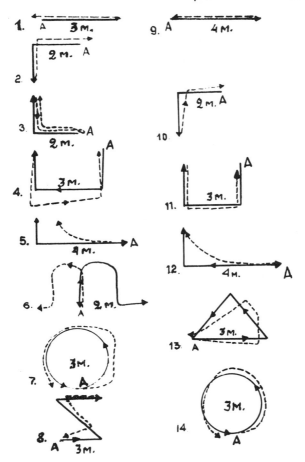

Fig. 29

Deaf-mute boy, GP, 10 years old, labyrinths functioning, blindfolded. *1,* Carried in a chair along a straight line; *2,* at an angle; *3,* after the second transfer at an angle, child went to the end point, then spontaneously returned to the starting place; *4,* carried along a figure U; *5,* after being carried 4 meters then turned at right angle; *6,* carried along the Russian letter Π and backwards; *7,* carried along a circle; *8,* carried along letter Z; *9,* led afoot along a straight line; *10,* led afoot at an angle; *11,* led afoot along the figure U; *12,* led along a straight line 4 meters then turned at right angle; *13,* led along a triangle; *14,* led along a circle. (Beritoff and Kherkheulidze, 1958a.)

serve to orient him. He can return to the starting point not only following a more or less complete original route, but also by a short cut which he has not experienced before (Figures 30 and 31).

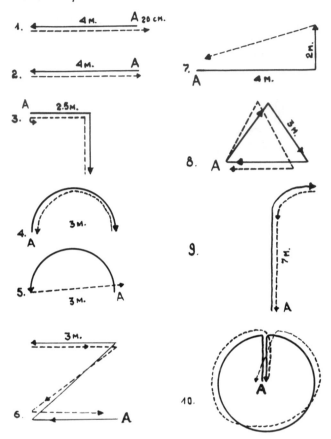

Fig. 30

Blind child, LT, 14 years old. *1* and *2*, Carried in a chair along a straight line; *3* and *4*, carried over an angle and along a half circle; *5*, the shortest path after being carried over a semicircle; *6*, carried along the letter Z; *7*, shortest path after being carried 4 meters along a straight line with a turn at a right angle; *8*, carried over a triangle; *9*, carried along a curve and a spontaneous return; *10*, carried from the center of a circle around its circumference and back to the center followed by a free movement from the center. (Beritoff and Kherkheulidze, 1958b.)

Comparing these results with those obtained in normal children of the same age, it is seen that the blind children are much better at retracing the routes they have gone over only once and the turns they have made, and are better able to localize them in space, than normal blindfolded children.

If a blind child is placed in a chair which is moved along a pattern

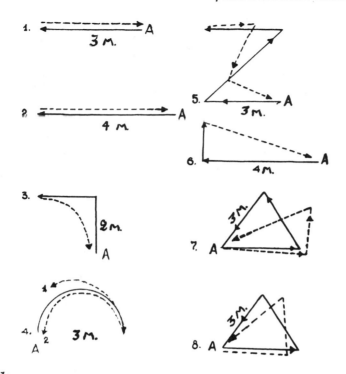

Fig. 31

Blind girl, KZ, 7 years old. *1* and *2*, Carried along a straight line; *3*, carried at an angle; *4*, first and second transfers (*1* and *2*) along a semicircle; *5*, carried over letter Z; *6*, shortest possible return after having been carried 4 meters with a turn at a right angle; *7* and *8*, carried along a triangle. (Beritoff and Kherkheulidze, 1958b.)

and is then brought to either the starting point or the end point of the pattern, he will be able to trace the same route almost without mistakes or with very little deviation (Figures 30 and 31). This makes us believe that the stimulation of the skin, muscle and joint receptors which arises during normal locomotion does not contribute materially to the orienting movements necessary to retrace a complex route. There are also indications that the auditory analyzer does not play any important role in the perception by a blind child of an experienced pathway. It is with the aid of the vestibular analyzer that the child achieves an image of the whole route, which he projects into space with almost the same precision as does a normal child when the latter perceives the same route visually.

Therefore, man orients himself in space basically with the aid of visual and vestibular receptors. It is also with the aid of these receptors that he projects into the environment all the objects that are perceived by other receptors, tactile, thermal, taste, and even olfactory and auditory ones. With the aid of the vestibular analyzer people achieve images of experienced pathways projected into space and the localization in the environment of all objects which were perceived in passing along this route. The result is an ability to orient locomotion.

Muscle and joint receptors do not play an essential role in spatial orientation because images of the experienced pathways are not formed on the basis of their stimulation. However, with repeated walking along the same route, stimulation of these receptors, simultaneous with labyrinthine stimulation, may contribute to the formation of conditioned signals which elicit motor behavior. By this mechanism a chain conditioned reflex may be established, i.e., a type of oriented locomotion which is accomplished automatically.

Perception of Obstacles at a Distance

It is known that blind people perceive obstacles at a distance. The distance at which they can perceive them will depend upon the size of the objects and the material of which they are made. This distance may vary from a few centimeters to a few meters. The ability of blind persons to perceive objects at a distance has usually been considered in explaining their ability to orient themselves in space. This is why we were interested in the study of this ability, at first in animals (cats and dogs) and then in man.

In a previous chapter, we made the observation that a blindfolded cat or dog does not run into large solid objects such as walls, screen, etc., provided it does not move too quickly. In fact animals ordinarily turn to avoid these objects at a distance of 20 to 50 cm. from the object. A net, however, cannot be perceived and avoided at a distance.

EXPERIMENTS WITH ANIMALS

By means of special experiments, we established the fact that the ability of an animal to avoid large obstacles at a distance, when these obstacles have a smooth surface, does not depend upon any smell originating from the objects or upon stimulation of the skin receptors by airwaves reflected from these objects. We observed that even if the whole head, except for the nasal orifices, or even the whole body was covered by a special coat made of a heavy material, the animal could still anticipate large objects at a distance. Thus, we eliminated the role of the skin receptors. We did find, however, that the ability to perceive objects at a distance disappears after a complete bilateral destruction of the labyrinths and also after putting wet cottonballs in the ears, i.e., after a certain decrease of hearing. On the basis of these observations, we concluded that blindfolded animals perceive objects at a distance on the basis of reflected sounds from the solid objects (Beritoff, 1958a).

However, the detours made by a blindfolded animal at a distance of 20 to 50 cm. seem to represent more than an unconditioned reflex in response to stimulation of hearing by reflected waves. The observed behavior strongly implies that this avoidance reaction is conditioned and is due to subthreshold auditory stimuli. In other words, an animal approaching a large solid object has already perceived it, subliminally, at a distance of 20 to 50 cm. As we discussed earlier in the book, Gershuni and associates (Gershuni 1949a, b, 1958–1959; Gershuni *et al.*, 1948) could form conditioned skin galvanic reflexes to subthreshold auditory stimuli, for instance, stimuli which were 8 to 12 decibels below the threshold. The conditioned detour is apparently formed as a result of several associations between the subthreshold auditory stimuli and the detours during the experimental trials. Dogs and cats have probably developed such conditioned capacity for avoiding objects at a distance during their locomotion at night. This ability in these animals is precluded by placing wet cottonballs in their ears so that soundwaves no longer effectively stimulate the hearing receptor.

However, animals that are blindfolded and have their ears plugged are still able to avoid familiar obstacles by making a correct detour. This must be accomplished by projecting into the environment an image which resulted from labyrinthine cues acquired during preceding movements in the same environment. This explanation is supported by the fact that after an operation involving bilateral destruction of the labyrinths, the animals lost the ability to avoid obstacles in a familiar environment and ran into them.

In Figure 32 behavior with detours is illustrated in the case of a very fearful and slowly moving dog, Pupsa. She had acquired an automatized food-getting behavior from the cage to the foodbox at a signal tone. At this sound, the blindfolded animal would go to the foodbox along the shortest possible path and after being fed would return to the cage along the same pathway. Then a wooden shield of one and a half square meters was placed across her pathway to the cage. At the auditory signal, the dog ran directly to the foodbox; then approach-

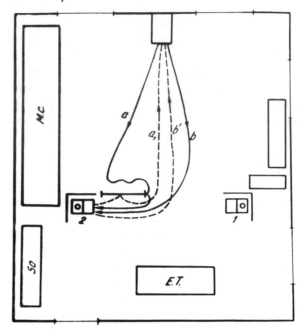

Fig. 32

Dog "Pupsa." Solid lines, paths along which dog went from cage to food-box; broken lines, returns to cage. First experiment with an obstacle (1.5 meters in length) in front of foodbox. See text.

ing the obstacle, it started to by-pass it while still at a distance of one-half meter from it and only touched the border of the shield (path *a*). After being fed, the dog headed back toward the cage, did not avoid the obstacle and then ran in a wider path and got around the obstacle (*a₁*). When the signal was given again, it by-passed the obstacle without touching it, both on the trip to the foodbox (path *b*) and the return trip to the cage (*b′*). This suggested that the animal acquired a clear image of the location of the obstacle.

Figure 33 well illustrates how precisely an animal differentiates a solid obstacle from open space. After the experiment shown in Figure 32, the shield was moved 0.5 m. from the foodbox. Now at the feeding signal the dog went toward the foodbox starting to detour, but on approaching it and perceiving that the pathway was free, it turned toward the foodbox and went directly there, without touching the obstacle. After being fed, the dog returned to the cage without touching the obstacle. The fact that this perception at a distance actually depends upon hearing is demonstrated in Figure 34. The dog's ears

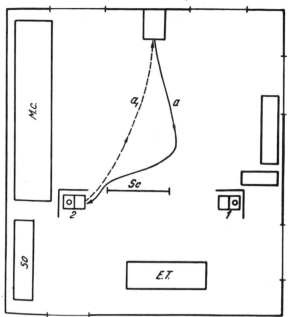

Fig. 33

Dog "Pupsa." Obstacle moved 0.5 meter from foodbox.

were blocked by wet cotton, and the obstacle was again placed in front of the foodbox. At the feeding signal the dog went to the foodbox by a short cut, but ran into the obstacle. It started to go around the obstacle, but again ran into it. After feeding, the dog detoured and avoided the obstacle on the trip back to the cage. This again suggested that the dog must have acquired a spatial image of the obstacle as a result of her previous experience.

The best proof of this is given by the behavior of the dog after destruction of the labyrinths. If one forms, in such blindfolded animals, an automatized alimentary approach behavior toward a definite foodbox by repeatedly leading the animal toward the foodbox, and then one places an obstacle in front of it, such an animal is no longer able to make a detour. It will move along the obstacle several times, touching it all the time with its sides but incapable of going around it. Even if it by-passes the obstacle, the dog is not able to orient toward the foodbox. In other words, a blindfolded dog without labyrinthine perception is not capable of projecting into space an image of the obstacle in front of the foodbox, because under such conditions the dog is not able to form an image of its location.

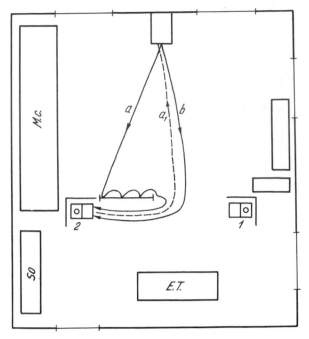

Fig. 34

Dog "Pupsa." Wet cotton in ears. (Beritoff, 1959b.)

EXPERIMENTS WITH HUMAN BEINGS

We conducted an analogous investigation in man. Together with Kherkheulidze (Beritoff and Kherkheulidze, 1958b), we studied perception of solid obstacles at a distance (Figure 35). A blind person does not perceive a net or mesh screen at a distance, but will always collide with it. The blind person perceives solid objects if they are located at the level of his head; if the objects are below this level, at the height of the knees or other parts of the body, he practically never perceives them. Also it does not matter whether the blind person walks alone toward the obstacle, whether he is rolled passively toward the obstacle while seated in a chair or even whether the obstacle is moved toward him while he is standing or sitting.

We found that if objects the size of a book were moved toward the head of a blind person, from either in front of him or to one side, the blind person clearly perceived them at a distance of 15 to 20 cm. If he were approached from above or from behind, toward the occiput, the object was not perceived. However, if a wooden board larger than

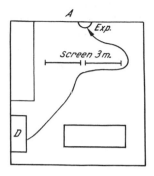

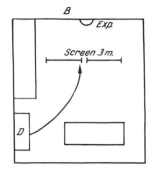

Fig. 35

A, A blind person was seated on a divan, *D*. Two screens each 1.5 meters long were placed in the room without his being aware of them. The experimenter standing at the far end of the room asked the subject to join him. The latter, at a distance of 30 to 50 cm. from the screens, went around them and approached the experimenter. *B*, Another blind person, under the same experimental conditions, continued toward the screen but stopped 40 cm. in front of them. (Beritoff and Kherkheulidze, 1958b.)

1 sq. m. was moved toward him from behind, the blind person would perceive it at a distance of 10 to 20 cm. If the same board was placed in front of the subject and moved toward his head, he would perceive it at a considerably greater distance, namely, 50 to 80 cm. Finally, a piece of felt could scarcely be sensed and small objects like a ruler could not be perceived even at the level of the face or forehead, a level which many specialists consider to be most sensitive for perceiving obstacles at a distance.

Some authors claim that such perception as has been described above is due to the stimulation of skin receptors by movements of the air or due to temperature changes in the immediate environment. However, we found that perception via facial skin receptors is of no importance since the blind person could perceive large objects approaching the back of his head and since the rather extreme procedure of covering the face with heavy material or a leather mask did not prevent perception of an obstacle in the pathway.

Other authors have considered the ability to perceive an obstacle at a distance to be based upon auditory stimulation (Worchal and Dollenbach, 1947, Worchal, Manness and Andrew, 1950). They believed that such perceptions arise from the reflection by solid objects of auditory waves of low frequency, below 200 per second, and also of subliminal auditory waves. In a large city there are continuous oscillatory air waves due to the movement of people and vehicles, and this creates a background noise which is usually not noticeable. The auditory waves being reflected by an obstacle are differentially perceived when they are a certain distance from the person.

The fact that auditory perceptions actually play an important role was demonstrated in the following way. We blocked the ears of subjects with wet cotton balls, put earphones on them and turned on a continuous tone; then the subjects were asked to avoid obstacles. The blind persons ran into obstacles, and only after doing so were they able to go around them. Obviously, in the absence of hearing, objects could not be perceived at a distance. Yet, blind children who served in these experiments said they were not aware of hearing any sounds which indicated the presence of obstacles. Our personal experience is that when we move solid objects toward our own ears, we can hear at a distance of 4 to 5 cm. a noise like a rustle, something like "ush" or "sss," and this sound is more intense the closer we bring the object to our ears. Also we continued to hear the noise, as long as we held the object at a short distance from our ears. If we approached this object from the front, we did not hear anything, obviously because of the longer distance from the ear. Of course, we expected that the blind person should be able to hear the same noise at a longer distance. Asked what they hear in these instances, blind persons describe a feeling such as the perception of a slight touch, pressure or cooling, particularly as far as their face is concerned. We would explain such perceptions as being due to a stimulation of the cutaneous receptors of the face by a shift of the skin, which is in turn elicited by a conditioned contraction of the smooth muscle of the face in response to subliminal auditory stimulation. As was mentioned above, an auditory stimulus which is 8 to 12 decibels below the threshold can become a conditional signal for skin galvanic reflexes. It can also produce changes in the electric activity of the brain, after being paired several times with painful stimulation of the skin (Gershuni, 1947, 1949a, b; Gershuni *et al.*, 1948).

We feel that the subliminal auditory perception of reflected auditory waves may become conditioned signals for the contraction of skin muscles in the forehead, in the following way.

Ordinarily, the experience of running into an obstacle results in a painful stimulation of the face, particularly of the forehead and nose. This, of course, elicits a skin galvanic reflex in the face, together with a contraction of the smooth facial muscles such as in a pilomotor reaction. There is also a contraction of the muscles of the neck and of the forearms, the latter being used in protecting the head from obstacles. After one or several encounters, subliminal auditory stimulation may serve to activate temporary connections, and the reflex contractions of the muscles of the face and neck may occur. In the case of the blind children in our experiments, it could be observed that at the moment of the perception of an obstacle, their eyelids would close and the muscles of their arms would become significantly more tense. It would seem that perception at the skin of the face, particularly the forehead, such as was reported by some of the blind subjects, arises as a result of very slight mechanical stimulation of the skin receptors of the forehead by the conditioned reflex of its smooth muscles.

In summary, we believe that a blind person judges the presence of an obstacle at a distance on the basis of the perceived stimulation of the skin receptors of his face. The latter are actually stimulated by the contractions of smooth muscles due to a previous conditioning. This conditioned reflex occurs in response to the subthreshold stimulation of the auditory apparatus by auditory waves reflected from an obstacle with a large, solid surface.

While the occurrence of perceptions at a distance may create an impression of smell or heat being emitted by objects, such factors are not significant in spatial orientation inasmuch as they are not projected at sufficiently long distances. In addition, these perceptions do not arise from all the objects which a blind person is able to avoid at a distance.

Finally, with regard to a blind person's orienting himself in space, the perception of objects at a distance is not the significant factor because such orientation occurs from labyrinthine perceptions involving the activity of the vestibular analyzer.

PART III BASIC NEURAL PROCESSES: SPINAL CORD AND CEREBRAL CORTEX

9 INHIBITION AND FACILITATION PROCESSES IN GENERAL

Neuronal Mechanisms for the Integration of Behavioral Acts

Each behavioral act, be it instinctive or individually acquired, image-driven or conditioned chain reflex, implies participation of the entire nervous system. This must involve the presence of states of excitation in certain neuronal circuits concomitant with the presence of states of inhibition in other nervous structures. Widespread inhibition constitutes the basic factor in integration of the central nervous system during behavioral reactions. Thus, we saw examples of food-getting behavior driven by images associated with a depression of automatized food-approach behavior. General inhibition arises in the central nervous system and spreads over almost all areas of the brain, with concurrent focal states of excitation in only limited neuronal circuits. This integration in central nervous system activity allows for a dynamic process in which one state may give way to another, whether it be inborn or individually acquired.

We shall show below that there are structures in the cerebral cortex that are probably responsible for the general inhibition sustaining there the integration of the nervous processes. However, integrative action is not specific to the cerebral cortex. It also occurs in all the other divisions of the brain, particularly the brainstem cerebellum and spinal cord. Obviously, one must find in all of these subdivisions of the central nervous system structures, underlying widespread inhibition and the physiologic mechanisms for its generation.

We have studied the integration of the central nervous system in its various parts, and in regard to all kinds of behavioral reactions. Such investigations began in 1911, and are still continuing. At first, studies were done with regard to the integrating function of the spinal cord. In 1916 we started to investigate conditioned reflexes and then automatized-individually-acquired behavior (1916–1932); later we studied inborn behavioral reactions (1927–1937) and finally, image-

161

driven behavior (1933–1947). We have continued to study the neuro-physiologic mechanisms underlying these various types of behavior.

In this and the following chapters we are going to discuss (1) the facilitation and inhibition processes in general, (2) central inhibition in the spinal cord (the simplest structure of the central nervous system), (3) the brainstem and (4) the structure of the cerebral cortex as related to behavior.

General Inhibition and Facilitation in Normal and Decerebrate Animals

Reciprocal Inhibition and Rebound Contraction

Sherrington and his associates established the fact that in each reflex action excitation of one group of muscles is associated with inhibition of their antagonists. With an increase in the intensity and duration of activation in one group of muscles, there is a reciprocal increase in intensity and duration of inhibition in the antagonistic group of muscles. Accordingly, in the central nervous system, there is a type of inhibition which is reciprocally associated with the excitation of motor neurons.

Furthermore, Sherrington and his associates observed that, after the suspension of the stimulation, reciprocal inhibition is replaced by excitation; i.e., the previously inhibited muscle now contracts. This contraction, which they called "rebound contraction," was observed by Sherrington on extensor muscles in the decerebrate cat. Sherrington called the physiologic law, according to which this phenomenon arises, "successive spinal induction."

However, the same phenomenon was discovered later in other preparations, for example, in lumbar animals. Furthermore the rebound contraction was found not only in the extensors, but also in the flexors provided that muscle tone predominated in the flexors and that the position of the head was favorable to such a distribution of muscle tone (Beritoff, 1915a, b, 1922a, b). In these experiments, the excitatory aftereffects (rebound), following reciprocal inhibition, were regularly found.

Moreover, many of the experiments showed that in each reflex act there is not only a reciprocal inhibition of antagonists, but also a partial inhibition of the agonists; in other words, the contracted muscles themselves, as well as a great deal of the remaining musculature, may be subjected to a more or less pronounced inhibition. Therefore, in all reflex acts inhibition involves more or less broad areas of the central nervous system equally affecting flexors as well as extensors.

General Inhibition

General inhibition is very often followed by an exaltation of excitatory processes, just as the reciprocal inhibition at the end of a triggering stimulation is followed by a general contraction. It was established that this rebound expresses the onset of a general facilitation (Beritoff, 1937a, b, 1941).

THALAMIC STIMULATION. The regular occurrence of general inhibition in the central nervous system has been known for a long time. It was first described by Setchenov (1863), who observed that electrical, mechanical and chemical stimulation of the thalami could elicit inhibition of the defensive flexor reflexes in the hind legs of a frog.

Herzen (1864) verified the experiments of Setchenov and observed the inhibition of reflexes in the whole body of the frog not only by stimulating the thalamus, but also other divisions of the brain. Moreover, he found that it occurs during the stimulation of the sensory nerves. Herzen concluded that in general whenever either the peripheral or central nervous system is stimulated, there is a concomitant intense and general inhibition of reflexes. Setchenov came to agree with this statement in his subsequent publications. However, he found that stimulation of the thalamus produces a more pronounced and more constant depression of the reflexes than the stimulation of other divisions of the brain, since in the latter case some reflex movements may occur prior to the onset of the depression. Like Herzen, Setchenov could observe depression of reflexes during the stimulation of sensory nerves or skin areas (Setchenov and Paschutin, 1865).

Somewhat later Setchenov (1868) studied reflex activity in detail while stimulating sensory nerves. He found a general inhibition of reflex activity with strong electrical stimulation of afferent nerves, as well as when the nerve was stimulated by chemical substances. Under these conditions, the general inhibition was expressed in the form of a relaxation following an initial motor response, and by the absence of reflex reactions to cutaneous stimuli. Setchenov also found that after the cessation of such stimulation, strong contractions occur at once. It is of interest from the historical point of view to note that

Setchenov described the phenomenon of rebound contraction following general inhibition much earlier than it was described by Sherrington in the case of reciprocal inhibition.

RELATION TO NATURAL AND SPECIFIC REFLEX ACTION. The phenomenon that we call general inhibition is usually observed in connection with muscular activity, in other words, in association with the
reciprocal inhibition and excitation of muscles. Even following the
stimulation of thalamic structures and other divisions of the brain
widespread inhibition is associated with excitatory events. This phenomenon also occurs in such natural reflex acts as urination and
defecation; simultaneously with movements involved in these acts,
there occurs a general inhibition in almost all skeletal musculature
(Meltzer, 1882, Uchtomsky, 1911). However, for a long time this
aspect of reflex activity was not subjected to any special investigation.
Following the first publication of Sherrington concerning reciprocal
excitation and inhibition, all the attention of physiologists was concentrated upon the study of these phenomena.

We conducted the first study of general inhibition in relation to
a specific reflex action in 1922. We disclosed that following the reflex
action involving one motor system, there is a general inhibition of
almost the entire remaining musculature. We were even led to formulate a general principle of the action of the central nervous system:
Each time a strong stimulus elicits a reflex contraction of certain muscles in one or several motor systems, the other muscles of the same
motor system and elsewhere in the organism are inhibited. We considered this principle to be an extremely important biologic factor in
animal behavior; because of this functional arrangement, the coordinated reflex movement of a given motor system could be free from
disturbances which could occur if other coordinated systems were
available to carry out a competitive reflex action.

Systematic investigation of general inhibition associated with reflex
action was started in 1935. Short-term and long-term experiments were
conducted in normal as well as in decerebrate animals including cats,
rabbits, pigeons and frogs. In all these cases, general inhibition was
elicited at the very onset of a stimulation and was associated with a
specific motor reaction, and persisted for a certain time after the
stimulation. It occurred also with subliminal stimuli, which are capable
of affecting respiration only, without causing any motor reaction.
Because of this, one cannot explain inhibition as an expression of a
"pessimal" state,* in other words, by asserting that it is a refractory

* In Russian terminology "pessimal" is opposite to an "optimal" state. (Editor.)

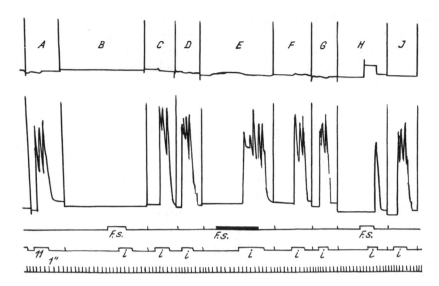

Fig. 36

General inhibition elicited by skin irritation in a normal rabbit. Upper trace shows movement of left hindleg; lower trace, movements of right hindleg. Faradic stimulation (lower signal) of the right hindleg produces its flexion (experiment *A*). If this stimulation is applied as one squeezes the skin of the left foreleg (upper signal, *F.S.*), the reflex of the hindleg is inhibited (experiments *B* and *H*). During a light tactile stimulation (stroking with a brush) of the foreleg, the reflex of the hindleg is somewhat decreased (experiment *E*). Lowest trace, time in seconds. (Dzidzishvili, 1939.)

state induced by an excessive rate of stimuli (Wedensky, 1903) or a "parabiosis," described by Wedensky as occurring under the influence of chemical or physical agents.

General inhibition is very well manifested in normal young rabbits following stimulation of their skin (Dzidzishvili, 1939, 1940a). Reflex movements which are elicited by stimulation of the hindleg skin are inhibited by mechanical stimulation of another part of the body or by pressure, particularly by a strong squeezing of the skin over an area 20 mm. square (Figure 36). Widespread inhibition was also observed during faradic stimulation of the skin, the stimulation being sumliminal with regard to its ability to elicit movements, although movements would occur in certain cases after the cessation of stimulation (a rebound contraction) (Dzidzishvili, 1939).

General inhibition was particularly easy to elicit by cooling the skin. The cooling was produced by circulating water, cooled to 3°C., through a metallic receptacle that was applied to the shaved skin. In this manner reflex movements elicited in the hindlegs, by electrical stimulation of the skin of the same legs, could be inhibited; and since this same inhibition could be elicited by cooling various areas of the body, from the thighs to the head, it was concluded that the inhibition was a diffuse one. During these experiments respiratory movements were also inhibited. The cooling alone would not produce any motor reactions (Figure 37). In some experiments following the cooling one could elicit a process of facilitation; that is, with a background of reflex contractions, cold stimulation would at first inhibit the contractions, but after such stimulation ceased there was facilitation.

General inhibition was also observed during warming of the skin, provided this was not severe enough to burn.

Similar experiments with general inhibition during skin stimulation were conducted by Beritoff and Bakuradze (1943b) on decerebrate cats. In this case recordings were made of the contractions in dissected antagonistic muscles, quadriceps and semitendinosus of both

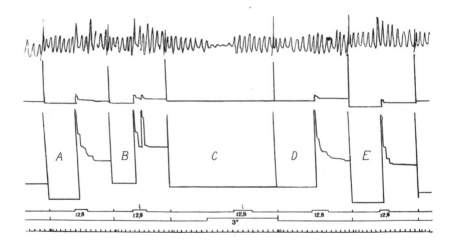

Fig. 37

Diffuse inhibition from application of cold water in normal rabbit. Upper record, respiration; middle record, left hindleg; lower record, right hindleg stimulated by a faradic current (upper signal). General movements occur during stimulation (experiments A, B, D, and E). Cold circulating water (3°C.) is applied to the back (lower signal). This stimulation does not elicit any movement, but suspends respiration as well as the reflex reaction elicited by the electrical stimulus (experiment C). Lowest trace, time in seconds. (Dzidzishvili, 1940a.)

hindlegs; inhibition was elicited by stimulation consisting of squeezing or touching different areas of the body. In the meantime, the tibial nerve was stimulated electrically in order to elicit reflex contractions in these muscles. Reflex contractions were inhibited by mechanical stimulation of the skin, but after the stimulation ceased, they recurred with an increased amplitude (Figure 38).

General inhibition and facilitation were also observed following auditory and visual stimulation of the animals. During a study of frogs, the effect of sound and light upon reflex activity following skin stimulation was ascertained; in general, sound increases reflex movements, while light depresses them (Johannes, 1930, Beburishvili, 1937).

During prolonged periods of stimulation, general inhibition in normal animals may last for several minutes and at times for hours. In frogs after prolonged stimulation of the skin and muscle receptors of the head by the application of a firm bandage, depression of reflex activity lasted 3 or 4 hours; all this time, the frog lay motionless and if placed on its back, would not turn over. Furthermore, if one of the

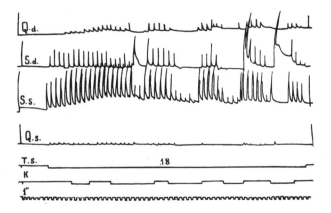

Fig. 38

Decerebrate cat 2 to 5 hours after the operation. Recordings of contractions of quadriceps on the right, *Q.d.*, and left, *Q.s.* sides; semitendinosus on the right, *S.d.*, and left, *S.s.* Left tibial nerve, *T.s.*, is stimulated by 1/sec. faradic shocks (18 cm. between coils). Lowest trace, time in seconds. Reflex contractions are seen on three muscles.

In addition, the skin on the right flank, *K*, was squeezed five times eliciting inhibition in all three muscles after the first negative trail. After the end of the squeezing, contractions increased in amplitude (rebound). During some trials, stimulation of the skin elicited a slight flexor reflex with reciprocal effects. (Bakuradze, 1943.)

hindlegs was passively extended, it would remain extended. Respiratory movements become very rare, and their reaction to pinching of the leg was very weak. Only after 3 to 4 hours did the frog start trying to get free of the bandage and finally succeed in making a jump. If the bandage was applied to one leg, instead of the head, the same condition lasted about 20 to 25 minutes.

When the skin of the head is squeezed in rabbits and puppies, the decrease in reflex activity lasts more than 30 minutes; while if the bandage is applied to the leg, it lasts only 15 to 25 minutes. The younger the animal, the shorter is this stage; in 8- to 14-day-old puppies, it lasts only 5 to 8 minutes (Chichinadze, 1946).

As we indicated above, a prolonged motionless state with decreased reflex activity follows widespread inhibition. The latter occurs in response to stimulation of the skin; however, a few minutes later it is followed by sleep or a sleep-like condition, an animal hypnosis, which results mainly from the disappearance of the effects of skin, muscle and labyrinthine stimuli, due to the immobilization of the animal during the widespread inhibitory state.

ANIMAL HYPNOSIS

General inhibition was observed and described by many authors who studied so-called "animal hypnosis." Heubel (1877) studied it in frogs. He placed the animal on its back and held the flexed hind legs in a fixed position while the head was immobilized by a clamp. After several minutes, he could take his hand away, and the animal remained motionless for several hours. Its eyes were closed; respiration and pulses slowed down, and muscles relaxed. Also, the reflex excitability was greatly decreased; pressure and pinching stimulations of the skin or of the digits would not elicit any reaction. Analogous phenomena were observed with pigeons. This sleep-like phenomenon was found not only in normal frogs but also after ablation of the hemispheres, diencephalon and mesencephalon.

Danilewsky (1881) later studied this phenomenon in frogs and in dogs the same way that Heubel did. In addition, he could elicit a widespread depression of reflexes either by applying a bandage over the abdomen, the chest or even only one leg or by pinching the skin. In the state produced, respiration was arrested for some time, the eyes were closed, the extremities remained in a fixed position and skin stimuli were ineffective.

Richet (1883) studied inhibition resulting from the chemical excitation of sensory nerves, following the example of Setchenov. He introduced concentrated saline solution in the dorsal lymph sac and produced a general immobilization of the animal, as well as a general depression of reflex activity.

The phenomenon of so-called "animal hypnosis," occurring as a result of skin stimulation or forced fixation of the animal, was also studied by Mangold and Eckstein (1919), Eckstein (1919) and others. We studied it in frogs and puppies and were able to elicit the depression of reflex activities with different types of stimulation, i.e., squeezing of the head, bandaging the chest and abdomen, intensely stretching the hindlegs and forelegs and compressing the big toe. In puppies, general inhibition can be elicited by squeezing and fixing the head, stretching or squeezing the tail, introducing different food substances into the mouth, violent sounds or stretching the skin (Beritoff, 1927, 1929b). All these stimuli could elicit some movements with simultaneous depression of reflexes to other stimuli.

The above phenomena were observed both in normal and in decerebrate animals. Hence, we concluded that the observed general inhibition is not dependent upon the presence of the hemispheres (Beritoff, 1927).

In my experiments with the immobilization of an animal, such immobilization consisting of forcibly placing the animal on its back and holding it in a fixed position for several minutes, a sleep-like state occurred. We studied this phenomenon in detail in 1929 and came to the conclusion that in this tranquilization of the animal, one can differentiate two states; the first stage involves an active immobilization of a part of the animal, consisting of a general central inhibition of most of the musculature, triggered as a result of the stimulation of the skin and muscle receptors. If this phase lasts sufficiently long, it is followed by sleep. The second phase is a passive one, the so-called "hypnotic condition." This phase seems to occur because in the first phase, during the general inhibition of the central nervous system, all the exteroceptive and, more important, the proprioceptive and labyrinthine activities are suspended as a result of the immobilization of the animal. This cessation of afferent stimuli, together with central inhibition, in turn brings about a very marked decrease in excitability of the central nervous system, so that following the phase of active inhibition, the animal continues to lie motionless and does not react to outside stimuli.

This phenomenon of general inhibition with the following hypnotic state was studied by Gerebtzoff (1940, 1949) in the rabbit, cat and dog, while working in the laboratory of Bremer. He used the method of Richet (stimulation of the spinal nerves by introduction of sodium chloride into the spinal lymph sac) and came to the conclusion that the general decrease in reflex activity results from an activation of the inhibitory centers of the cortex and mesencephalon.

GENERAL FACILITATION

As stated earlier, the general inhibition following stimulation is replaced by a general facilitation, i.e., a general increase in central excitability. This is observed after stimulation of the receptor mechanisms, afferent nerves or the surface of the cortex. Only under certain conditions, however, is it elicited with great regularity. Thus, we observed that facilitation occurs following inhibition only in cases where inhibition is terminated rather quickly, after 1 to 2 seconds. If the state of inhibition terminates during the course of stimulation, then no facilitation occurs after the end of the stimulation. Facilitation occurs most strongly 1 to 2 seconds following inhibition; then it very quickly subsides a few seconds later (Beritoff, 1937a, Beritoff, Bakuradze and Narikashvili, 1937).

The degree of facilitation depends upon the intensity of the inhibition. It is all the more pronounced when the preceding inhibition has been intense. The facilitation is usually expressed by rebound contractions; i.e., the same muscles which were inhibited now show a contraction. But this is best observed when these muscles have been in tonic contraction or if the animal was generally in an excited state, in other words if the motoneurons were subjected to some spontaneous activation. However, if this is not the situation, rebound contractions may not occur, but facilitation may be easily elicited by a stimulation of receptors or afferent nerves immediately after the end of the inhibition-inducing stimulation. Because of the facilitation, the reaction to the additional stimulus will be increased (Figure 38).

We established the fact that general inhibition and facilitation which may follow it occur during stimulation of receptors and afferent nerves in any segment of the body. Diffuse inhibition was observed in frogs during squeezing of the head or skin or during stimulation of the cranial nerves (the trigeminal, for example) (Narikashvili, 1937, Tevzadze, 1951), or by stimulation of the vagus (Gedevani, 1941). It was observed also during mechanical or chemical stimulation of the cutaneous nerves of the extremities, the abdomen and chest in frogs (n. spinalis, n. cutaneous femoralis lateralis) (Gogava, 1939, Beritoff and Gogava, 1937). In all these cases general inhibition was revealed by depression of movements and decrease of tonic and defensive reflexes. Also, in all these cases, a quickly subsiding inhibition was followed by facilitation.

Inhibition also involves contracted muscles. This is revealed when one elicits inhibition against a background of more or less intense clonic reflex movements, such as usually occur if one stimulates an afferent nerve by isolated faradic discharges every 1 to 2 seconds. These clonic effects are decreased or completely suppressed during tetanization. The state of inhibition is made manifest by the occurrence of rebound contractions (Figure 39) (Beritoff, 1937a).

General Inhibition and Facilitation in Spinal Preparations

We have just considered phenomena of general inhibition and facilitation in normal and decerebrate animals. One might assume that this diffuse inhibition followed by facilitation originates only in the brain. Yet widespread inhibition and facilitation also occur in each reflex activity of spinal and lumbar preparations. In these animals general inhibition may occur not only in relaxed muscles but in those which are partially contracted.

General inhibition was fully investigated in lumbar preparations of cats and dogs. Stimulation was applied to the skin and muscle receptors, as well as to afferent nerves, dorsal roots, viscera and autonomic nerves. Pinching the skin triggers inhibition in the lumbar preparations much better than any other stimulation. Mechanical stimulation by direct touch or by a brush very often elicited reflex clonic movements (Bakuradze, 1943).

STIMULATION OF AFFERENT NERVES OR DORSAL ROOTS

Diffuse inhibition occurs in lumbar animals during stimulation of afferent nerves or dorsal roots, and it results not only from stimulation that elicits a motor reaction but also from subliminal stimuli. However, subliminal stimuli produce weaker and more circumscribed inhibition than do stimuli which produce a motor effect. In the latter case, inhibition is revealed not only in relaxed muscles but also in those which are partially contracted. Moreover, with an increase in the intensity of stimulation of afferent nerves, inhibition involves more distant areas of the spinal cord. This is very well illustrated in Figures 40

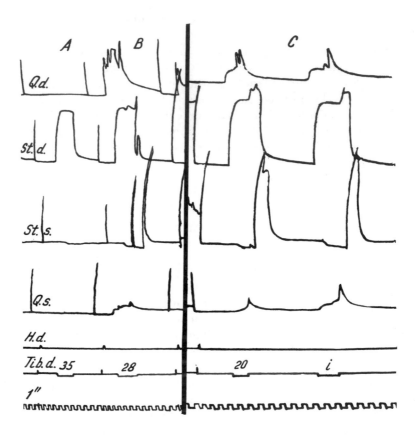

Fig. 39

Inhibited contraction during an increase of a tetanic stimulation (decere-brated cat). Contractions of the following muscles are recorded: Right, *Q.d.*, and left, *Q.s.*, quadriceps; both semitendinosus, *St.d.*, *St.s.* First the right tibial nerve, *Tib.d.*, was stimulated with a threshold faradic current (35 cm. between coils); during this stimulation, only semitendinosus of the corresponding side was activated. Then the stimulation was increased to 28 and 20 cm. During this stimulation, the extensors on both sides also showed contractions. However, these muscles, as well as the flexor on the contralateral side, were partly inhibited; when the stimulation stopped, a rebound contraction appeared. (Beritoff, Bakuradze and Narikashvili, 1937.)

and 41, which represent experiments on lumbar preparations in cats involving stimulation of the dorsal root. With minimal stimulation, inhibition involves only ipsilateral muscles (Figure 40); with more intense stimulation, when a flexor reflex occurs on the corresponding

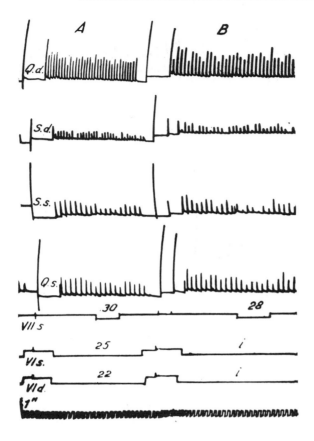

Fig. 40

General inhibition during subliminal stimulation of a dorsal root. Lumbar preparation of a cat. Stimulation of the sixth dorsal root on the right, *VId.*, and left, *VIs.*, sides with single electrical discharges elicits single reflex clonic movements in all recorded muscles: quadriceps, right, *Q.d.*, and left, *Q.s.*, semitendinosus right, *S.d.*, and left, *S.s.* Subliminal stimulation of the left seventh dorsal root, *VIIs.*: single twitches decrease only ipsilaterally. The numbers on signal lines signify on this and the following figures, the intensity of stimulation expressed as a distance between the primary and secondary coils of the inductorium. (Beritoff, 1941.)

side, the muscles of the opposite side also show inhibition (Figure 41) (Beritoff, 1941).

During stimulation of the tenth (sacral) dorsal root supplying the tail, we made the following observation. A tetanizing stimulation did not elicit any motor reaction in the extremities with whatever intensity of the current was used: we could observe only inhibition (Figure

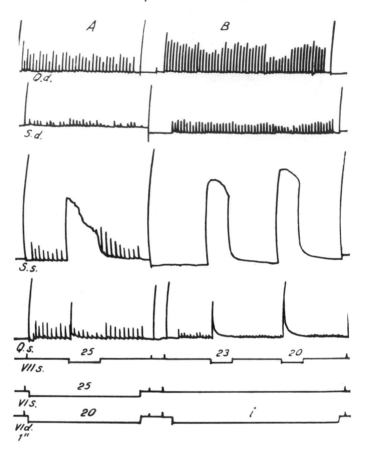

Fig. 41

Same experiment as Figure 40. When one applies, along with stimulation of the sixth dorsal root, a strong tetanic stimulation of the seventh dorsal root on the left side, *VIIs.*, one elicits a flexor reflex (experiment *A*). The ipsilateral flexor contracts while the left extensor is strongly inhibited (reciprocal inhibition). With a stronger tetanic stimulation applied against the background of the right-sided stimulation with single electrical discharges (experiment *B*) both recorded muscles on this side are partially inhibited. This is an expression of a general inhibition. (Beritoff, 1941.)

42). As is known, stimulation of the tail causes it to move, while reflex movement is inhibited in the hindlegs (Beritoff, 1928). This confirms that this reaction to the stimulation of the tail is transmitted through the tenth dorsal root.

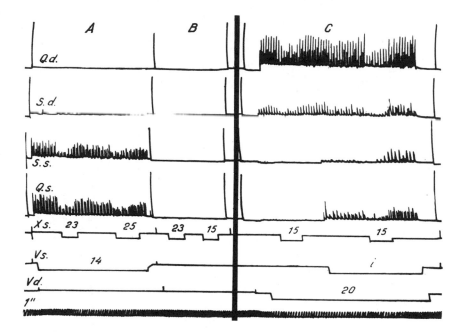

Fig. 42

General inhibition and general facilitation in a lumbar preparation of a cat. General inhibition during stimulation of the tenth dorsal root. Contractions of quadriceps, *Q.d.*, *Q.s.*, and semitendinosus, *S.d.*, *S.s.*, on both sides are recorded. Stimulation of the tenth left dorsal root, *Xs.*, which is very thin (of the order of 0.1 mm.). This stimulation does not produce contractions in the recorded muscles whatever the intensity of stimulation is (experiment *B*), but it inhibits reflex contractions in these muscles which are elicited by stimulation of the fifth dorsal roots on the left, *Vs.*, and right, *Vd.*, sides (single stimuli). At the end of the stimulation, facilitation is observed (experiment *C*). (Beritoff and Bakuradze, 1941.)

Stimulation of afferent nerves and dorsal roots elicits a general inhibition concurrently with a reflex contraction. During a prolonged stimulation, the contraction progressively fades out, while inhibition persists; i.e., inhibition in general lasts longer than excitation. For this reason, even if the contractions of a given muscle subside, it will still show inhibitory effects in response to the stimulation of the other nerves (Figure 43).

During prolonged stimulation, a diffuse inhibition may last for several minutes in lumbar preparations and then slowly decrease. If the stimulation is suspended after a short period of time, inhibition also

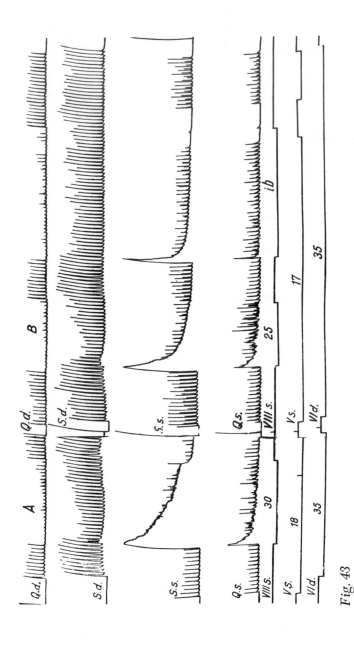

Fig. 43

General inhibition of contracted muscles, lumbar cat. Contractions of quadriceps, *Q.d.*, *Q.s.*, and semitendinosus, *S.d.*, *S.s.*, on both sides are recorded. Stimulation of dorsal roots, *Vs.*,*VId.*, by single faradic stimuli produce single clonic contractions in all muscles. Tetanic stimulation of the eighth left dorsal root, *VIIIs.*, elicits, however, a flexor reflex with a very strong contraction. During the decrease in amplitude of this flexor reflex, contralateral reflex clonic twitches remain inhibited. (Beritoff and Bakuradze, 1941.)

subsides very shortly afterward. Thus, Figure 44 illustrates a case when faradic stimulation was applied for a relatively long time to the spinal cord of the cat (dorsal column in the thoracic segment) while reflex twitches were elicited by stimulation of a dorsal root. General inhibition lasted as long as the stimulation was maintained (8 minutes), and the aftereffects of inhibition persisted for several seconds. When the stimulation is prolonged and inhibition progressively subsides, there is no facilitation or increase in excitability after the end of stimulation. This is also shown by Figure 44.

General inhibition is elicited in lumbar preparations not only by a tetanizing stimulation of the afferent nerves but also by single faradic stimuli. As was indicated above, such stimulation simultaneously elicits single twitches in the antagonistic muscles of the corresponding hindleg. These contractions are also associated with widespread inhibition. Figure 45 shows that following a stimulation of one dorsal root, stimulation of another dorsal root applied a few seconds later

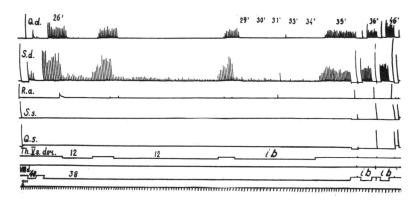

Fig. 44

Prolonged general inhibition, thoracolumbar cat. Contractions of both quadriceps, *Q.d.*, *Q.s.*, and semitendinosus, *S.d.*, *S.s.*, are recorded bilaterally, as well as the rectus abdominalis, *R.a.* Stimulation of the eighth right dorsal root, *VIIId.*, by single faradic stimuli elicited single reflex twitches in the muscles of the right side. During this stimulation, a tetanizing current was applied to the left posterior column in a thoracic segment, *Th.Vs.dor.* At the onset, the stimulation of the dorsal column elicited a slight contraction of the abdominal muscles. The first time the stimulation lasted 20 seconds, the second, 1 minute and the third, 6 minutes. In the last case, the kymograph was stopped five times, each time for 1 minute. Reflex twitches were almost completely inhibited. After the end of the inhibitory excitation, the reflex twitches were restored in 10 to 15 seconds. Lowest trace shows time in seconds. (Beritoff and Bakuradze, 1943a.)

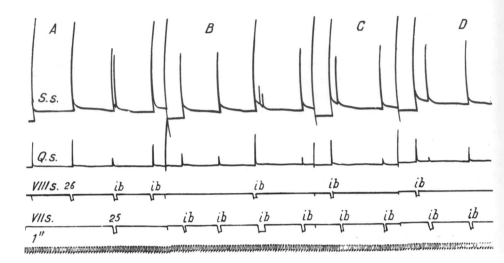

Fig. 45

General inhibition from single peripheral impulses, lumbar preparation of a cat. Contractions of quadriceps, *Q.s.*, and semitendinosus, *S.s.*, on the left side are recorded. Seventh, *VIIs.*, and eighth, *VIIIs.*, dorsal roots on the left side were stimulated by single faradic stimuli, resulting in contractions of both muscles. In experiment *A*, stimulation of the seventh dorsal root preceded stimulation of the eighth root by 1 second; the effect of the latter stimulation was partially inhibited. In experiment *B*, stimulation of the eighth dorsal root preceded stimulation of the seventh root by 2 seconds and in experiments *C* and *D*, by 3½ and 5 seconds, respectively. Each time there was a weakening of the effect from the test stimulus. (Beritoff and Bakuradze, 1940b.)

elicits a rather weak effect. This experiment reveals that a single volley of peripheral impulses is capable of eliciting a diffuse inhibition which spreads over neighboring segments. This inhibitory effect must be responsible for the depression of the reflex reaction following the initial effect triggered by a tetanizing stimulation in the preceding experiment.

STIMULATION OF MUSCLE RECEPTORS

A very marked general inhibition is observed following the stretching of the muscle resulting in a stimulation of muscle proprio-

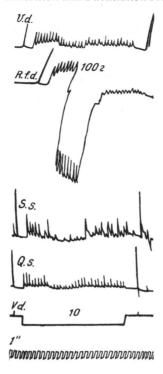

Fig. 46

General inhibition from the proprioceptive impulses, lumbar preparation of a cat. Contractions recorded in right vastus lateralis, V.d.; right rectus femoris, R.f.d.; left semitendinosus, S.s.; left quadriceps, Q.s. The spinal cord was exposed but all the dorsal roots were intact. Stimulation of the fifth dorsal root on the right side, Vd., elicited reflex clonic twitches in all muscles. At the same time, the right rectus femoris was stretched by a weight of 100 Gm. On the stretched muscle, the clonic twitches increased, while all other muscles showed an inhibition of twitches. (Beritoff and Bakuradze, 1941.)

ceptors or by direct stimulation of the muscle nerves. These experiments were carried out in spinal preparations in cats (Beritoff and Bakuradze, 1941) and frogs (Narikashvili, 1936). Stretching of the gastrocnemius or triceps, as well as stimulating of the nerves, elicits a diffuse inhibition of all the muscles of the hindlegs with the exception, of course, of the one which is stretched; the latter exhibits a contraction (Figure 46).

Inhibition occurs for each muscular reflex, even when the reflex results from stimulation of the muscle nerves or tendon receptors by a single faradic stimulus (Hoffmann, 1934; Kostyuk, 1956). The investigation of Kato (1934) showed that a general inhibition, without excitation, may occur with any stimulation of some afferent muscle nerves—also during their tetanizing stimulation, or even under conditions of strychnine poisoning. These afferent fibers are on the order of 9 to 10 microns. Fibers of lesser diameter, on the order of 6 to 7 microns, elicit a reflex excitation. According to Kato, during the stimulation of a mixed nerve with a relatively weak current, one will activate large fibers and therefore elicit inhibition; whereas, with a more intense stimulation, fibers of a smaller diameter will be activated and contractions observed. In the experiments of Kostyuk (1956), since the electrical pulses were brief, more excitable fibers of a larger diameter were stimulated, and therefore only inhibition was produced.*

Usually the inhibition which is elicited by proprioceptive stimuli is also followed by facilitation and an increase in excitability (Hoffmann, 1934, Kostyuk, 1956).

STIMULATION OF VISCERA

Diffuse inhibition is also elicited in thoracolumbar and lumbar preparations during stimulation of the viscera, such as the stomach, rectum or bladder, by stretching them or by stimulating afferent autonomic fibers. Facilitation usually occurs, following this stimulation (rebound contraction) (Figure 47) (Beritoff and Bakuradze, 1943b). Figure 48 shows that during a weak distension of the rectum all the muscles are inhibited; following this stretching, facilitation takes place, evidenced by an increase in single twitches (experiment A). During a more pronounced stretching, the flexors are only partially contracted, and following the suspension of stretching, there is a rebound contraction.

Afferent fibers originating in the bladder and rectum enter the sacral region of the spinal cord. Therefore, a general inhibition arises in the sacral region and diffuses from there along the spinal cord. The

---

*Our own recent studies showed that such inhibitory processes are responsible for the tremor observed in parkinsonian patients and probably for the clonus in patients with pyramidal tract lesions. Single brief electrical stimuli applied to the median nerve are capable of prolonging the interburst period of the parkinsonian tremor of the thumb; if these stimuli are repeated, the tremor is reset each time (Liberson, W. T., EEG Clin. Neurophysiol. (Suppl. 22), pp. 79–89, 1962). More recently, Liberson and Paillard (Proc. 12th Annual Spinal Cord Injury Conf., Veterans Adminstration, Hines, Illinois, 1963) showed that rubbing of the sole of the foot produces a prolonged inhibition of the proprioceptive reflexes of the soleus muscle before any contraction is seen in its antagonist. This might constitute another example of widespread inhibition. (Editor.)

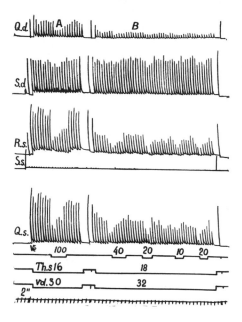

Fig. 47

General inhibition from interoceptive impulses, thoracolumbar preparation
of a cat. In the lumbar area, the dorsal roots were sectioned except for the
fifth lumbar root on the right side, *Vd.* Contractions of the quadriceps,
Q.d., Q.s., were recorded as well as those of the semitendinosus, *S.d., S.s.,*
on both sides, and the rectus abdominalis, *R.s.* Stimulation of the dorsal
column at the level of the fifth thoracic segment on the left side, *Th.s.,*
and of the fifth dorsal root of the right side, resulted in reflex twitches.
During this stimulation, the bladder, *Ve.,* was distended by means of a thin
rubber balloon inflated to a pressure of 10 to 100 mm. of mercury. All the
muscle twitches were partially inhibited. (Beritoff and Bakuradze, 1943b.)

sacral region contains a coordinating apparatus for the flexor reflex
and the motoneurons of the semitendinosus (Beritoff, 1923). This
must explain why the flexor motoneurons were activated during certain experiments with the strong stimulation described above.

STIMULATION OF VISCERA AFTER SECTIONING OF BOTH DORSAL AND VENTRAL ROOTS

There is considerable literature indicating that some afferent fibers
enter the spinal cord through the ventral roots and also along the vessels. We are referring to the well-known clinical investigations of

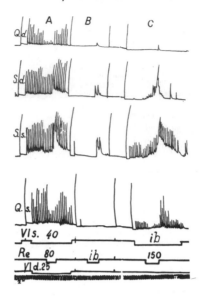

Fig. 48

General inhibition and facilitation due to the interoceptive impulses, lumbar preparation of a cat. Sixth dorsal roots were sectioned bilaterally, *VId., VIs.;* contractions of quadriceps, *Q.d., Q.s.,* and semitendinosus, *S.d., S.s.,* on both sides were recorded. Stimulation of the sixth dorsal root on either side by single faradic stimuli, elicited reflex twitches in all muscles. The rectum, *Re,* was then distended in experiments *A* and *B* to 80 mm. of mercury and in experiment *C* to 150 mm. of mercury. (Bakuradze, 1943b.) (See text.)

Förster (1927), and Fröhlich and Meyer (1922). Morphologic studies of Sherrington (1894) and Michailow (1909) suggest that the afferent fibers of pain perception pass from the visceral, muscle and joint receptors through the ventral roots. We also investigated this problem in the thoracolumbar preparations of the cat (Beritoff and Bakuradze, 1943b, c). We completely sectioned dorsal roots and partially sectioned ventral roots without injuring the vessels which enter the spinal cord together with these roots. We then investigated influences on the reflex activity of the spinal cord resulting from stimulation of visceral receptors, by the distension of the bladder, stomach, duodenum and rectum with small rubber balloons placed within these organs. A myographic recording was made of the contracting antagonistic muscles of the hindlegs, as well as of the contractions of the abdominal muscles.

As indicated above, stimulation of the viscera elicits both excitation of the skeletal muscles and their inhibition. In spite of the section of dorsal roots caudad to the spinal cord transection in the thoracic, lumbar or sacral regions, stimulation of the viscera and of the corresponding autonomic nerves continued to elicit general inhibition (Figure 49). Figure 49 shows that with the distension of the rectum, inhibition is manifest in all the recorded muscles on both sides. The knee flexors are supplied by the sixth, seventh and eighth segments, the extensors by the fourth, fifth and sixth segments and the abdominal muscles by the thoracic segments. In these experiments general inhibition takes place without any concomitant motor reaction.

In view of the foregoing, the question of how the interoceptors influence the spinal cord had to be investigated. Does this influence occur through the ventral roots or through the fibers traveling with the vessels penetrating the cord together with the roots?

Care was taken to avoid damaging the vessels during sectioning of the roots. The ventral roots were cut after sectioning the dorsal roots with the exception of those roots which supply the muscle whose contractions were to be recorded. We found that after sectioning all the dorsal and ventral roots, with the exception of one or two pairs for the study of motor reactions, we still could induce a diffuse inhibition during the stimulation of visceral receptors (Figure 50).

We concluded, therefore, that the visceral afferent fibers penetrate the spinal cord not only through the dorsal and ventral roots but also with the vessels. However, since, after the section of the dorsal roots, stimulation of the viscera would not elicit contractions of the skeletal muscles, we also concluded that reflex twitches of the skeletal muscle, following stimulation of the viscera, occur only by means of the afferent impulses passing via dorsal roots.

STIMULATION OF VENTRAL ROOTS AFTER SECTIONING DORSAL ROOTS

We also tried to stimulate the ventral roots after sectioning the dorsal roots. That is, after sectioning all the dorsal roots, starting with the second or third lumbar segments to the end of the spinal cord, we stimulated the sixth, seventh and eighth ventral roots and looked for the effects in the quadriceps and semitendinosus muscles on both sides. As is known, the semitendinosus is supplied by the ventral roots of the seventh, eighth and ninth segments and the quadriceps by the fourth, fifth and sixth segments and much less often through the seventh ventral root. If we sectioned one of these roots and stimulated its central segment, no motor effect was observed in any of these muscles. Reflex motor effects also failed to appear when the stimulation was

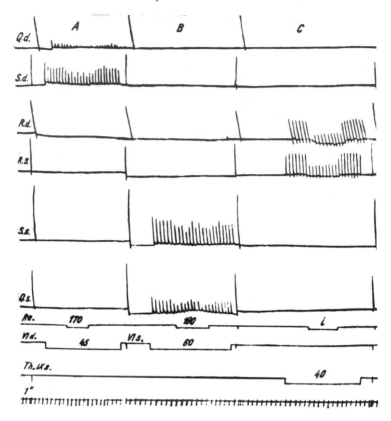

Fig. 49

General inhibition resulting from interoceptive impulses, deafferented thoracolumbar preparation of a cat. Spinal cord sectioned at two levels, sixth to seventh thoracic segment and the second to third lumbar segment. On both sides, all dorsal roots sectioned. Contractions of quadriceps, *Q.d.*, *Q.s.*, semitendinosus, *S.d.*, *S.s.*, and rectus abdominalis, *R.d.*, *R.s.*, recorded on both sides. In experiment *A*, the stimulation of the right sixth lumbar dorsal root, *VId.*, by single faradic stimuli elicited single reflex twitches in the muscles of the right hindleg. In experiment *B*, the same effects were elicited in the left hindleg by stimulation of the left lumbar dorsal root, *VIs*. In experiment *C*, stimulation of the left ninth thoracic dorsal root, *Th.IXs.*, elicited single twitches in the abdominal muscles. In all three experiments, a distension of the rectum, *Re.*, to 170 to 180 mm. of mercury elicited an inhibition of recorded muscles. (Beritoff and Bakuradze, 1943b.) (See text.)

applied to any of the nonsectioned ventral roots. If, for instance, one stimulated the seventh or eighth ventral roots, this would produce a peripheral motor effect on the semitendinosus muscle but would not

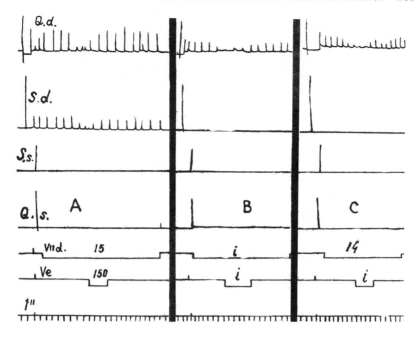

Fig. 50

Diffuse inhibition produced by interoceptive impulses, lumbar preparation of a cat (section between second and third lumbar segments). All dorsal roots sectioned bilaterally. Contractions of the flexors, *S.d.*, *S.s.*, and extensors, *Q.d.*, *Q.s.*, recorded bilaterally. Single faradic stimuli were applied to the seventh right dorsal root, *VIId.*, and elicited reflex twitches in the muscles on the right side. Distension of the bladder to 150 mm. of mercury produced inhibition, *Ve.* In experiment *A* all ventral roots also were sectioned except the third to seventh; in experiment *B* except the third to fifth; in experiment *C* except the third and fourth. In all these experiments, distension of the bladder elicited inhibition of reflex twitches. (Beritoff and Bakuradze, 1943b.)

elicit any contraction of the other muscles attached to the myographs. When stimulation of the ventral root was applied against a background of reflex twitches elicited by stimulation of the dorsal roots, we found a definite, but slight, inhibition of these twitches. This inhibition also spreads over the muscle on the other side (Figure 51). Therefore, the inhibition which was triggered via the ventral roots had a widespread character. This inhibition is, however, significantly weaker than when dorsal roots or the afferent nerves are stimulated and does not occur in all the preparations with the same consistency.

As is known, antidromic stimulation, transmitted along the axon,

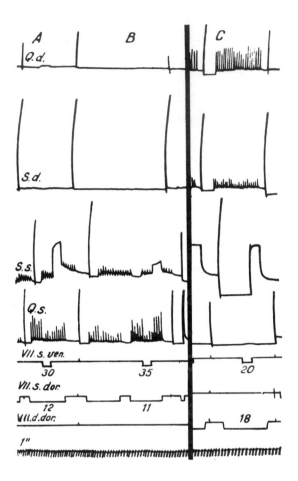

Fig. 51

General inhibition elicited by stimulation of a ventral root. Lumbar preparation of a cat with all lumbar, sacral and coccygeal dorsal roots sectioned. Contractions of quadriceps, *Q.d.*, *Q.s.*, and semitendinosus, *S.d.*, *S.s.*,
recorded on both sides. In experiments *A* and *B*, stimulation of the left
seventh dorsal root, *VII.s.dor.*, induced reflex twitches in the muscles of the
ipsilateral side. Then a tetanizing stimulation of the nonsectioned left
seventh ventral root, *VII.s.ven.*, elicited contractions in the flexor, while the
extensor was inhibited. In experiment *C* reflex twitches were elicited on the
muscles of the opposite side by stimulation of the seventh dorsal root on
the right side, *VII.d.dor.* Tetanizing stimulation of the same ventral root
partially inhibited both muscles. Numbers on the signal lines signify the
distance between the primary and secondary coils of the inductorium.
(Beritoff and Bakuradze, 1941.)

affects motoneurons and elicits facilitation. That is, for several seconds afterward these motoneurons will react to orthodromic impulses more intensely than before the application of the antidromic stimuli (Bremer, 1936). Therefore, the stimulation of the ventral roots induces on one hand facilitation of the corresponding motoneurons, due to the stimulation of the motor fibers, and on the other hand it generates general inhibition of other motoneurons.

It is possible that inhibition during the stimulation of the ventral roots depends, to a certain degree, upon the recurrent collaterals of the stimulated motor fibers. Many histologists described recurrent collaterals of the axons of the motoneurons before their emergence from the anterior horn. At first Golgi (1883) disclosed that the ventral roots give off collaterals which run in the gray matter of the anterior horn. This was confirmed in mammals, including man, by a number of outstanding histologists, such as Ramon y Cajal (1899), Philippson (1905), Lenhossek (1895) and Golgi (1883), who found these collaterals in almost all motor axons with a considerable consistency. Lenhossek found that in the spinal cord of the rabbit these recurrent collaterals even form a whole neurofibrillar net in the vicinity of the anterior horn, being interlaced with the dendrites of the motoneurons (Figure 52). The authors do not find that these collaterals penetrate the dorsal half of the spinal cord. However, there are observations that they may partially penetrate along the anterior commissure on the opposite side of the cord. Dendrites of the motoneurons also cross the midline by this commissure, as was described by Ramon y Cajal in the spinal cord of the frog and by Bechterew (1926) in the newborn kitten. Bechterew gave a very striking picture of the contacts between the axonal collaterals, on the one hand, and the dendrites of the motoneurons, on the other, in the commissure itself (Figure 53). The presence of these contacts of the recurring collaterals with the dendrites of the motoneurons of the one or the other side suggests that these recurring collaterals participate in the origin of the general inhibition. But the way these synapses of the recurring collaterals may be responsible in inhibition will be discussed in more detail below.

Pain Perception and General Inhibitions

Our collaborators, Tzkipuridze and Chichinadze (1944a, b), carried out an extensive investigation on patients who were experiencing intense pain, i.e., patients with causalgia or with headaches, toothaches,

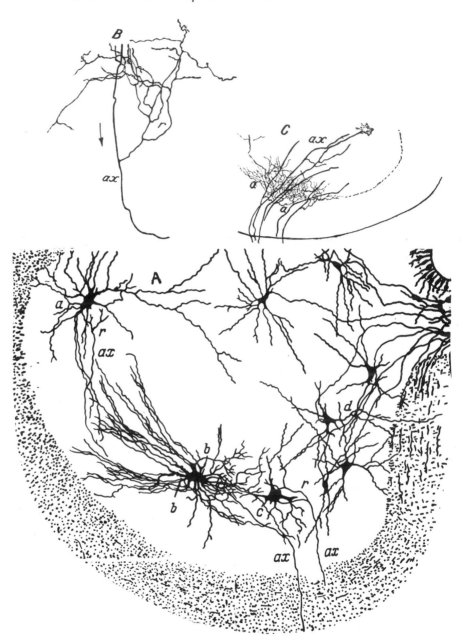

Fig. 52

Recurring collaterals of the ventral root fibers. A, Preparation of the spinal
cord of a 30 cm. human embryo; *a, b, c,* motoneurons; *ax,* axons; *r,* recurrent

gangrene, neuritis, other inflammatory processes, phantom pain, etc. They were able to elicit widespread inhibition in these patients by stimulating skin and muscles of the extremities and of the chest. In order to obtain a more precise evaluation of the degree of stimulation, it was accomplished by means of compression with the aid of a Riva-Rocci sphygmomanometer.

They found that pain, along with its objective manifestations (e.g., respiration, facial expressions, etc.) and subjective feelings, is considerably decreased or even suspended with a pressure of only 15 to 20 mm. of mercury. This pressure did not disturb the circulation. In order to achieve inhibition of pain, both a certain duration and a certain level of compression were necessary. Inhibition thus elicited lasted 4 to 5 hours and sometimes longer. During the course of this inhibition, the pain would recur for brief episodes but could be extinguished quite rapidly. Following the inhibitory stimulation, pain would recur in from 10 seconds to 10 minutes; it recurred earlier in cases where it had been more difficult to inhibit.

The site of the compression of skin and muscle receptors was not a significant factor in achieving inhibition. For example, causalgia in one extremity was relieved or even disappeared during the compression of another extremity. But phantom pain in an amputated extremity was not relieved by the compression of the skin and muscles in the opposite extremity. Apparently phantom pain involves a different mechanism.

These data suggest that stimulation of the skin and muscle receptors elicits general inhibition of not only the coordinating apparatus of motor structures but also neuronal elements responsible for the pain perception. Because the inhibitory action is prolonged, we think that the stimulation of muscle receptors which are not easily adaptable plays a very important role in this phenomenon. But, of course, the compression of skin and muscles cannot be considered the sole factor in the suppression of pain. For instance, the application of cold may be equally effective, and it is actually used by patients; as we saw before, it is capable of eliciting general inhibition.

---

collaterals; *d*, commissural cells. B, Preparation of the spinal cord of a fully developed rabbit embryo; *ax*, fiber of a ventral root with a very markedly divided recurrent collateral, *r*. C, Preparation of the spinal cord of a newborn rabbit; *a*, a fine reticulum made of divided recurrent collaterals near the lateral limits of the spinal cord. (Lenhossek, 1895.)

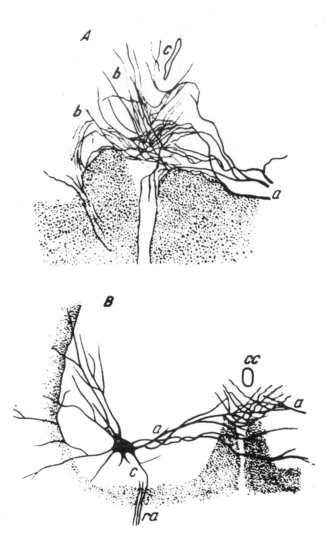

Fig. 53

Anterior commissure of the spinal cord of a newborn kitten. A, Golgi preparation; *a*, dendrites of motoneurons on the left side synapse with *b*, the
collaterals of the axons of the right anterior horn; *c*, central canal. *B*, A
motoneuron of the anterior horn sends protoplasmic processes, *a*, toward
the anterior horn on the other side through the ventral columns; *c*, axons
with a recurrent collateral; *ra*, the ventral root; *cc*, central canal. (Bechterew, 1926.)

Origin of General Inhibition and Facilitation

Since 1936–1937 we have discussed, from the theoretical point of view, the mechanisms of general inhibition in the light of the histologic investigations of Herrick (1930–1934), Coghill (1929, 1936), Lorente de Nó (1934) and others who found that the central nervous system contains a neurono-neuropillar structure. That is, the central nuclei and pathways form neuronal circuits with their axonal synaptic endings on cell bodies of other neurons. Integration and transmission of stimuli is effected through these neuronal circuits, i.e., those coming from the receptors into the cerebral hemispheres and, conversely, those originating in the forebrain and running toward the motoneurons. The remaining mass of central nervous system consists of neural nets, the so-called neuropil, the main part of which are dendrites and axonal collaterals of neurons forming neural circuits as well as numerous ramifications of afferent fibers. The neuropil comprises also its own neurons with branching neuron processes.

In this reticulum axons form synapses with cell bodies and their dendrites just as in the central nuclei. The neuropil occupies large portions of certain regions of the central nervous system, being located in between the conducting pathways and nuclei, and freely penetrates them. It is also located on the periphery of the brain, forming perimedullar and subpial layers (Kölliker, 1902, Nemilov, 1913). The most compact formations of neuropil were considered to be the reticular formation in the brain and the substantia gelatinosa dorsalis of Rolando in the spinal cord.

Yet the use of the term "neuropil" to denote any neural reticulum or any neuronal net leads to semantic difficulties. Thus, from the time of Bethe (1903) a neuropil was considered to be any syncytial structure of the nervous system usually found in lower invertebrates; this was contrasted with the neuronal structure of the nervous system in vertebrates. Well-known neurologists such as Herrick (1930–1934), Ariens Kappers (1927), Zavarsin (1941) and others started to apply this term to mean any plexus made of nerve processes, even those in which axons synapse with dendrites. Therefore, it was very difficult to be absolutely sure in any particular case which meaning was being given to this term by one or another writer. Originally, following the example of Herrick, we applied the term "neuropil" to any reticulum, even a synaptic one. But now, in order to avoid difficulty in interpretation, we have decided not to use the term "neuropil" in regard to neuronal nets where a syncytium is lacking.

On the basis of certain electrophysiologic studies such as the investigations of Beck (1914), Umrath (1933, 1934), Hughes and Gasser (1934a, b), Barron and Matthews (1935), Adrian and Buytendijk (1931) and others, some 30 years ago we came to the following conclusion: The recorded rapid electrical potentials in the brain reveal the excitation of neuronal circuits, in the conducting pathways; whereas, the slow potentials result from the activation of the neuropil, particularly its dendritic mass. We assumed also that the potentials produce an electrical field which affects the neighboring neuronal elements electrotonically by inducing in them electrotonic increases in excitability (facilitation), or decreases in excitability (inhibition) (Beritoff, 1937a, b).

The same general concept was extended to the cerebral cortex. We assumed that here also diffuse inhibition is due to the electrotonic effects upon neuronal circuits of slow potentials generated by the dendritic mass.

However, later it became known that bioelectric potentials originating during the activation of neuronal elements do not spread in the cortex by purely physical mechanisms for any significant distance. For example, a discharge of pyramidal neurons of the fifth layer is not recorded from the interstitial fluid when the electrode is located only 20 to 30 microns away from the cell body, while the recorded potential from the tip of the recording microelectrode touching the cell body may be as high as 5 mv. (Li, Choh and Jasper, 1953). In the spinal cord ganglia, potentials originating from a single cell can be recorded at a distance of no more than 80 microns from the cell's surface (Svaetichin, 1951). Because of this, one would assume that the influence of the electrical field may be felt only in its immediate vicinity as in a nerve trunk. Here excitation of certain nerve fibers elicits in neighboring fibers first an anelectrotonic decrease of excitability, as the current enters them. Then at the point of exit of the current from the fiber, a catelectrotonic increase of excitability is seen, followed by a phase of depression which can be observed at the cathode subsequent to the polarization. Experimentally, it was proved that the conduction of impulses in the neighboring fibers is made difficult during the positive phases, and may even be blocked (Granit and Skoglund, 1945a, b). For instance, our collaborator, Gogava, found that during relatively strong stimulation of the nerve trunk of a frog, with stimulation of group B fibers, the amplitudes of the potentials in group A fibers are somewhat decreased (Figure 54) (Beritoff and Gogava, 1958).

Another of our collaborators, Djavrishvili (1959), revealed analogous interactions between the alpha and beta subgroups of A fibers.

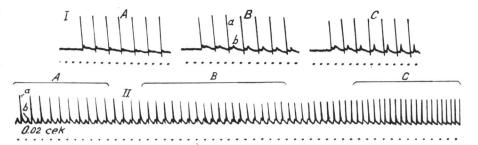

Fig. 54

An anelectrotonic effect of B fibers upon A fibers. Sciatic nerve of a frog. *I*, The lumbosacral plexus stimulated with 0.5 msec. shocks. Potentials recorded from the tibial nerve in the region of the knee. Cathode ray oscillograph and AC amplifiers used. *A*, At a threshold stimulation (10 volts; 30 per sec.) spikes recorded from A fibers; *B* and *C*, same with the intensity of 15 and 25 volts respectively. After the spikes of A fibers, *a*, spikes of B fibers recorded, *b*. *II*, *A*, Increase of the frequency of the stimulation to 65 per sec.; when spikes, *a*, occur shortly after spikes, *b*, their amplitude significantly decreases, *B*. With further increase of frequency of stimulation to 100 per sec., *c*, brief spikes disappear because of the refractory state. At the same time, the amplitude of spikes, *a*, increases. (Beritoff and Gogava, 1958.)

When, with an increase of the stimulating current, beta fibers started to be involved, the potentials of the alpha fibers were significantly decreased (Figure 55).

It follows that there may be in the central nervous system an active anelectrotonic influence exerted by activated cell bodies and dendrites. It must be even much more pronounced here than in the nerve trunks because in the central nervous system, we deal not only with rapid but also slow potentials. The latter are summated by stimulation at a relatively high rate and therefore may form a steady potential, thus creating a continuous electric field in the intercellular fluid which should affect neural elements exactly as an anode of a constant direct current. The emergence of a steady electric potential in the central nervous system may be well seen in Figure 56, where the recording of the potentials of the dorsal root was done with a DC amplifier. When the DC amplifier is used, such steady potentials can also be recorded from the ventral roots. Therefore, they originate within the spinal cord as the result of a summation of dendritic and local cell body potentials, which then electrotonically spread through the roots.

It is clear that the presence of electric fields due to steady potentials of a relatively high amplitude cannot fail to depress neuronal elements

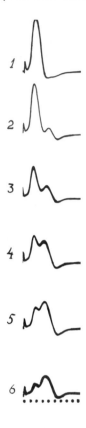

Fig. 55

Anelectrotonic influence of beta fibers on alpha fibers. Sciatic nerve of a frog stimulated by 0.5 msec. shocks. Potentials recorded by a differential AC amplifier and a cathode ray oscillograph. Progressive increase in strength of stimuli: *1*, 0.1 volts; *2*, 5.0 volts; *3*, 6 volts; *4*, 7 volts; *5*, 9 volts, *6*, 20 volts; with the occurrence and increase of potentials of beta fibers, those of alpha fibers decreased in amplitude. (Djavrishvili, 1959.)

which are found in this field. Probably the strong depression observed in the spinal cord during tetanizing stimulation of dorsal roots or afferent nerves is due, to a great degree, to the electrotonic effect of such electric fields. We must also keep in mind the fact that during the stimulation of nerves or roots considerable electrical potentials arise in the spinal cord because of the simultaneous activation of a great number of neural elements. Therefore, it is unavoidable that great shifts in electric fields occur in the interstitial fluid.

One may be sure that the phenomenon observed by Barron and

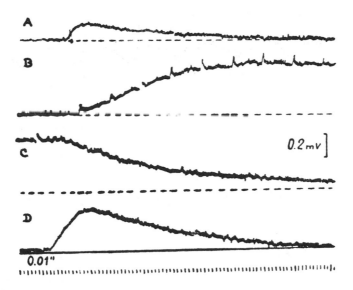

Fig. 56

Slow potentials recorded from a dorsal root during stimulation of trigeminal nerve. Curarized frog with an exposed spinal cord, intact circulation at 16°C. Potentials recorded from the ninth dorsal root by bipolar electrodes 2 mm. from the spinal cord. Intra-electrode distance is 7 mm. DC amplifier recording with a mirror oscillograph. The ophthalmic branch of the trigeminal nerve on the ipsilateral side was stimulated by electrical shocks of maximum intensity. A, Effect from a single stimulus; B, onset; C, end of a brief tetanizing stimulation with a frequency of about 12 per sec.; D, effect of four stimuli with a frequency of 40 per sec. Upward deviation indicates negative activity under the proximal electrode. (Roitbak, 1950a, b.)

Matthews in 1935, namely, an intermittant conduction of impulses along the posterior column, is due to the anelectrotonic effects of the electric fields arising in the gray matter of the spinal cord. Indeed, since stimulation of the dorsal column, as well as of the receptors, activates the gray matter of the spinal cord, one should expect the emergence there of electric shifts which cannot fail to influence fibers of the same dorsal roots running in the posterior column.

In fact, we observed the presence of slow electric potentials in the spinal cord, using microelectrodes placed in the dorsal horn. It was clearly seen that with pronounced shifts of the electric potentials in the spinal cord, the activity in the dorsal root fibers running within the cord was inhibited. Figure 57 gives one such illustration.

Yet widespread inhibition which is seen in each coordinated movement of some effectors must be originated in a different way. Indeed,

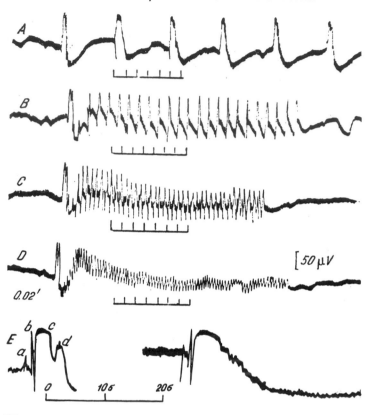

Fig. 57

Depression of dorsal root spike potentials. Barbiturized lumbar preparation of a cat; all ventral roots cut. Potentials recorded from the depth of dorsal horn of seventh lumbar segment on the left side; left tibial nerve stimulated (4 volts). A, Rhythm of stimulation 10 per sec.; B, 50 per sec.; C, 100 per sec.; D, 200 per sec.; E, single potentials recorded with higher speed; a, artifact of stimulation; b, dorsal root potential; c, summated local potential of nerve cells and dendrites; d, potential due to spreading excitation. The presence of a prolonged positive oscillation is due to an artifact of the AC amplifier. (Beritoff, Bakuradze and Roitbak, 1948.)

diffuse inhibition can occur during the stimulation of an area on the skin of only a few millimeters or during the stimulation of one afferent nerve fiber. Such stimulation does not evoke any reflex movement. Obviously, one cannot explain the diffusely spreading inhibition occurring in such cases by the emergence of electrical fields in accordance with the above-discussed mechanism.

It follows then that widespread inhibition, under normal physiologic conditions, does not entirely depend upon the formation of such electrical fields. We feel that we may assume that in all the divisions of the central nervous system of vertebrates, inhibition is due mainly to a synaptic activation of dendrites. We believe that local potentials aris-ing in the dendrites generate currents which flow from the dendrites into the cell body and which, by flowing from there outward in the subsynaptic areas, block the synapses by their anelectrotonic effects. In this regard, we must keep in mind the fact that, according to de Castro (1951), motoneurons of the spinal cord are covered, just as are the pyramidal cells of the cortex, by a glial layer considerably thin-ner in the subsynaptic region. Also, according to Portugalov *et al.* (1958), the activity of succidehydrase in the dendrites of these cells is lower than in the cell body. Also the protein content, judged by the presence of amino acids, is lower in dendrites than in the cell bodies. All this favors the dendritic hypothesis of inhibition, as it suggests a low intensity in the local dendritic process and the outward flow of the dendritic electrotonic current mostly through the synaptic areas.

There is a variety of data showing general inhibitory effects of slow potentials in the spinal cord and the brainstem. We are going to consider only those observations which made us assume the essential role, in the process of diffuse inhibition, of the slow potentials arising in the dorsal half of the spinal cord. These are discussed in the follow-ing paragraphs.

Experiment one. If one records biopotentials from the dorsal horn and from the ventral roots of the lumbar cat during the stimulation of the afferent nerves of the hindleg, one may observe that together with a widespread inhibition there are slow potentials which occur in re-sponse to even subliminal stimuli. The presence of discharges in ven-tral root fibers, that is, in the motoneurons, is found only during a more intense stimulation; when this occurs, slow potentials also in-crease, just as does the widespread inhibition. Figure 58 illustrates this finding.

A simultaneous recording of biopotentials in the dorsal and ventral roots also shows that slow potentials are recorded in the dorsal roots with weaker stimuli than those required to elicit rapid spike poten-tials, or even slow potentials in the ventral root of the same segment (Figure 59). As indicated above, a widespread inhibition can occur as a result of stimuli which do not produce any external effect.

Experiment two. The occurrence of spinal cord slow potentials is shown to be associated with depressing effects in the internuncials as well as in the motoneurons. This is clearly revealed by the recording of potentials in the ventral and dorsal roots. Using a slow rate of

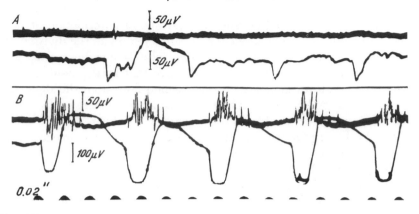

Fig. 58

Slow potentials recorded from the depth of the dorsal horns. Lumbar preparation of a cat; all ventral roots sectioned. Recording made from the left eighth ventral (first sacral root; upper trace), and from the left dorsal horn of the seventh segment (lower trace). Mirror oscillograph; AC amplifier. Experiment A with subliminal stimulation (0.05 volts); experiment B with a more intense stimulation (2 volts) and the same frequency of stimulation (10 per sec.). In experiment A during marked slow potentials, the ventral roots were not activated (see text). (Beritoff, Bakuradze and Roitbak, 1948.)

stimulation of the afferent nerve, the potential elicited by the first stimulus is large; but then, as the stimulation continues, the effects from ensuing stimuli occur against a background of slow potentials due to the first stimulus and are relatively more or less inhibited (Figure 60) (Beritoff, Bakuradze and Roitbak, 1948).

The records in Figure 60 demonstrate that, during an intense reflex activity, as soon as slow potentials make their appearance, the activity of motoneurons and internuncials resulting from ensuing stimuli becomes very much decreased. In experiment A, the first group of rapid oscillations, *a*, expresses excitation of motoneurons directly influenced by the fibers in the dorsal roots, which participate in a monosynaptic reflex arc; these spikes disappear with the occurrence of stimuli following the first volley. In experiment B, in the same roots and under the same conditions, the second group of rapid oscillations, *b*, reflecting the influence of the impulses arising from the internuncials is also lacking.

In addition, in experiment A (Figure 60) a more distant ventral root (the fifth) is almost devoid of any rapid oscillations. It shows only slow potentials, and this in two phases. The first results from the activity of fibers in the dorsal root, and the second results from the

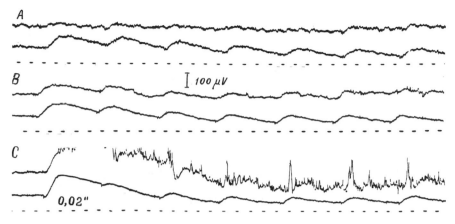

Fig. 59

Slow potentials of dorsal and ventral roots. Spinal preparation of a frog. Activity of the ninth ventral root (upper trace) and tenth dorsal root (lower trace) on the right side recorded by the two-beam cathode ray oscillograph; AC amplifiers. Right sciatic nerve stimulated. Intensity in experiment A is 0.5 volts; in experiment B 1 volt; in experiment C 2 volts. In experiment A potentials are barely seen in the ventral roots while they are quite manifest in the dorsal roots. The oscillations of a low amplitude are AC artifacts. In experiment B only slow potentials are recorded from the ventral root because of local excitation of the motoneurons. In experiment C spike potentials in the ventral roots also arise from excitation of the axons. (Beritoff and Roitbak, 1950a.)

influence of the internuncials. This root contains motor fibers which mainly supply the quadriceps. With the stimulation of the peroneal nerve, as was the case in this experiment, this muscle was inhibited. This is why we may assume that the slow potentials derived from the fifth ventral root result mainly from those slow potentials which effected inhibition of the motoneurons of the knee extensor. The beginning of the first phase of slow potential in the fifth ventral root occurs slightly earlier than the discharge of fast potentials in the seventh ventral root. It almost coincides with the beginning of the slow potential of the sixth dorsal root, experiment B. One should therefore conclude that this first phase of the slow potential recorded via the fifth ventral root expresses general inhibition, whereas the second phase probably expresses the reciprocal inhibition of the extensor.

Experiment three. When electrical changes are pronounced, one may show a decrease of dorsal root spike potentials inside the spinal cord. This was seen in Figure 57 where, during a tetanizing stimula-

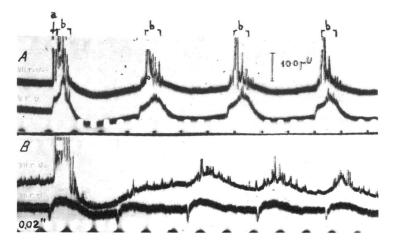

Fig. 60

Depression of spike potentials during the occurrence of the slow wave. Lumbar preparation of a cat; all ventral roots cut. Left tibial nerve stimulated 15 times per sec. Recording of the bioelectric potentials on the left side, using bipolar electrodes, differential amplifiers, and mirror oscillograph. *A*, From the seventh ventral root (upper trace) and from the fifth ventral root (lower trace). *B*, From the sixth ventral root (upper trace) and from the sixth dorsal root (lower trace). In these experiments, *a*, indicates on the oscillogram spike potentials of the motoneurons elicited by a monosynaptic reflex arc; *b*, indicates spike potentials elicited through the internuncial neurons. (Beritoff, Bakuradze and Roitbak, 1948.) (See text for detailed explanation.)

tion of the tibial nerve, the dorsal root spikes are initially decreased against the background of slow spinal cord potentials, experiment *D*. These depressing effects are particularly pronounced at the time of the first large slow potential. The decrease in amplitude of the dorsal root potentials at that time leads in turn to a decrease in the local processes evoked by them. Because of this the slow potentials of the spinal cord are also decreased, and accordingly their inhibiting effects upon the dorsal root fibers are weakened.

One must keep in mind the fact that the prolonged positive deflection against which we observed a particularly pronounced depression of spikes in Figure 57, and in other figures, is distorted by the AC amplifier. When a DC amplifier is used instead, a steady progressively decreasing negative aftereffect is recorded, as can be seen in Figure 61 (spinal frog).

The steady negative aftereffects recorded by a DC amplifier in the

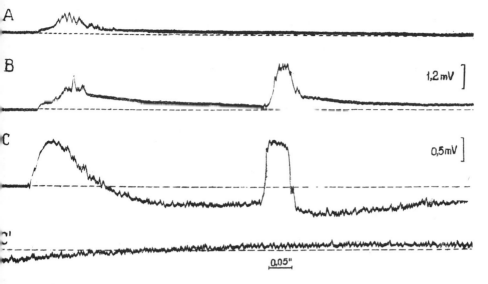

Fig. 61

Spinal preparation at a temperature of 10°C. (after administration of strychnine). Potentials are recorded from the ninth ventral root 3 mm. from the spinal cord. Sciatic nerve stimulated on ipsilateral side with 16 volts. In experiments A and B potentials recorded through DC amplifier. A, Effects from a single stimulus; B, from two stimuli at 0.5 sec. intervals; C, AC amplifier, 16 volts, two stimuli at 0.5 sec. intervals; C', continuation of C. (Beritoff, Kvavilashvili and Roitbak, 1950.)

ventral roots, such as those represented in Figure 61, probably are a summation of local potentials arising in the subsynaptic regions of dendrites and of the cell bodies of motoneurons. They arise under the influence of impulses arriving there directly along fibers of the dorsal roots as well as indirectly through the internuncials. The slow potentials derived from the ventral root do not evoke inhibition by a direct action upon the motoneurons; one would rather expect their activation. The inhibition of the motoneurons must result mainly from the emergence of the major component of the dendritic current coming out of the soma and flowing through the synapses located on the cell bodies, producing there an anelectrotonic block. Thus, the cell is deprived of the usual continuous bombardment of stimuli of peripheral and intercellular origin, and therefore its excitability decreases.

However, there is no doubt that to a certain degree the decrease of activity of motoneurons is determined by the depression of the internuncials. High amplitude slow potentials recorded from the depths of the dorsal horn must originate mostly from the local dendritic processes in this horn. Therefore, clearly, the dendritic potentials may inhibit internuncials by spreading their currents into the cell and the adjacent synapses, and also by the effects of electrical fields in the interstitial fluid upon the axons and the cell bodies of these internuncials.

Experiment four.   When potentials are recorded in the ninth ventral root in spinal frogs during a combined stimulation of the ipsilateral and contralateral peroneal nerves, interesting results are observed. When only contralateral stimulation is applied, slow potentials occur; during ipsilateral stimulation, fast potentials are recorded; whereas, in the case of combined stimulation, fast potentials are decreased just as the slow potentials emerge (Figure 62) (Beritoff and Roitbak, 1948). The same kind of inhibition of fast ventral root potentials is observed in the lumbar region of frogs during slow potentials elicited by the stimulation of the brachial nerve.

Experiment five.   A good illustration of the inhibition of spinal cord cells by slow potentials was revealed during the following experiment of Roitbak (1950a, b), when he combined stimulation of the trigeminal nerve with stimulation of the afferent nerve of the hindleg (Figure 56). Stimulation of the head skin or of the trigeminal nerve

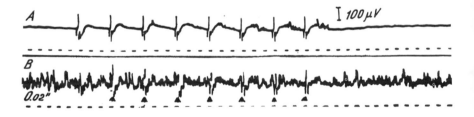

Fig. 62

Slow potentials during reciprocal inhibition in a frog. All ventral roots cut; recordings made from ninth ventral roots on left side. Experiment A, right sciatic nerve stimulated (2 volts) 15 times per sec. Each stimulus artifact is followed at first by a dorsal root spike and then after a certain interval, a slow potential which increases with the repetition of stimuli. Experiment B, stimulation of left peroneal nerve alone (0.25 volts) 40 times per sec. During a reflex discharge made of fast oscillations, the stimulation of the right (contralateral) sciatic nerve is added (seven stimuli in all, indicated by pointers). After the second stimulus, the fast oscillations decrease significantly in amplitude and almost disappear completely at the time of slow potentials. (Beritoff and Roitbak, 1948.)

in frogs elicits a diffuse inhibition of the animal. Locomotion, tonic and statokinetic reflexes as well as respiration and defensive reflexes are inhibited (Beritoff and Gogava, 1937). At the same time slow potentials are recorded in the lumbar area from the dorsal roots. They are summated during a tetanizing stimulation, and this summated effect lasts as long as the stimulation is applied, as can be seen in the DC recordings of Figure 56. If the stimulation is applied to the trigeminal nerve during the recording of electrical discharges in the ventral roots, i.e., those elicited by stimulation of the peroneal nerve, these discharges are depressed with the onset of slow potentials resulting from activation of the trigeminal nerve. Not only are fast potentials inhibited in this instance, but also inhibited are those slow potentials simultaneously recorded from the dorsal roots, i.e., those which resulted from the activation of the peroneal nerve (Figure 63).

These dorsal root slow potentials reflect the activation of dendrites in motoneurons as well as in internuncials. One must assume that the secondary slow hump which is seen in the first slow potential, occurring during stimulation of the peroneal nerve, depends entirely upon the activation of internuncial dendrites; in Figure 63 this hump is indicated by an arrow. It was found that during the association of this stimulation with the stimulation of the trigeminal nerve, the hump disappears. It became clear from this observation that stimulation of the trigeminal nerve elicits inhibition of the motoneurons as well as of the internuncials in the lumbar region of the spinal cord.

Experiment six. As the reflex mechanisms become fatigued, ventral root spikes disappear much earlier than the ventral and dorsal root slow potentials. During tetanizing stimulation, slow potentials may persist several minutes after the cessation of the ventral root spike potentials. Obviously during a prolonged stimulation the dendrites, as well as the cell bodies of the spinal cord, continue to generate local processes. As indicated above, general inhibition also may outlast the state of excitation of the motoneurons; this was revealed by the continued absence of contractions in corresponding muscles (Beritoff and Roitbak, 1950a).

Moreover one may note that when the dorsal root slow potentials progressively disappear as the result of a prolonged stimulation of the peroneal nerve, the stimulation of another nerve, for instance the tibial nerve originating in the same receptive fields, also elicits slow potentials of a decreased amplitude. After several minutes of rest, slow potentials will again occur in response to stimulation of the peroneal nerve (Figure 64). This shows that the dorsal root slow potentials do

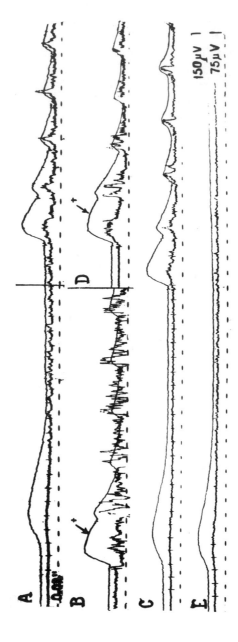

Fig. 63

Inhibition of reflex activity of spinal cord under the influence of stimulation of the trigeminal nerve. Potentials recorded from ninth dorsal root (upper tracings) and ninth ventral root (lower tracings); AC amplifier recording; two-beam cathode ray oscillograph. *A*, Trigeminal nerve stimulated on ipsilateral side (inhibiting stimulation 10 volts, frequency 50 per sec.). After 400 msec., stimulation of the peroneal nerve added on ipsilateral side (excitatory stimulation 1 volt, frequency 15 per sec.). *B*, Effect of stimulation of peroneal nerve alone; *C*, same experiment as *A*; *D*, another trial of peroneal nerve stimulation alone; *E*, effect of stimulation of trigeminal nerve alone. The interval between experiments is about 3 minutes. Time scale: 0.02 sec. (Roitbak, 1950b.) (See text for details.)

204

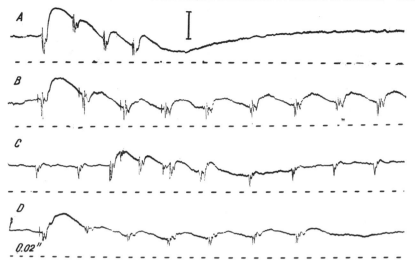

Fig. 64

Changes of dorsal root slow potentials with fatigue in spinal frog. The recordings are made from the right eighth dorsal root by an AC amplifier and cathode ray oscillograph. A, Stimulation of tibial nerve (15 per sec., 1 volt); B, beginning of a prolonged stimulation of peroneal nerve (15 per sec., 2 volts); C, continuation of stimulation of peroneal nerve 5 minutes later when slow potentials practically disappeared. An additional test stimulation of the tibial nerve (1 volt) elicited weaker effects than in experiment A; D, stimulation of peroneal nerve after 5 minutes of rest. Again relatively high amplitude responses with slow potentials arise. (Beritoff and Roitbak, 1950a.)

not express synaptic processes of excitation, but rather the post-synaptic local processes taking place in the dendrites and cell bodies. Obviously, these local processes spread to a certain distance from the synaptic areas. Being fatigued from stimulation of the peroneal nerve, the dendrites and the cells apparently remain fatigued when the tibial nerve is stimulated because the afferent fibers of the tibial nerve synapse upon dendrites and cell bodies in the same vicinity as do the afferent fibers of the peroneal nerve.

Experiment seven. The ability of slow potentials in the spinal cord to generate anelectrotonic effects has been investigated by Motsny (1956). He introduced a microelectrode into the area of motoneuron nuclei in the spinal cord, of the spinal preparation of the cat, and passed through it an exponentially increasing and decreasing current of a certain duration (about 60 msec. of 6 to 8 microamperes). He observed that when the current was increasing, if the electrode was negative, the reflex excitability of the motoneurons was enhanced. The contraction of the flexors, being elicited by the stimulation of the ipsilateral tibial nerve, increased in amplitude. When the current was decreasing, excitability was lowered and contractions of the flexors elicited by the ipsilateral anterior tibial nerve were weak. Also the change of the flexor reflex during cathodal polarization was the same as that which occurred during stimulation of the contralateral inhibitory nerve.

From this and other similar observations we may conclude that central inhibition in the spinal cord, reciprocal as well as diffuse, is determined by the anelectrotonic effect of slow potentials upon the neuronal elements which generate spikes. Inasmuch as these slow potentials which are recorded from the dorsal roots or from the depths of the posterior horn, are essentially the result of summation of dendritic local potentials, one may assume that the basis of inhibition is the anelectrotonic influence of dendritic slow potentials mostly upon the synapses located on the cell bodies of the corresponding neurons.

The phenomenon of facilitation, i.e., the increase of excitability in the inhibited neuronal element, can be explained from the point of view of the anelectrotonic nature of inhibition. As is known, when direct current is flowing in the nerve trunk in the vicinity of the anode, excitability decreases due to anelectrotonus. When the current is turned off, excitability increases for a short period of time in the anodic region. The same physiologic phenomenon must take place with the anelectrotonic block of axosomatic synapses under the influence of dendritic potentials. At the moment of the block the excitability is decreased in these synapses, and it is simultaneously decreased in the cells because the peripheral and intercellular impulses stop influencing the cell body. After the cessation of anelectrotonic effects from dendritic potentials, just the opposite changes occur in the synapse; the excitability is increased, and the cell is again influenced by impulses bombarding its synapses.

When the direct current is turned off gradually there is no increase of excitability at the anode. The same may be observed in regard to facilitation, when anelectrotonic inhibition is occurring, under the influence of dendritic potentials. That is, as we indicated above, when inhibition progressively decreases facilitation does not occur following the cessation of inhibitory stimulation.

Therefore, a brief facilitation of central nervous system activity, which is observed during a sudden suspension of general inhibition, is due to the same law of physiologic electrotonus applicable to occurrences in the nerve trunk in the anodic region when the DC current is turned off.

10 SPECIFIC COORDINATING MECHANISMS

Mechanism of Reciprocal Inhibition

A long time ago we asserted that the reciprocal inhibition of motoneurons during phasic movements of extremities is due to the activation of an apparatus for coordinating flexion and extension (Beritoff, 1911–1913). This coordinating apparatus consists of internuncial neurons in the dorsal horn, which are located ventrally to the substantia gelatinosa of Rolando in those areas of the spinal cord where the afferent nerve fibers arrive. Thus, for instance in cats, the coordinating apparatus for flexor reflexes is located mostly in the seventh lumbar and the first and second sacral segments, while the apparatus for extensor reflexes is located mostly within the limits of the fourth, fifth and sixth lumbar segments (Beritoff, 1922a).

The coordinating mechanisms of each inborn reflex are located in that part of the cord where the afferent fibers from the corresponding receptive field terminate. This location may be proved by local application of strychnine to these structures. If strychnine is locally applied to the dorsal surface of the ninth and tenth segments of the cord in frogs, the flexor and extensor reflexes in the hind limbs become enhanced. The afferent fibers from the receptive fields of flexion and extension end in these segments. At the same time, the rubbing reflex, which can be elicited from the neighboring dorsal roots of the seventh and eighth segments, remains unchanged. If the latter are locally treated with strychnine, then the rubbing reflex becomes augmented while the flexor and extensor reflexes remain unchanged (Beritoff, 1911–1913). The coordinating mechanisms of the rubbing reflex of the hind limbs seem to be located in the seventh and eighth spinal segments while those of the flexor and extensor reflexes appear to be located in the ninth and tenth spinal segments.

Following activation of one of these coordinating centers, excitation of the motoneurons in one group of cells occurs simultaneously with the reciprocal inhibition of neurons corresponding to the antagonistic group of muscles. Some time ago we suggested a hypothesis according to which the axons of the internuncial neurons located in each of the coordinating centers synapse with the cell bodies in one group of motoneurons, while they synapse with the dendrites in the antagonistic group of neurons (Beritoff, 1948, 1949). Thus, some axons from coordinating apparatus of the flexor reflex synapse with the cell bodies of the motoneurons of flexors eliciting their excitation, while other axons synapse with the dendrites of the motoneurons of extensors, thus eliciting their inhibition. It is also quite possible that an internuncial neuron in the dorsal horn would synapse by one group of collaterals with the cell bodies of flexor motoneurons, while some other of its collaterals synapse with the dendrites of extensor neurons. Another internuncial will show just the reverse synaptic relationships.

Experimental evidence for dendritic origin of reciprocal inhibition was offered by Sprague (1958). During stimulation of the second and third dorsal sacral roots on the ipsilateral side, muscles of the tail are contracted; on the contralateral side they are inhibited. Sprague studied the degeneration of synaptic terminals of dorsal root fibers after sectioning the second and third sacral dorsal roots in rabbits. He has shown that ipsilateral synaptic terminals degenerate both on somas and dendrites of motoneurons, while contralateral ones degenerate only on the dendrites (Figure 77–I, p. 231). Inasmuch as the contralateral motoneurons of the tail become inhibited, the author concluded that the inhibition of these motoneurons is accomplished by means of the activation of their dendrites. Thus, one may prove morphologically that the reciprocal inhibition of motoneurons in a monosynaptic reflex occurs by means of activation of their dendrites. We may suggest that in the case of polysynaptic reflexes, reciprocal inhibition of motoneurons also occurs by means of activation of their dendrites through the internuncial neurons.

It is noteworthy that a local application of strychnine to any coordinating structure enhances and prolongs, not only the excitation of a definite group of motoneurons, but also the inhibition of the antagonistic group as well (Beritoff, 1911–1913). This seems to prove that the same internuncial neurons may elicit in the antagonistic muscles excitation and inhibition, respectively. Therefore, these antagonistic processes may be reciprocally interrelated.

On the basis of recent electrophysiologic studies of the electrical activity of the spinal cord following strychnine application, it was concluded that when the concentration of strychnine is low, the excitability of both cell bodies and dendrites of motoneurons as well as of internuncials tends to become enhanced. As a result of this, the inhibitory as well as the excitatory action become increased (Beritoff and Roitbak, 1950b).

The inhibitory effect in the motoneurons, following a single peripheral stimulus, lasts at least the same time as the duration of the slow dendritic potential, approximately 10 msec. A knee flexor reflex (contraction of the semitendinosus muscle) elicited by a stimulation of the peroneal nerve on the same side, at a frequency of 100 to 200 per second, will be inhibited by the stimulation (30 to 100 c./sec.) of the peroneal nerve on the opposite side (extensor reflex); it is possible to observe a dropping out of one impulse at a time in response to each inhibitory stimulus. We have studied this phenomenon in spinal as well as in decerebrate cats (Beritoff, 1914, 1924a).

However, it is obvious that if the internuncials of the coordinating apparatus respond with high frequency repetitive discharges to each peripheral impulse, there may be a summation of slow dendritic potentials so that the inhibition from a single external stimulus may last a longer time (Samojloff and Kisseleff, 1927). During a series of rapidly following discharges in internuncial neurons, one may observe a rhythmic inhibition which represents modulations by slow potentials at the rate of stimulation.

Generally during moderate stimulation of the peroneal nerve the rhythm of excitation in the ipsilateral flexors is about the same as the rhythm of reciprocal inhibition in the contralateral flexors. This finding is consistent with the explanation according to which both the impulses eliciting excitation of the cell bodies of the motoneuron on the ipsilateral side and those causing activation of the motoneuron dendrites on the opposite side, arise from the same stimulated internuncials in the coordinating apparatus. Analogous conclusions were made with regard to the synchronous, rhythmic occurrence of reciprocal excitation of the extensors and inhibition of the flexors in the experiments of Adrian (1924) on the extensor reflex.

Role of the Substantia Gelatinosa of Rolando in General Inhibition

As we have seen, an external stimulus elicits not only a coordinating movement involving certain muscles, but a simultaneous partial inhibition of the remaining musculature. Our study suggests that this widespread inhibition is carried through the substantia gelatinosa of

Rolando; we believe that each time peripheral impulses affect the coordinating apparatus they also affect this substance.

STRUCTURE OF THE SUBTANTIA GELATINOSA

Substantia gelatinosa, together with the zona marginalis, occupies the tip of the dorsal horn. According to the recent investigations of Pearson (1952) most of the cells of the substantia gelatinosa are very small, 6 to 14 microns, and have a multitude of small dendrites. These dendrites are located in the plane parallel to the dorsolateral aspect of the spinal cord. Also, axons of these cells are very short and very thin. The cells are interconnected through these axons. Moreover, some longer axons penetrate into the lateral funiculis and then return into the substantia gelatinosa. According to Pearson, they are very difficult to follow and only rarely do they give off collaterals which disappear into the dorsal horn (Figure 65).

Medially, substantia gelatinosa is limited by the nucleus proprius. This is a conglomeration of relatively large cells. Most of their dendrites penetrate into the substantia gelatinosa and almost reach its dorsal boundary. These dendrites are covered with small thorn-like processes or spines. The cell axons run directly ventral to and partly in the anterior commissure toward the opposite side.

From the medial, ventral and lateral aspects, the substantia gelatinosa is in contact with a special kind of large cell called "pericornual cells." Their dendrites permeate the substantia gelatinosa extensively and quite deeply. They are also densely covered by thorn-like spines or gemmules. Their axons are directed ventrally, but can be followed for only a short distance. Some of them penetrate into the lateral funiculis and divide themselves into two branches—one ascending and one descending—which then turn into the substantia gelatinosa. Figure 65 shows all these cellular structures as described by Pearson.

Large fibers of the dorsal roots or more exactly the large collaterals of the fibers, running in the dorsal columns for the most part, go around the substantia gelatinosa from the medial and lateral sides. However, there are also some large fibers which go through the substantia gelatinosa without giving off any collaterals as they pass through. The thin collaterals of the fibers of dorsal roots forming the Lissauer tract completely penetrate the substantia gelatinosa up to its ventral boundary. They branch there and synapse on cell bodies as well as on dendrites. These branchings of the thin fibers form, together with the dendrites, a very thick reticulum (Figure 66).

The thin collaterals are mainly related to the fibers for pain and

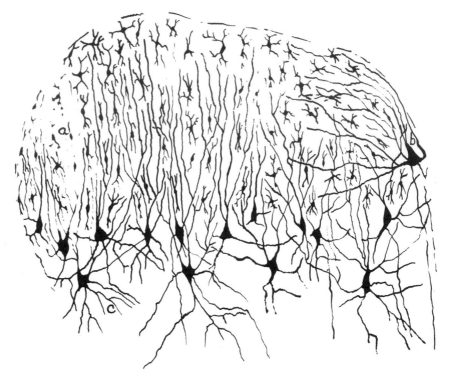

Fig. 65

Schematic representation of the substantia gelatinosa, *a*, in its relationship to the neurons of the nucleus proprius, *b*, and to the pericornual cells, *c*. A transverse section (Golgi preparation) of the spinal cord of an infant. (Pearson, 1952.)

temperature perception. In a bilateral local injury of the substantia gelatinosa, the transmission of pain is disturbed (Ranson, 1915, Ranson and Billingsley, 1916, Earle, 1952). But these thin fibers may be also related to proprioceptive and interoceptive sensitivity.

On the basis of the above-mentioned data concerning the structure of the substantia gelatinosa of Rolando, one may make the following conclusions.

1. Substantia gelatinosa may transmit ascending as well as descending excitation.

2. Substantia gelatinosa is directly activated by the thin afferent nerve fibers which originate in the exteroceptors of the skin, the proprioceptors and interoceptors.

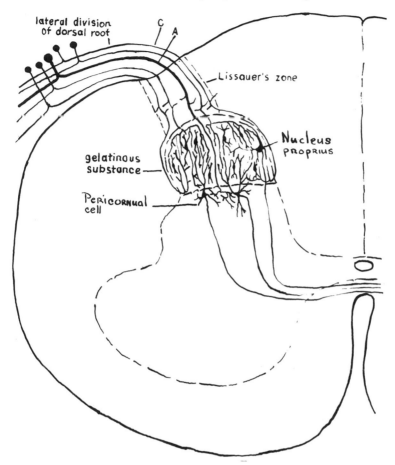

Fig. 66

Schematic representation of transverse section of human spinal cord show-ing relationship of fibers of lateral division of dorsal root to neurons of dorsal horn. *A*, Myelinated fibers of large diameter which run through substantia gelatinosa and synaptically terminate on the cell bodies of the nucleus proprius; *C*, thin fibers of the dorsal root terminating in the sub-stantia gelatinosa. The small cells of the substantia gelatinosa are repre-sented as interneurons. Among the cells of the nucleus proprius and peri-cornual cells are shown those which give off axons to the lateral spinal thalamic tract of the opposite side. (Pearson, 1952.)

3. These afferent fibers penetrate the substantia gelatinosa from its dorsal to its ventral boundaries, synapsing with cell bodies as well as with dendrites.

4. The dendrites of the large pericornual cells also penetrate sub-

stantia gelatinosa. These cells are, in turn, activated by the large fibers of the dorsal roots.

5. Dorsal dendrites of the cells of the nucleus proprius penetrate substantia gelatinosa and run parallel to the fine fibers of the dorsal roots. There is reason to believe that they both enter into mutual contact; that is, that the fibers of the dorsal roots form multiple contacts with the thorny processes of the dendrites.

6. Because each fiber of the dorsal roots running in the posterior column gives off collaterals all along its length, the activation of the substantia gelatinosa by a fiber will occur all along the length of this fiber.

7. The cells of the nucleus proprius are activated by the large diameter fibers in the dorsal roots, which run alongside or through the substantia gelatinosa.

8. Axons of the cells of the substantia gelatinosa run along the dendrites of the cells of the nucleus proprius. Therefore, they not only may serve for the integration of the cells of the substantia gelatinosa, but also for the activation of the dendrites of the nucleus proprius.

The structural relationship between the substantia gelatinosa and the nucleus proprius suggests to us that it has an important dual function. First it conducts excitatory processes along the spinal cord, particularly those which arise within it under the influence of the thin dorsal root fibers. Second it inhibits the cells of the nucleus proprius through the activation of its dendrites.

We may assume that the cells of the nucleus proprius constitute the internuncials which are responsible for the reciprocal excitation and inhibition of antagonist groups of motoneurons. Then one may assume that the general inhibition of spinal reflexes may occur as a result of inhibiting internuncials of the nucleus proprius by means of the substantia gelatinosa.

Effect of Various Stimuli on Substantia Gelatinosa

PAINFUL AND THERMAL STIMULI.   The inhibitory function of the substantia gelatinosa is consistent with the experiments of Dzidzishvili. As was mentioned before, this experimenter observed a widespread inhibition of the hindlegs when hot or cold stimuli were applied to the skin of normal rabbits. He also observed it following a tetanizing stimulation of the skin or after pinching the skin. According to the experiments of Bakuradze (1943), painful stimulations elicited diffuse inhibition in lumbar cats. It is known that the fibers transmitting pain and temperature synapse in the substantia gelatinosa which is an intermediary station for pain and temperature sensitivity (Pearson, 1952). Therefore there is reason to believe that diffuse inhibition elicited by thermal and painful stimuli is carried out with the help of the substantia gelatinosa. Our investigations with direct stimulation of the spinal cord in lumbar cats further reinforced this point of view. Beritoff and Bakuradze (1943a) revealed that stimulation of the lateral aspect of the cord often elicits inhibition even when one applies a low intensity stimulus. This area contains a layer of secondary proprioceptive fibers as well as the Lissauer fasciculus containing the primary pathways of pain and temperature sensitivity (Figure 67).

In the lower half of the lateral zone under the superficially located layer of the secondary proprioceptive pathways are found secondary pathways for pain and temperature sensitivity contained by the tractus spinothalamicus. Stimulation of this entire lateral area with lower intensity stimuli than those necessary to generate motor effects elicits diffuse inhibition (as is shown in Figure 67).

Inhibition elicited by stimulation of the dorsolateral zone on one side spreads over several segments and also to the contralateral side. This must be explained by the structural peculiarities of the dorsal root fibers and the substantia gelatinosa. The dorsal root fibers entering a segment give off collaterals to the preceding and succeeding segments. Moreover, the axons of the cells of the substantia gelatinosa enter the lateral zones and activate the neighboring areas of the substantia gelatinosa through the recurrent fibers. The inhibition in the contralateral spinal cord must be carried out by means of the dorsal root fibers or the axons of the internuncials crossing the middle line in the anterior and posterior commissures and activating mainly the dendritic mass of the motoneurons there.

STIMULATION OF THE VENTRAL CORD. General inhibition results also from stimulation of the dorsal and the ventral columns. General inhibition resulting from stimulation of the dorsal column is elicited together with reflex contractions, just as it occurs during stimulation of the dorsal roots; therefore, it is probably due mainly to activation of the substantia gelatinosa. During stimulation of the ventral cord involving mainly descending tracts (tractus corticospinalis ventralis, vestibulospinalis, reticulospinalis), weak motor effects occur manifested by some extension of the extremities. Simultaneously general inhibition arises which increases with an increase in the intensity of stimulation (Figure 68). These experiments were carried out

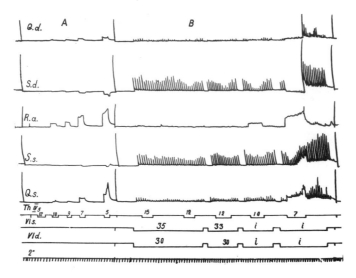

Fig. 67

General inhibition from stimulation of the lateral funiculi. Thoraco-lumbar preparation of a cat; dorsal roots of the lumbar region are cut. Quadriceps, *Q.d.*, *Q.s.*, and semitendinosus, *S.d.*, *S.s.*, recorded on both sides, as well as rectus abdominis, *R.a.* The lateral aspect in the middle of the fourth and fifth thoracic segments of the left side was stimulated, *ThIVs*. In experiment *A* this stimulation was applied separately, while in experiment *B* it was combined with the stimulation of the sixth pair of the dorsolumbar roots, *VId.*, *VIs.*, by single faradic stimuli. In this experiment a weak stimulation of the lateral area elicited, with about 10 cm. between the coils of the inductorium, an activation of the rectus abdominis and quadriceps of the ipsilateral side, while the semitendinosus remained relaxed. However, when the same stimulation was applied during the presence of single twitches generated by stimulation of the dorsal roots, inhibition was observed with weaker stimulation, the coils being 12 to 15 cm. apart; at the same time all flexors and extensors on both sides were inhibited; in other words, there was widespread inhibition. (Beritoff and Bakuradze, 1943a.)

on thoracolumbar cats. The above-mentioned tracts have hardly any direct connections with the substantia gelatinosa. This is why we believe that this diffuse inhibition is elicited through activation of the dendritic mass of the motoneurons by means of the fibers running from these tracts. However, it is possible that with more intense stimulation the associative fibers of the fasciculus proprius are also activated; it surrounds the anterior and lateral horns and consists entirely of axons of the internuncials connecting neighboring regions

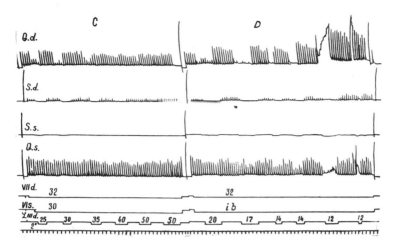

Fig. 68

General inhibition from stimulation of the anterior funiculi. Lumbar preparation of a cat. The same muscles recorded as in preceeding figure. Tetanizing stimulation of the ventral surface in the area of the third and fourth segments, *LIIId.*, upon the background of single reflex twitches elicited by the stimulation of the sixth and seventh dorsal roots, *VIs.*, *VIId.* The numbers signify the intensity of stimulation expressed in centimeters between the primary and secondary coils of an inductorium. *C*, Relatively weak stimulation of the anterior funiculi (35 to 25 cm.) elicits inhibition of the reflex twitches only on the ipsilateral side; *D*, with a more pronounced stimulation (20 to 14 cm.) the twitches are inhibited also on the contralateral side, and with 12 cm. there are inhibited tetanic contractions in both extensors, followed by rebound contraction. (Beritoff and Bakuradze, 1943a.)

of the spinal cord. In other words, it is the stimulation of these neurons which probably is responsible for the increased inhibition of the motoneurons that arises during a relatively intense stimulation.

COMPARISON WITH THE RETICULAR FORMATION. In normal animals the brain structures may elicit inhibition in the spinal cord in other ways than transmitting impulses through the descending direct pathways toward the dendritic mass of the motoneurons. As is known, substantia gelatinosa extends into the medulla, terminates there in the vicinity of the reticular formation and is directly continued by the nucleus of the spinal tract of the trigeminal nerve. Ariens Kappers *et al.* (1936) explicitly suggested a very close relationship between the descending root of the trigeminal nerve and the substantia gelatinosa.

According to Bechterew, the axons of the nucleus of the fifth nerve enter directly into the substantia gelatinosa in the medulla. Thus a close connection seems to exist between the substantia gelatinosa and the reticular formation (Bechterew, 1926).

It follows from the foregoing that the impulses originating from nuclei of the trigeminal nerve as well as from the reticular formation, as a result of the stimulation of the medulla or of the fifth nerve itself, should first be conducted toward the substantia gelatinosa in the medulla and in the cervical segments of the spinal cord. These impulses then spread caudad along the short neural connections of the substantia gelatinosa proper toward the sacral division of the spinal cord. This may explain the observation of Roitbak made in frogs (1950) that slow potentials, which we described above, and inhibition elicited by stimulation of the trigeminal nerve arise in the lumbar area of the spinal cord following a very long latency, approximately 18 to 60 msec.

EFFECTS OF CHEMICAL SUBSTANCES.   We also studied the function of the substantia gelatinosa by applying different chemical substances, such as acetylcholine (solutions of 1:1000 to 1:50,000), potassium chloride (25 per cent to 5 per cent) and nicotine (1:1000 to 1:5000). These experiments were carried out in thoracolumbar cats, under ether and chloralose anesthesia. The active substance was applied within the limits of one or two segments, along the dorsolateral surface of the spinal cord, in one area on one side. Observations were made on the antagonistic muscles of the knee. In animals under ether, application of acetylcholine to the dorsolateral surface of the cord in all active concentrations, at first elicited inhibition lasting a score of seconds. Then if the concentration was low, inhibition would wear off without any muscle excitation or even without any phase of facilitation (Figure 69).

With higher concentrations, reciprocal effects could be observed; namely, with the contraction of one muscle simultaneous inhibition of the antagonistic muscle could be seen. During this period the single twitches produced by stimulation of dorsal roots were markedly increased (Figure 70).

These observations lead us to conclude that acetylcholine in small doses (in lumbar animals under ether) elicits activation of the substantia gelatinosa with a resulting general inhibition. However, when the concentration of acetylcholine is higher, and this agent penetrates deeper into the cord, it activates the internuncials of the coordinating apparatus. This accounts for the reciprocal effects upon the moto-

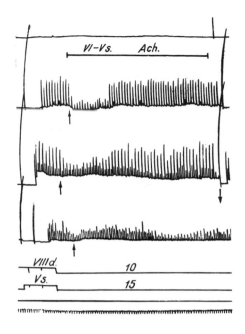

Fig. 69

Influence of acetylcholine upon the substantia gelatinosa. Lumbar preparation of a cat; ether narcosis. The antagonistic muscles of the knee (from top to bottom: right quadriceps; right semitendinosus; left semitendinosus; left quadriceps). Single twitches elicited by stimulation of left fifth dorsal root (lower signal) and right eighth dorsal root (upper signal) by single faradic stimulus. Acetylcholine applied (horizontal line) to the dorsal lateral surface at level of fifth to sixth segment (1:20,000). The action of acetylcholine (indicated by the horizontal line) is expressed in all muscles by an inhibition of reflex contractions (beginning of the application). (Beritoff and Bakuradze, 1940a.)

neurons. In this case, the acetylcholine probably reaches the motoneurons themselves, and thus produces an increase of muscle twitches in the ipsilateral muscles.

Acetylcholine in the dosages used in these studies does not affect the dorsal roots or ventral root nerve fibers. Obviously, during the application of this substance to the surface of the spinal cord, it penetrates the cellular regions and thus activates them. In view of this spread of the active influence of acetylcholine over several segments, particularly on the side of the application, one may assume that acetylcholine is also transmitted by capillaries and not only as a result of diffusion. However, inhibition occurs bilaterally. This indicates that

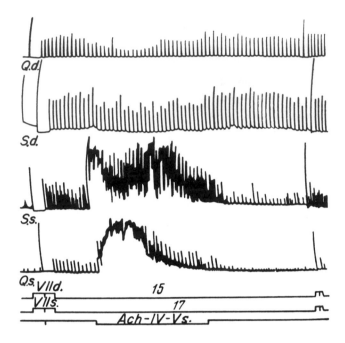

Fig. 70

The same experiment as in Figure 69. Stimulation of the seventh pair of dorsal roots (both upper signals) elicited single twitches from all muscles. Acetylcholine, concentration 1:2000, was applied (lower signal) to fourth and fifth segments of left dorsolateral surface of the cord. On the left side reflex twitches increased in amplitude with a simultaneous reciprocal reaction; at first, the flexor contracted, then the extensor contracted while the flexor was inhibited. In the muscles on the opposite side, single reflex twitches decreased. (Beritoff and Bakuradze, 1940c.)

to a certain degree acetylcholine also penetrates the contralateral side. It is possible, however, that in animals under ether, the inhibiting structure, substantia gelatinosa of the contralateral side, is activated through the internuncials.

During the application of acetylcholine to the ventral surface of the spinal cord, provided that low concentrations were used, reflex activity as evidenced by single twitches did not change. However, with higher concentrations of acetylcholine, effects were observed similar to those caused by dorsolateral application of the substance. Presumably, this was due to the penetration of the acetylcholine into the substantia gelatinosa.

In the animals under chloralose, showing a decreased reflex activity, acetylcholine elicited inhibition followed by facilitation; no reflexes with reciprocal excitation and inhibition were observed.

Incidentally, these experiments have important theoretical significance for the role of acetylcholine in the transmission of excitation and origin of inhibition. Our experiments show that given decreased reflex excitability, acetylcholine may only increase the excitability, but will not elicit a motor reaction. At the same time, stimulation of a dorsal root elicits considerable reflex action. If nerve impulses reaching synapses generate excitation of the cells by manufacturing acetylcholine at the nerve endings, then the acetylcholine reaching the same cells through the blood would also activate them.

Furthermore, our experiment showed that the effect of acetylcholine, expressed by an increase in excitability, may last no longer than 1 minute. This cannot be ascribed to the action of the tissue cholinesterase. The same is observed if acetylcholine is applied to the animals injected with eserine. After initial application of acetylcholine to the spinal cord, 5 minutes must elapse before a new application of the drug is able to elicit either inhibition or facilitation (Figure 71). However, during this 5-minute period dorsal root stimulations as well as application of other chemical substances, such as potassium chloride or nicotine, continued to be effective. One must assume that the excitable system very quickly adapts itself to the stimulating effect of the acetylcholine. In our judgment these observations do not support the ascribing of any essential role to acetylcholine in the transmission of excitation in the spinal cord.

Could one ascribe an essential role to acetylcholine with regard to inhibition? We saw that acetylcholine elicits diffuse inhibition just as stimulation of the dorsal root does, but inhibition in the case of acetylcholine did not last more than a score of seconds and could not be repeated for several minutes after the first application. On the other hand, stimulation of the dorsal root or posterior columns may produce inhibition lasting many minutes. If the inhibition weakens as a result of fatigue, it is sufficient to interrupt the stimulation for only a few seconds in order to again elicit considerable inhibition. Therefore, on the basis of our investigations, we conclude that acetylcholine does not play any essential role in the transmission of excitation or in the generation of inhibition in the central nervous system.

STIMULATION WITH MICROELECTRODES.   Recently in connection with the increased interest in the role of the reticular formation in reflex

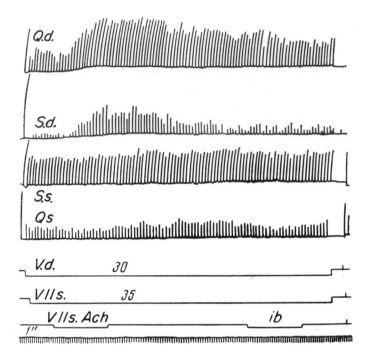

Fig. 71

Adaptation of the spinal cord to acetylcholine. Lumbar cat; chloralose. Contractions of quadriceps, *Q.d.*, *Q.s.*, and semitendinosus, *S.d.*, *S.s.*, recorded on both sides. Stimulation of right fifth dorsal root, *Vd.*, and of left seventh dorsal root, *VIIs.*, repeated faradic stimuli. Acetylcholine (1:2000) was applied. *VIs.Ach*, two times, with an interval of 80 seconds, to the sixth segment over the right lateral surface. During the second application, no effect was produced although the stimulation of the dorsal roots did elicit the same reactions as initially. (Beritoff and Bakuradze, 1939a.)

activity, we again investigated the substantia gelatinosa, which constitutes an analogous formation in the spinal cord. Our associate, Ioseliani (1958), introduced microelectrodes of 10 to 15 microns in diameter into this substance in lumbar cats and stimulated it with electrical pulses of variable frequency. When the stimulation of the substantia gelatinosa was done by single electric shocks from an electronic stimulator, the recordings showed that the muscles on the ipsilateral side responded with single twitches. At a frequency of 2 to 5 per second these twitches were decreased in amplitude; at a rate of

5 to 7 per second they were completely suspended (Figure 72). This inhibition increases with further increases in the rate of stimulation, the optimum inhibition being achieved at a rate of 40 to 50 per second. During stimulation with single electric shocks, contractions occur only in ipsilateral muscles; on the contralateral side, inhibition occurs without contractions. No matter which lumbar segment is stimulated, inhibition spreads over all the muscles of the hindlegs.

The reflex twitches elicited by stimulation of the substantia gelatinosa are observed mainly in those muscles which are supplied by the stimulated segment. It seems, therefore, that they are due to the spread of current to the dorsal root fibers involved in monosynaptic reflex arcs passing through the substantia gelatinosa or around it. These reflex twitches, together with diffuse inhibition due to the action of the substantia gelatinosa, are elicited with single stimuli. Inhibition occurs after a longer latency than the monosynaptic excitation, and because of this the latter is not prevented. However, in view of

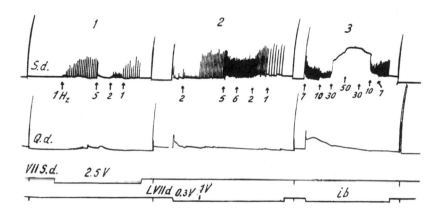

Fig. 72

Reflexes during stimulation of the substantia gelatinosa and the nucleus proprius. Lumbar preparation of a cat. In experiment *1* substantia gelatinosa of Rolando was stimulated through a microelectrode in the seventh lumbar segment, *VIIS.d.* Frequency of stimulation at the beginning was 1 per sec. Single twitches of the right quadriceps, *Q.d.*, and mostly the right semitendinosus, *S.d.*, were of increasing amplitude. When the frequency was changed to 5 per sec., the twitches disappeared. With a frequency of 2 per sec., twitches reappeared with low amplitude. In experiments *2* and *3* the seventh dorsal root, *LVIId.*, was stimulated. Now with the increase in frequency of stimulation (1 volt), single twitches became more frequent and with 30 to 50 c./sec. stimulation, there was a tetanus. (Ioseliani, 1958.)

the fact that the inhibition lasts not less than 200 msec., increasing the rate of electrical stimuli of 5 to 7 per second inhibits these motor effects.

During stimulation (at a rhythm of 5 to 10 per second) of the dorsal root which contains gross nerve fibers along with fine ones, twitches occurred at the rate of stimulation, while with a stimulation of 20 to 50 per second reciprocal tetanic contractions were seen (Figure 72, experiment 2 and 3).

Figure 73 illustrates the extent to which reflex contractions elicited by stimulation of the dorsal fibers, are inhibited during activation of the substantia gelatinosa.

Stimulation of the substantia gelatinosa elicits not only widespread inhibition, as each time at the end of the stimulation diffuse facilitation also occurs. It is revealed in flexors, as well as in extensors. Also, it does not make much difference which segment is stimulated; for instance, the seventh one (as in Figure 74). The facilitation is also short lived, as is usually the case with inhibition.

When the microelectrodes are located in the posterior horn under the substantia gelatinosa, tetanizing stimulation elicits a coordinating reaction involving excitation of certain muscles and inhibition of others but at the same time inhibition occurs in all of the remaining muscles bilaterally. Figure 74 shows (experiment A) a tetanizing

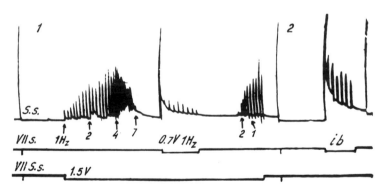

Fig. 73

Inhibiton during the stimulation of the substantia gelatinosa. Lumbar preparation of a cat. Reflex contractions of the left semitendinosus, S.s., recorded; microelectrode in substantia gelatinosa of seventh lumbar segment on left side. *1*, Substantia gelatinosa was stimulated, VIIS.s., with frequencies of 1 to 7 per sec. When the contraction disappeared, the seventh dorsal root was stimulated, VIIs., by single stimuli; *2*, stimulation of seventh dorsal root alone. (Ioseliani, 1958.)

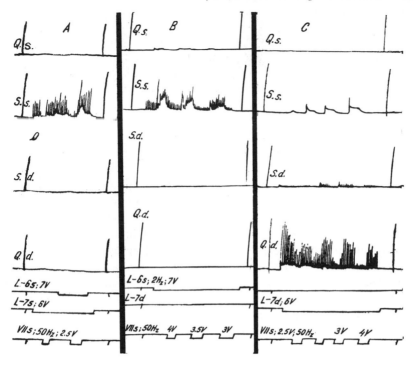

Fig. 74

Reciprocal effects during stimulation of the nucleus proprius. Lumbar pre-paration of a cat. Reflex contractions of the quadriceps, *Q.s., Q.d.,* and the semitendinosus, *S.d., S.s.,* recorded bilaterally. Stimulation of seventh, *7s,* and sixth, *6s,* dorsal roots on left side and seventh dorsal root on right, *7d,* elicited reflex twitches in the ipsilateral muscles. In experiment *A* this stimulation was associated with the tetanizing stimulation of the substantia gelatinosa, *VIIs,* and in experiments *B* and *C* with the tetanizing stimulation of the nucleus proprius, *VIIs.* (Ioseliani, 1958.) (See text for further explanation.)

stimulation of substantia gelatinosa on the left at the seventh seg-ment. This elicits pure inhibition of single reflex twitches in flexors, with a rebound contraction following the end of stimulation. These twitches could be elicited by stimulation of the seventh dorsal root on the same side. When the stimulating electrode was pushed down into the nucleus proprius, stimulation elicited contractions of a flexor with facilitation of its reflex twitches (experiment *B*). In other words, a flexor reflex was observed. The same stimulation elicited inhibi-tion of reflex twitches in both antagonistic muscles of the contra-lateral side, in other words widespread inhibition (experiment *C*).

It seems, therefore, that stimulation of the dorsal horn activates not only the internuncials of the coordinating apparatus but also the substantia gelatinosa. It is most probable that current spreads into the nerve fibers entering this substance.

However, when the microelectrode is located in the ventral horn, a tetanizing stimulation up to 70 c./sec. elicits a tetanus of the muscles on the corresponding side and a very weak diffuse inhibition of the muscles on the contralateral side (Figure 75) (Ioseliani, 1958).

Stimulation of the anterior horn elicits excitation of those muscles which correspond to the stimulated segment. Inhibition is then completely absent in these muscles. As Figure 75 shows, stimulation at a rate of 1 per second results in single twitches at the same rhythm. At the rate of 30 to 47 c./sec., a clonic tetanus is observed; while at the rate of 70 c./sec., there is complete tetanus of high amplitude. Inhibition is present, in very slight degrees, in contracting muscles.

Therefore, the experiments with local stimulation of the spinal cord confirm that (1) the coordination of the flexor reflexes or the extensor reflexes, with reciprocal excitation and inhibition, occurs with the participation of the nucleus proprius of the dorsal horn, (2) diffuse inhibition, followed by a diffuse facilitation, is due to the activation of the substantia gelatinosa, and (3) the anterior horn and its motoneurons do not play an important role in the coordination of the reflexes or in the general inhibition.

STRYCHNINE

Recently, we studied the influence of strychnine upon general inhibition. Stimulation of muscle and visceral receptors was tested in different stages after a local application of the strychnine to the dorsal surface of the lumbar segments as well as after a general poisoning of the animal. These stimuli, as mentioned before, usually elicit widespread inhibition of skeletal musculature. After strychnine poisoning, when the reflex contractions of antagonist muscles were significantly enhanced, these stimuli continue to produce widespread inhibition. The latter even was enhanced by strychnine. It was possible to elicit widespread inhibition even during convulsive contractions occurring in response to a light shock to the stand or to a stimulation of sensory nerves. The jerks ceased or significantly weakened during stretching of muscle or of visceral organs (Oninani, 1958).

General inhibition failed to occur when the reflex contractions were of maximal amplitude. This also is the case with normal preparations. When reflex activity decreased under the influence of the long

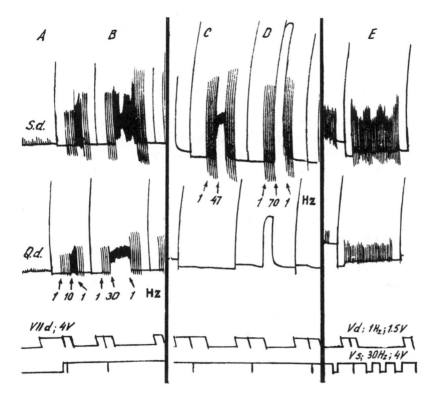

Fig. 75

Stimulation of the anterior horn; motor effects. Lumbar preparation of a cat. Contractions of quadriceps, *Q.d.*, and semitendinosus, *S.d.*, on right side recorded. In experiments *A*, *B*, *C* and *D* stimulation of the anterior horn of seventh segment on the right side, *VIId*, was performed. *A*, Stimulation at 1 to 10 c./sec., *Hz*, produced single twitches; *B* and *C*, single stimuli replaced by tetanizing stimulation (30 to 47 c./sec.) with which clonic tetanic contractions occurred; *D*, single stimuli replaced by 70 c./sec. stimulation and a complete tetanus observed; *E*, stimulation of fifth dorsal root on the right side, *Vd*, elicited single twitches of both antagonistic muscles. At the same time, stimulation of the opposite anterior horn at the same segment produced slight inhibition of the flexor. Downward deflexion indicates that signal is on. (Ioseliani, 1959.)

lasting action of strychnine, general inhibition weakened as well. The latter completely disappeared before the cessation of reflex movements (Oninani, 1958).

The experiments with local strychninization of the spinal cord were carried out on cats during stimulation of substantia gelatinosa also. These experiments convinced us that the widespread inhibition set up by stimulation of substantia gelatinosa did not decrease after strychninization. On the contrary, it was even increased. Reflex contractions arising in response to dorsal root stimulation markedly increased. These enhanced reflexes were inhibited during repetitive stimulation of the substantia gelatinosa. Stimulation of the substantia gelatinosa inhibited even strong convulsive contractions (Ioseliani, 1959).

One may assume that this enhancement of general inhibition during the action of strychnine is conditioned by the increase of excitability of the cells and dendrites of the substantia gelatinosa of Rolando.

Therefore, in all these simple and complex reflex reactions, in other words in any segment of behavior, general inhibition occurs in a considerable number of internuncials and motoneurons, over a large portion of the spinal cord. This inhibition occurs together with the activation of certain coordinating centers for reciprocal excitation and inhibition. A similar diffuse inhibition occurs in the brain through activity of the reticular formation of the brainstem, while in the spinal cord it is effected by the substantia gelatinosa. Both are activated by the stimulation of almost all of the receptors. The general inhibition is activated even earlier than the coordinating centers are, and because of this the former may precede the reciprocal excitation.

Taking into consideration the known facts concerning the structure of the spinal cord and the foregoing physiologic explanations, one may represent the role of neuronal formations of the spinal cord in the coordinated innervation of skeletal muscles and in general inhibition as shown in Figure 76.

DEPOLARIZATION AND HYPERPOLARIZATION OF MOTONEURONS AND INTERNUNCIALS

Now we are going to attempt to apply the concept which I have developed here, relative to the origin of reciprocal and general inhibition in the spinal cord, to the understanding of those remarkable facts which have recently been reported by Eccles (1957), Kostyuk (1958a, b) and others in connection with intracellular recordings from motoneurons and internuncials. We will use mostly the factual material of Kostyuk. It is known that with a single stimulus applied to a proprioceptive nerve, a depolarization occurs in certain motoneurons participating in the corresponding monosynaptic arc and a hyper-

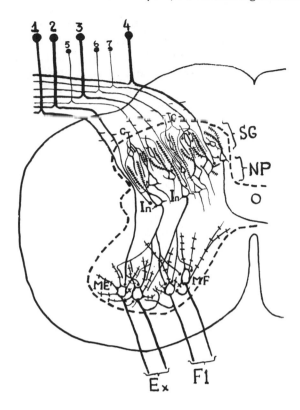

Fig. 76

A schematic representation of the neuronal structures responsible for monosynaptic reflexes, coordinated flexion of an extremity and general inhibition
in the spinal cord. *SG*, Substantia gelatinosa of Rolando; *NP*, nucleus proprius;
In, internuncials; *ME*, motoneurons (extensor); *MF*, motoneurons (flexor).
1, Neuron passing through dorsal root and connected monosynaptically with
the motor neurons of the extensors. *2* and *3*, Neurons passing through dorsal
root and connected with the interneurons, *In*, ending on cell bodies of the
flexor motoneurons and dendrites of the extensor motor neurons; in this way
a reciprocal stimulation and inhibition of antagonistic muscles is carried out.
4, The fibers running in the dorsal root and connected with the interneurons
giving origin to the spinothalamic tract. *5*, *6* and *7*, Thin fibers running in
the dorsal root and terminated in the substantia gelatinosa where they in-
nervate the cells of this substance and the dendrites of the neurons of the
nucleus proprius. The activation of these dendrites elicits inhibition of the
nucleus proprius, in other words, a general inhibition. *C*, Collaterals of fibers
running in the dorsal root originating from the neighboring segments. They
also terminate in the cells of the substantia gelatinosa and in the dendrites
of the neurons of the nucleus proprius and elicit a general inhibition.

polarization in other motoneurons; both lasting about 10 msec. The level of the depolarization does not exceed 10 mv.; the maximal hyperpolarization equals several millivolts and is associated with the inhibition of spikes in the motoneurons. It is generally accepted that these effects are due to local processes elicited in the cells and the cellular membrane by synaptic impulses. However, the motoneurons experience depolarization not only under the influence of the stimuli applied to the receptor elements or to the afferent nerve, but in addition to a continuous bombardment from the internuncials which, according to Kostyuk, send discharges incessantly, sometimes at a high rate of 100 to 200 per second. This continuous bombardment experienced by the motoneurons may also be derived from the tonic, respiratory and other centers of the brain. Therefore, the motoneurons must be continually depolarized. In view of this, if for some reason this bombardment is arrested or decreased, the motoneurons must repolarize; the level of this hyperpolarization must be higher in cases when the preceding spontaneous depolarization was pronounced. This is what we think is observed during the activation of a monosynaptic reflex arc.

As indicated above, according to the data of Sprague, the coordinated movement of the tail is accomplished by means of monosynaptic excitation of ipsilateral motoneurons and monosynaptic inhibition of contralateral ones. This inhibition is accomplished through activation of the dendrites of these neurons.

Frank and Sprague (1959) have shown by means of intracellular recordings that during the inhibition of the motoneuron, hyperpolarizing potentials are recorded (Figure 77). As in the experiments of Eccles (1955, 1957) and Kostyuk (1958a, b), this hyperpolarizing potential is much weaker than the depolarizing one. However, its latency may at times be only 0.3 msec. longer. This time is not sufficient to activate even one internuncial neuron.

What is the origin of the hyperpolarizing potentials observed during the monosynaptic inhibition of the motoneurons? Each monosynaptic reflex is accompanied by general inhibition as well. At this time motoneurons in a number of segments are inhibited.

We believe that widespread inhibition is due to the excitation of the substantia gelatinosa from collaterals of monosynaptic afferent nerve fibers. This results in activation of the dendrites of the internuncials in the nucleus proprius, and because of this activation, spontaneous rhythmic activity in these neurons is either immediately arrested or decreased. At the same time there is a decrease in the initial depolarization of the motoneurons and an apparent hyperpolarization occurs.

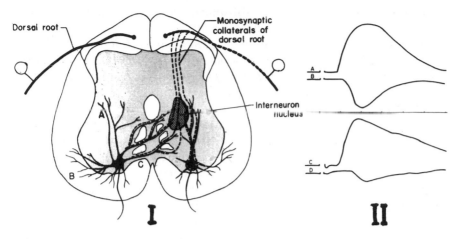

Fig. 77

I, Schematic representation of the afferent neuron endings in a monosynaptic reflex arc. A degenerated nerve fiber sectioned proximally to the sacral spinal ganglion is shown by a broken line. It ends ipsilaterally both on the dorsal dendrites and on the soma of the motoneuron, and contralaterally only on medial dendrites of the motoneuron. (Sprague, 1958.) *II*, Intracellular postsynaptic potentials of a motoneuron following stimulation of different strengths of monosynaptic arc. The upper tracings were obtained by a single strong stimulus, the lower by a weaker single stimulus. In both upper tracings, *A, C,* the negative potentials recorded ipsilaterally are represented; the lower tracings, *B, D,* represent the positive potentials recorded contralaterally. (Frank and Sprague, 1959.)

It is understandable that the level of this hyperpolarization in each cell will depend upon the number of impulses which arrived previously from the internuncials. If the motoneurons generated spikes spontaneously or did so under the influence of some stimuli, these spikes should disappear during hyperpolarization. The hyperpolarization should last as long as the depolarization from nerve stimulation because local processes in the motoneurons and in the dendrites of the interneurons, elicited by a single peripheral impulse, last approximately the same time. They originate under the influence of nerve impulses carried by the same proprioceptive fibers.

The longer latency of the hyperpolarizing potential may be explained by the fact that the latency of the depolarizing potentials depends on the time of transmission through axosomatic synapses, while the latency of the hyperpolarizing potential is conditioned by the transmission of the dendritic depolarization through axodendritic synapses as well as by the establishment of anelectrotonic block of axosomatic synapses by dendritic currents.

During polysynaptic excitation of motoneurons, following a single stimulus of the afferent nerve, depolarization is more intense and lasts longer, up to 0.1 to 0.2 seconds. The hyperpolarization also lasts longer and is higher in amplitude, reaching up to 15 mv.; correspondingly, the inhibition is increased and becomes more prolonged. This considerable hyperpolarization, according to our concept, depends upon the participation of internuncials of the coordinating apparatus in the polysynaptic excitation. These internuncials supply synapses on one hand with the cell bodies of some motoneurons, eliciting depolarization and spikes in them and, on the other hand, with the dendrites of antagonistic motoneurons, generating an anelectrotonic blockade of cell synapses. This, in turn, determines the hyperpolarization of the cells and depression of the spikes. Under the influence of the dendritic potentials, the anelectrotonic blockade occurs in the axosomatic synapses derived from the interneurons as well as from the descending tracts; this is why hyperpolarization will reach a considerable amplitude, up to 15 mv. Characteristically such a high hyperpolarization is observed following stimulation of the ipsilateral nerve and, therefore, after a considerably increased spontaneous bombardment of the interneurons.

During a study of the intracellular activity of the internuncials, Kostyuk observed that when inhibition was generated by a stimulation of a contralateral afferent nerve, only a slight hyperpolarization was elicited, preceded by a slight depolarization. During such hyperpolarization, spontaneous reflex activity would be suspended. But not infrequently, the depression of spontaneous discharges occurred without hyperpolarization and, in general, without any change in membrane potential.

We assumed that the occurrence of only a slight hyperpolarization, or even the absence of it in internuncials in the presence of an obvious inhibition, may be explained by the absence of a significant original spontaneous depolarization by the internuncials. This is why hyperpolarization may be lacking when an anelectrotonic blockade of the cell synapses occurs, resulting from the activation of their dendrites in the substantia gelatinosa. Moreover, the internuncials may even experience in this instance a slight depolarization as a result of the catelectrotonic effects of dendritic potentials upon the subsynaptic cell membrane. This action of dendritic potentials should also explain the fact that depolarization may precede hyperpolarization.

According to the observations made by Kostyuk, the internuncials may discharge in response to peripheral impulses, as well as spontaneously, without at first being depolarized. This indicates that under the conditions of the experiment the excitability of the internuncials is so high that they are able to be activated and generate spikes without a preliminary spatial or temporal summation of local potentials, but with the slightest disturbance of ionic equillibrium between the inner and the outer millieu. It is most probable that such an increase of excitability is created artificially during the operation. It is known that, after exposing the spinal cord, a single shock applied to a dorsal root may elicit contractions of all the muscles of the corresponding extremity.

Significance of General Inhibition

We may assert from the foregoing observations that each time any kind of activation takes place in the central nervous system, the resulting motor reaction occurs along with a widespread inhibition. Therefore, together with reciprocal inhibition and excitation of antagonistic muscles, diffuse inhibition of the central nervous system becomes a factor to be considered. During stimulation the resulting inhibition lasts longer than excitation, and it may continue for several minutes before it progressively decreases. Following termination of stimulation, inhibition ceases for several seconds and is followed by short-term facilitation.

The biological significance of general inhibition is that (1) the organism is protected from unnecessary energy expenditures which would otherwise be incurred because of responses to a multitude of weak external stimuli, (2) excitatory processes are limited to those neuronal circuits which are involved in the ongoing external reaction to a given stimulus, and (3) the activation of other neuronal circuits can be effected only by significant external or internal stimuli. Thus the dominant motor reaction is not disturbed. It seems that the mechanism of general inhibition is functionally interrelated with the excitatory process during each segment of a behavioral reaction causing a spatial limitation of this process. In other words diffuse inhibition contributes to the integration of a behavioral reaction, simple or complex, in that together with the activation of certain neuronal complexes in various divisions of the brain, there is inhibition of activities in the remaining brain structures.

During the study of the embryonal development of behavior in low vertebrates, Coghill (1936) came to the same conclusion regarding the biologic significance of widespread inhibition. The presence of diffuse inhibition, according to Coghill, is revealed at the earliest stage of embryonal development, when peripheral stimulation starts to elicit general reflex reactions involving the whole organism; it then develops progressively. In Coghill's experiments on *Amblyostoma,* inhibition originally occurred following tactile stimulation of an extremity and was limited to the involved extremity; the whole organism with the exception of the stimulated extremity, was in an active state. In the next stage of development, movement occurred in the stimulated extremity in response to a tactile stimulation, but inhibition was not present; in contrast in the third stage, tactile stimulation elicited inhibition of the entire organism. In the fourth stage, tactile stimulation elicited isolated movements of the stimulated extremity, as a definite localized reflex, with inhibition of the remaining organism. It follows that widespread inhibition constitutes practically as primary an effect as excitation itself, and that it increases progressively with the development of the reflex action. Coghill found that individualization and localization of movements is conditioned by the presence of widespread inhibition, which plays a decisive role in this process. According to him, local reflexes become possible because of the presence of general inhibition. Gonzalez (1932) also found that the process of the individualization and specialization of certain reflexes is due most of all to this diffuse inhibitory activity which depresses all the primary and basic integrated reactions.

We are going to consider general inhibition in cerebral activity and behavior in Part IV; we shall first consider the morphologic and functional organization of the cortex.

11 STRUCTURE OF THE CEREBRAL CORTEX AS RELATED TO BEHAVIOR: MORPHOLOGIC AND FUNCTIONAL CHARACTERISTICS

The cerebral cortex of higher vertebrates is the structure responsible for subjective reflection of the outside world, regulation of all types of behavior, namely, all forms of adaptation to the conditions in the environment; the instinctive acts of adjustment, as well as conditioned behavior, and those behavioral acts which are image-driven, being directed by mental representations of the outside world.

How can we approach the problem of finding out whether there are specific neuronal elements for psychoneural processes which would be responsible for reflection of the outside world in terms of feelings, perceptions, images and other mental representations? It would be desirable to determine which neuronal elements and which divisions of the cerebrum participate in the production of temporary connections during the formation of conditioned reflexes. The contemporary state of our knowledge of the finer structure of the cerebral cortex is such as to make us believe that we can suggest specific answers to these questions.

We are going to review the factual material concerning the architectonics of the cerebral cortex and at the same time we will try to elucidate the psychophysiologic significance of one or another type of neuron in the total activity of the cortex. As we believe that pyramidal neurons are subjected to the same type of inhibition that we just described at the level of the spinal cord, we are going to consider these neurons first. Afterward, we will review the newest contributions to our knowledge concerning the other cellular elements of the cortex.

Pyramidal Neurons

MORPHOLOGIC CHARACTERISTICS

Pyramidal neurons are found in all the layers of the cortex with the exception of the first. Their apical dendrites rise mostly toward the

level of the first layer, while some of them do not reach even as high as the second layer. The great number of other dendrites which arise from cell bodies, so-called basal dendrites, are relatively short and usually do not reach beyond the layer where the cell bodies are located (Figures 78 and 79).

The axons of certain small- and medium-sized pyramids do not leave the cortex. We will call these neurons internuncial neurons. They interconnect stellate and other neurons with pyramidal neurons of different layers. They are found in all the layers except the first and are particularly numerous in the second to the fourth layer of the cortex (Figure 78: cells 3, 7, 8, 9 and 10). The axons of a considerable number of the medium-sized pyramids penetrate the subcortical white matter. They serve to interconnect different regions of the same hemisphere or both hemispheres through the corpus collosum. These neurons are usually called association neurons; they are located in all layers of the cortex except the first and are particularly numerous in its intermediary layers (Figure 79).

The large pyramids which are located in the fifth and sixth layers essentially belong to a projectional efferent system. Their axons run through the white subcortical matter toward the lower divisions of the brain, forming pyramidal and extrapyramidal tracts (Figure 80: neuron 8; Figure 87: neuron 13).

Axons of associational and projectional pyramidal cells have a great number of collaterals which travel essentially horizontally and synapse in the lower layers of the cortex, usually with the dendrites of neighboring pyramidal neurons or even with the dendrites of the same neurons (Poljakov, 1958). Several collaterals ascend into the upper layers; these are so-called "recurrent" collaterals (Figure 80); most of them reach the first layer. They end mostly in the first and second layers on the apical dendrites of the pyramidal neurons.

Dendrites of pyramidal neurons in the cortex of man are very densely covered by characteristic morphologic formations. First Sukhanov (1899) and then many other investigators studied these club-like or thorn-like formations in detail. In recent years Poljakov and

---

Fig. 78

Cellular distribution and afferent systems of the parietal region of the cortex (mouse). *1, 2, 5, 17,* Stellate cells with short axons. All other cells are those of the pyramidal neurons of various sizes; *a* and *b,* specific afferent fibers from the thalamus; *c* and *d,* nonspecific afferent fibers from the thalamus; *e* and *f,* afferent fibers from the association neurons. On the left are represented cytoarchitectonic layers of the cortex. (Lorente de Nó, 1944.)

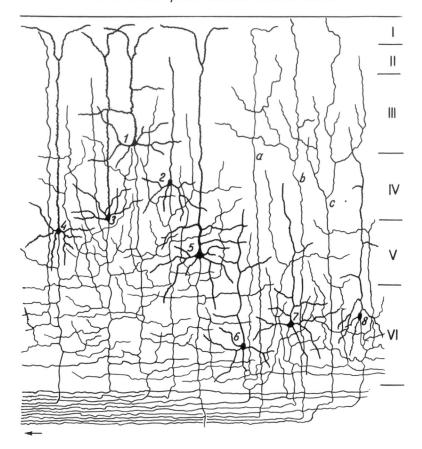

Fig. 79

Association neurons in the cortex of the hemispheres. On the left are represented the cells of association pyramidal neurons which are distributed in
the third to sixth layers. On the right, their endings are shown in the three
upper layers. (After Chang, 1952.)

Sarkisov (1949) and Chang (1952) found that the spheroid heads of
these thorns are connected with the dendrites by a fine pedicle of 0.5
micron in length, and in view of this feature, they may very easily be
torn off. The form and size of these formations are very variable. They
are found on the dendrites of pyramidal cells in all mammals
(Zhukova, 1953). There are many more thorn-like formations on the
dendrites of pyramidal neurons of the cerebral cortex than on the
neurons of the lower divisions of the cerebrum, and they are relatively
rare in the spinal cord (Poljakov and Sarkisov, 1949).

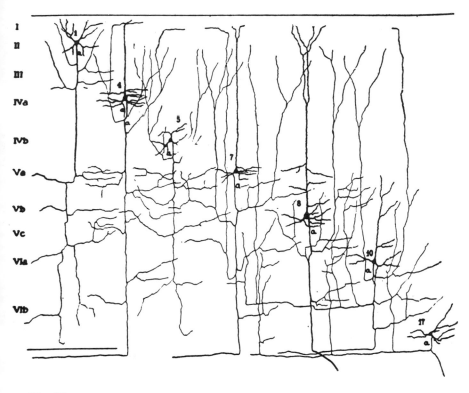

Fig. 80

Axonic ramifications of pyramidal neurons with descending axons (main types). *1* and *5,* Internuncial neurons — their axons do not leave the limits of the cortex; *4, 7, 10* and *17,* association pyramids; *8,* projectional neurons. (Lorente de Nó, 1944.)

According to Poljakov the number of thorn-like formations on the dendrites of one single pyramidal neuron may reach 6000. They are particularly numerous on the apical dendrites of pyramidal neurons in the upper layers of the cortex. Poljakov, Chang and others noted that the soma of these neurons and the proximal region of the dendrites are deprived of these formations which predominate over the distant endings of the apical dendrites (Figure 81).

According to Poljakov and Sarkisov (1949), these "thorny" spines begin to appear in man relatively late in his ontogenesis, almost at the time of birth. As regards the different types of nerve cells, these formations are found the earliest in most of the early maturing large pyramidal cells of the fifth layer; in other cells, they appear only

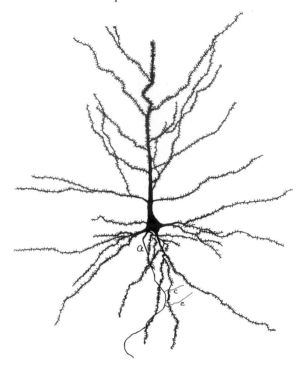

Fig. 81

Pyramidal neuron. Note spine-like formations on all the dendrites; they begin at a certain distance from the cell. The cell body itself and more or less thick portions of dendrites are deprived of these formations. It is clear that they are more densely distributed upon the apical dendrites than over the basal ones. The dendrites of this pyramidal neuron have 3497 spine-like formations. *a*, Axons; *c*, collaterials. (After Poljakov, 1953.)

when the cells are mature. They are very sensitive to a variety of noxious agents. For example, half an hour following a ligature of the carotid artery, there is a considerable change in the structures of the "spines," and they completely disintegrate during a more prolonged disturbance of the metabolism of the nerve tissue.

In the opinion of Sarkisov, Poljakov and Chang, these formations constitute a receptor apparatus. Indeed, it is through them that physiologic changes are effected in the dendrites. Axon fibers are in contact with them through their terminal branchings (Figure 82). The synapses on the "spines" are also found in dendrites of subcortical nuclei in mammals (Leontovitch, 1958) as well as in the spinal cord (Poljakov and Sarkisov, 1949).

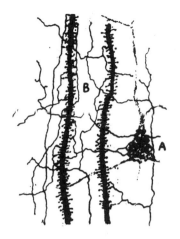

Fig. 82

Synaptic interconnections on dendrites and cell bodies. *B*, Two dendrites with spine-like formations some of which are in contact with the lateral and terminal synapses of ascending ramifications; *A*, a pyramidal cell all covered by synapses forming a reticulum, a basket-like net around the cell and a large portion of its dendrites. (After Chang, 1952.)

Pyramidal nerve cells and their dendrites are entirely covered by a layer of glial elements. Because of this, the surface of the neuron does not enter into contact with the intercellular tissue fluid. In the synaptic regions, the glial layer is still present, but is much thinner (Figure 83) (De Castro, 1951). However, according to electronic microscopy, the glial layer may be absent between the surface of the cells and synaptic endings (DeRobertis, 1959). In view of the fact that glia contains myelin, it is a poor conductor of electricity, just as in the case of the myelin sheath of nerve fibers. This observation has considerable significance for the understanding of the physiologic processes which take place in the nerve cells.

The reception of impulses by the soma and by the initial segments of the dendrites, where the thorn-like formations are not present, must take place directly through the local synapses. Synapses are found on the cell body in a considerable number, and are sometimes concentrated in certain limited areas (Zurabashvili, 1951), occasionally forming a complex reticulum, a basket-like nest around the cell bodies (Figure 82A). During synaptic activation a local process is generated in the cell under the corresponding synapse. The potential which arises there is responsible for the current flowing outward

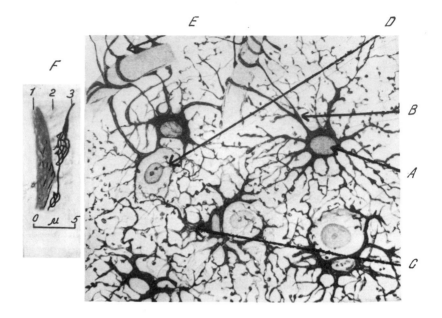

Fig. 83

Glial elements in the cerebral cortex. *A*, Glial cell; *B*, process of glial cell; *C*, glial cell on the surface of a pyramidal cell; *D*, a terminal process of a glial cell on a pyramidal cell; *E*, glial elements on a blood vessel; *F*, largely magnified structure of the synaptic ending on the surface of the cell body; *1*, the superficial segment of the cell; *2*, glial cell; *3*, synaptic ending. (De Castro, 1951.)

mostly through the hillock where the axon originates, or in the absence of the hillock it flows through the initial segment of the axon, free from the myelin sheath. According to Maximow, the inner structure of the hillock represents a transitional form between the cell body and the axon (Maximow, 1930). With a simultaneous excitation of a great number of cell synapses, a very marked depolarization takes place in the region of the hillock or in the initial segment of the axon, so that the generated current initiates a traveling impulse in the axon. This may occur during the activation not only of all the synapses on a given cell, but also of only some of them. From the hillock and the cell body the excitatory process cannot spread antidromically along the dendrites because of a marked decrement of the process in the dendrites. The initial segment of the axons thus constitutes a special apparatus for the generation, in the axon, of a conducted impulse.

Functional Characteristics

Excitation arising in the pyramidal cell does not spread over the dendrites because of the decremential dendritic conduction. But the electric current due to the cellular potential does spread electrotonically along the dendrites. Since the latter are covered by a glial sheath, these currents will flow outward mostly through the synaptic areas. Flowing into the synapses they will produce there an anelectrotonic

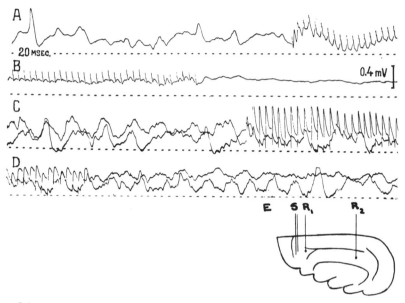

Fig. 84

Depression of a "spontaneous" electrical activity of the cat during stimulation of the cortex. Tracings *A* and *B* in a cat under deep pentobarbital (Nembutal) narcosis. Stimulating and recording electrodes located upon the gyrus suprasylvius; recording electrode applied at a distance of 2.5 mm. from stimulating one. *A*, Beginning of a tetanic stimulation (frequency 50 per sec., intensity 30 volts); *B*, after 10 seconds of tetanizing stimulation. Recordings *C* and *D* from another preparation. Relatively deep Nembutal narcosis. Stimulating electrodes, *S*, located on the gyrus sigmoideus. Potentials recorded simultaneously from the surface of the same gyrus, *R₁*, (upper tracings) at a distance of 2 mm. from the stimulating electrode, *S*, and from the surface of the gyrus suprasylvius, *R₂*, (lower tracings) at a distance of 10 mm. from *S*. *C*, Beginning of a short tetanic stimulation (50 per sec., 25 volts); *D*, end of stimulation; *E*, diagram of disposition of electrodes. (Beritoff and Roitbak, 1953.)

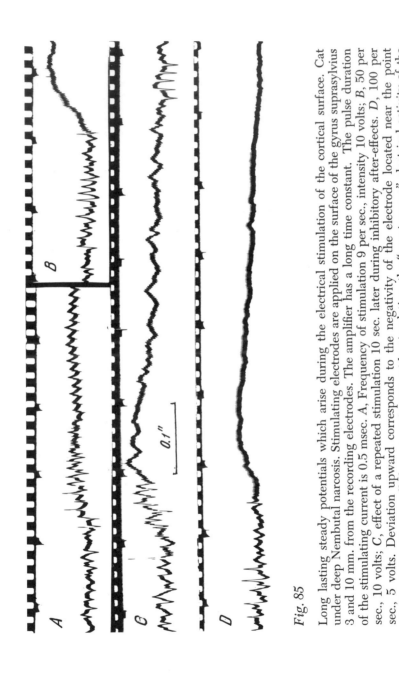

Fig. 85

Long lasting steady potentials which arise during the electrical stimulation of the cortical surface. Cat under deep Nembutal narcosis. Stimulating electrodes are applied on the surface of the gyrus suprasylvius 3 and 10 mm. from the recording electrodes. The amplifier has a long time constant. The pulse duration of the stimulating current is 0.5 msec. A, Frequency of stimulation 9 per sec., intensity 10 volts; B, 50 per sec., 10 volts; C, effect of a repeated stimulation 10 sec. later during inhibitory after-effects. D, 100 per sec., 5 volts. Deviation upward corresponds to the negativity of the electrode located near the point of stimulation. During all these experiments with stimulation, the "spontaneous" electrical activity of the cortex disappears. (Beritoff and Roitbak, 1953.)

244

block and therefore will inhibit activation of dendrites through the synapse in apical as well as basal dendrites. This is probably why during an alerting reaction, associated with a "desynchronization of the cortical electrical activity," spontaneous slow dendritic potentials disappear, and are present with a decreased amplitude only in response to direct electrical stimuli (Purpura, 1946).

As is known, slow negative potentials are recorded in the vicinity of electrically stimulated points of the cortical surface. Their generation is ascribed to the dendritic local processes, which are analogous to those recorded in the spinal cord and which were considered in the last chapter. These slow potentials may be associated with a depression of the spontaneous electrical activity of the cortex as well as of primary evoked potentials elicited in the cortex by the stimulation of afferent nerves (Beritoff and Roitbak, 1953).

In Figure 84, stimulation of the gyrus suprasylvius at a rhythm of 50 c./sec., elicits a complete depression of spontaneous electrical activity, depression persisting for a certain time after the cessation of the stimulation (oscillograms A and B). One can see on the graph that this depression is manifest at a distance of 2 mm. and is very slight at a distance of 10 mm. (oscillograms C and D).

Using an amplifier with a long time constant, one could clearly see that this depression of spontaneous activity arises during the negative potential evoked by tetanizing stimulation of the cortex. This can be seen in Figure 85, not only with the high frequencies of stimulation, such as 50 and 100 c./sec., but also with a low frequency of 10 c./sec. It follows that the depression in question cannot be considered to be the result of an increased frequency of stimulation or to be a refractory state of the neuronal elements which participate in the generation of spontaneous electrical activity.

In view of these observations, we may assert that surface negative dendritic slow potentials depress the soma and the axosomatic synapses of the corresponding neurons to the point of making them inexcitable through these synapses (Beritoff and Roitbak, 1955, 1956).

Characteristically during stimulation of the cortex the positive electrical oscillations evoked by a peripheral stimulation are also somewhat inhibited (Figure 86). Since these electrical oscillations are due to the excitation of pyramidal neurons located in the deep layers of the cortex, one may conclude that during cortical stimulation at the time of the surface negative slow potential, these pyramidal neurons are also subjected to some depression (Beritoff and Roitbak, 1953).

Dendrites of the pyramidal cells are stimulated mostly through the

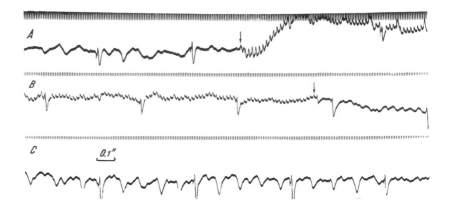

Fig. 86

Depression of spontaneous electrical activity and of primary responses to auditory stimuli during stimulation of the cortex. Cat under Nembutal narcosis. Active recording electrode is located over the middle ectosylvian gyrus, second recording electrode on sigmoidal gyrus; stimulating electrodes are on the surface of the middle ectosylvian gyrus 4 mm. from the recording electrodes. The amplifier has a long time constant. A, Effects of auditory stimuli at a frequency of 5 per sec. and of an additional stimulation of the cortex (frequency 50 per sec., intensity 12 volts); B, continuation of the combined stimulation 1.2 seconds later and then cessation of stimulation of the cortex, but continuation of the auditory excitation; C, direct continuation of B. (Beritoff and Roitbak, 1953.)

tangential synapses. This stimulation always generates a local process. The latter spreads with great decrement and does not reach the cell body (Adrian, 1936, Roitbak, 1955, 1956). One of the basic explanations for the rapid decrement of the excitatory process in the dendrites is the absence of a direct contact between the synapse and the dendrite due to the presence of a "thorny" spine in between. The spheroidal head of this spine is connected through a pedicle with the dendrites; therefore, the stimulating action of the synapse upon the dendrite must decrease considerably regardless of whether this action is electrical or chemical.

At the basis of this phenomenon, one may possibly consider those biochemical peculiarities which Portugalov described in 1958, in the motoneurons of the spinal cord; this has been mentioned in the previous chapter. Namely, the succinodehydrase in dendrites of the motoneurons is somewhat less active than in the cell bodies and in the synaptic area. In addition, in the dendrites, with the increase of the distance from the cell body, the content of amino acids, such as tryptophan, and of histamine is low in comparison with their amount found in the cytoplasm of the cell, these enzymes being found essentially in the neurofibrils. Therefore, one may wonder whether or not one of the causes of the decrement in the spread of local processes in dendrites of pyramidal neurons is the low intensity of the enzymatic processes which take place there.

The low intensity of oxidative processes results in a slow course of local excitation and, therefore, of the related electrical potentials. Furthermore, since the dendrite is stimulated successively from tangentional axonal fibers in different foci, the duration of the dendritic potential elicited by a volley is increased, and reaches 0.1 to 0.2 second. With repeated synaptic bombardment of the dendrite, local potentials summate, generating a continuous steadily increasing current. This slow current is spread electrotonically along the dendrite and reaches the cell body because the dendritic "thorny" appendices and glial sheath make it difficult for the current to flow through them. The dendritic currents flowing electrotonically inside the cell may flow outward from there, mostly through the synaptic regions where the glial layer is relatively thin. Flowing outward from the cell, this current must penetrate into the synapses and because of its inward flow there, produces an anelectrotonic blockade. Because of this, the synapses stop transmitting impulses to the cell body (Beritoff, 1956a). Of course, the dendritic currents flowing outward through the cell membrane toward the synapses and the initial segments free of any glia layer may produce a membrane depolarization of the cell segments. However, this depolarization is too small to cause a conducted excitatory process. On the other hand, as the synaptic blockade discontinues the constant bombardment which the pyramidal cells usually receive from the nonspecific facilitating system as well as from the activated pyramidal neurons, the usual background depolarization of the cell decreases. Therefore, the cell appears to become hyperpolarized. The result of this will be a decrease of excitability in the soma. Therefore, with blocked synapses, there will also be cell inhibition (Beritoff, 1959). This is how the dendrites of the pyramidal cells with their thorn-like spines and tangential synapses offer, according to our concept, specialized mechanisms for the generation of cell inhibition.

We said before that currents arising from the pyramidal cells, electrotonically spreading along the dendrites, produce an anelectrotonic blockade of the dendritic synapses, thus inhibiting them. Now we come to an analogous conclusion with regard to the inhibition of the pyramidal cells. Therefore, dendrites and cell bodies of the pyramidal neurons show reciprocal relationships! The increase in cell activation leads to inhibition of the dendrites and the increase in dendrite activation elicits inhibition of the cell body. These antagonistic relationships are well expressed by changes in electrical resistance of the superficial dendritic layer. Aladjalova (1960) showed that during the activation of the dendritic layer, expressed by slow wave activity, the resistance of this layer is lowered, and vice versa, with depression of the superficial dendritic layer resulting in disappearance of dendritic slow wave activity, the resistance of the layer increases.

The first layer of the cortex essentially consists of (1) branching apical dendrites arising from the majority of pyramidal cells located in the deeper layers and (2) fibers of different orgins, i.e., processes of the horizontal cells, recurring collaterals of the pyramidal neurons and axonal ramifications belonging to the fibers of associational neurons of the same or opposite hemisphere (Figure 87). All these fibers running in the upper layers of the cortex are tangential to the lateral thorn-like spines of the apical dendrites. They also terminate on the cells of the horizontal and other internuncial neurons which are found in this layer. The axons of these neurons run horizontally as well as vertically and end in the upper layers of the cortex in the same way, that is, upon the apical dendrites as well as on the cell bodies of the internuncial neurons (Bechterew, 1898, O'Leary and Bishop, 1938, Poljakov, 1953). These anatomic connections of the pyramidal and other neurons with the first layer of the cortex are seen in Figure 87 as described by Chang. Here in the first layer, are located the dendrites of the internuncial neurons, *3, 7, 8, 9* and *10*, the associational neurons with long axons, *11, 12*, and projectional efferent neurons, *13*. Here also run the fibers of the horizontal neurons, *4, 5*, and internuncial neurons, *3, 8*. In addition the axons of the spindle cells, *16*, penetrate this layer as do afferent thalamic fibers, *1*.

These inter-relationships of the neurons of the upper layers are also shown schematically in Figure 88 after Shkolnik-Yarros. Here in the first layer, the apical dendrites of the internuncial and associational neurons synapse with the axons of the horizontal cells and those of Martinotti. It must be noted that these fibers, *1*, run along the first layer, and are tangential to the apical dendrites of a great number of pyramidal neurons. In the second and third layers the apical dendrites,

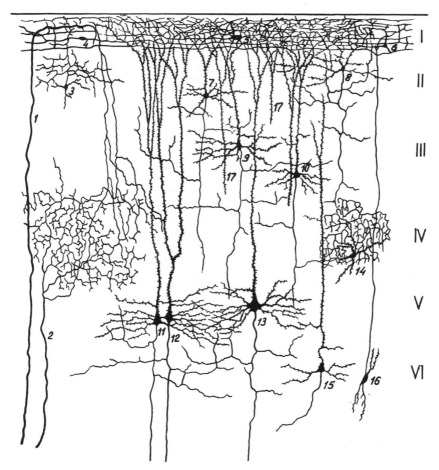

Fig. 87

General diagram for the distribution of neurons in the cortex. *1, 2,* Afferent thalamic fibers; *4, 5,* horizontal neurons; *3, 7, 8, 9, 10,* internuncial neurons; *14,* stellate neuron; *11, 12, 15,* association neurons; *13,* projection neuron of Betz; *16,* fusiform internuncial neuron. (After Chang, 1952.)

2, enter into contact with the afferents originating from the other divisions of the nervous system, the axons of the Martinotti cells and a great number of other axons. The ramifications of the apical dendrite in its lower third, *3,* enter into contact with collaterals, *c,* of axons of the Martinotti cells and also with collaterals of the axons of the same pyramidal cell (therefore a contact with itself). In Figure 88 the axons of the stellate cells and the collaterals of axons of pyrami-

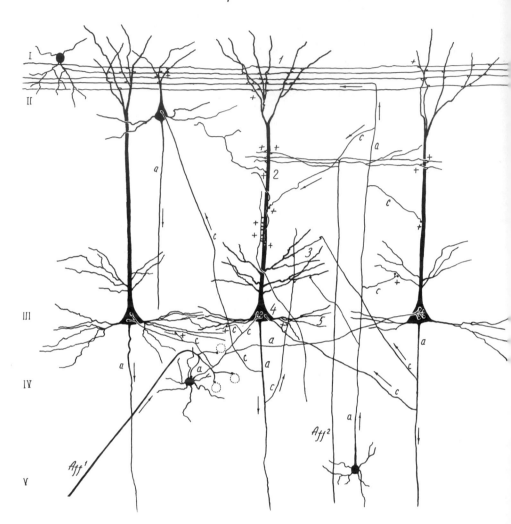

Fig. 88

Diagram of connections of afferent fibers with stellate and pyramidal cells of the cerebral cortex. Roman numerals indicate cortical layers; *1*, horizontal axons of cells of Martinotti and those of first layer; *2*, apical dendrite; *3*, initial ramification of the apical dendrite; *4*, cell body of the pyramidal neuron; *5*, basal dendrites; *Aff'*, specific afferent thalamic fibers; *Aff²*, non-specific thalamic fibers; *a*, axons; *c*, axonal collaterals; arrows indicate direction of transmission of stimuli. (Diagram by Shkolnik-Yarros (1958b) from detailed studies of her own material as well as that of Poljakov.) (See text for detailed explanation.)

dal cells enter into contact with the cell body, 4, of the other pyramidal cells. The same figure shows the connection with the associational neurons of the specific afferent thalamic fibers, *Aff¹*, through the stellate neurons (fourth layer), and also of the nonspecific thalamic fibers, *Aff²*, with the apical dendrites (upper area of second layer). One may assume that excitation of the associational pyramidal cells takes place through the specific fibers, whereas inhibition occurs through the nonspecific fibers.

According to the observations of Poljakov, the collaterals of pyramidal neurons enter into contact with the dendrites of neighboring pyramidal neurons and may have a recurrent branch which synapses with their own dendrites. This is shown in Figure 88 and is consistent with physiologic observations.

During antidromic activation of the pyramidal tract produced by stimulating it in the region of the medulla, neurophysiologists have recorded slow potentials in the cortex (Woolsey and Chang, 1948). These potentials seem to express the active state induced in those dendrites which are activated by the terminal collaterals arising from the involved pyramidal neurons. This is consistent with our concept of the genesis of inhibition through dendrites.

Landau (1956), with carefully localized stimulation in the pyramidal tract of the cat, found electrical potentials only in the sigmoid area, particularly in the anterior sigmoid gyrus where the Betz cells are found. Here slow positive potentials follow rapid negative oscillations. Landau considered the slow potential to be a result of the spread of excitation along the apical dendrites; however, it more probably arises from activation of the basal dendrites through the horizontal collaterals which branch off the axons immediately after their point of origin. We believe that when a certain group of pyramidal neurons and the dendrites of neighboring cells are energized simultaneously through the axonal collaterals, inhibition of these pyramidal neurons must take place. In this way, the cortical reactions may be well circumscribed. As we saw before, analogous mechanisms take place in the spinal cord. It is known that during antidromic stimulation of the motor fibers of a ventral root, reflexes elicited through neighboring ventral loops are inhibited (Beritoff and Bakuradze, 1941).

The collaterals of pyramidal neurons may synapse with their own dendrites, as seen in Figure 88. The activation of these dendrites, as was indicated before, must elicit inhibition of the cells. However, in some cases when the cell has just gone through a period of excitation so that its membrane has been considerably depolarized, the dendritic current arising in the neighboring short dendrites, activated by the recurrent collaterals of the same neuron, may elicit a local process in the cell or even a conducted impulse due to excitation by this current of the initial segment of the axon. Of course the dendritic current flowing outward from the cells under the synapses will also produce the blockade of these synapses to a certain extent; however, this situation may not prevent the above-mentioned effect on the initial segment of the axon. It is possible that a regular rhythmic discharge of 100 to 200 c./sec. or more, which is observed in the records derived from the pyramidal cells (Jasper *et al.*, 1958), depends in some way on this kind of auto-excitation of cells through their own collaterals.

Figure 89 is a diagram of the spread of dendritic electronic currents in the cerebral cortex and of the widespread cortical inhibition generated by this mechanism. As seen from this figure, and in accordance with our hypothesis, the dendritic inhibition of the cell may be partly due to the blockade of the synapses located in the vicinity of the activated dendrite. Such a pyramidal cell may be activated through other unblocked synapses located at a greater distance.

Figure 90 contains a diagram representing the activation of a pyramidal cell, and its excitatory effect upon the basal dendrites of a neighboring pyramidal neuron, the latter being inhibited locally thereby. Thus, during the activation of one or only a few axosomatic synapses, the pyramidal cells enter into a state of local excitation associated with the presence of a local potential; while after a stimulation of a number of synapses, the cell gives rise to a conducted impulse. The latter originates in the initial segment of the axon under the influence of electrical currents generated by local cellular potentials.

As in the previous figure, the first layer of the cortex and two pyramidal neurons are represented. The cell is activated through the synapses which are marked by plus and minus signs. The diagram represents an active state of the cell as a result of the effects of single impulses arriving through several synapses. The summated cellular current flowing outward activates the axon hillock and simultaneously produces an anelectrotonic blockade of axodendritic synapses. From the activation of neuron P^1 through its horizontal collateral c, the basal dendrites of the neighboring neuron P^2, are activated. As a result of this, the electrotonic currents flow inward into the cell and then outward from the cell through the synaptic regions where their anelectrotonic depression should occur.

On this diagram are also seen the records of the electrical potentials

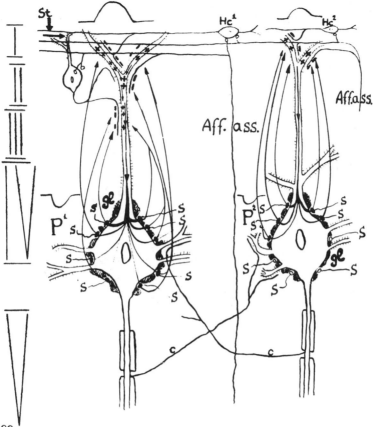

Fig. 89

Diagram of general cortical inhibition. This figure represents the first layer of the cortex and two pyramidal neurons. The dendrites are covered by thorn-like processes, and the cell body by the glial elements, *gl*, and synapses, *S*, from the internuncials and association neurons. The superficial layer of the cortex is stimulated, *St;* from there the excitatory state spreads along the association fibers, *Aff. ass.*, and horizontal neurons, *Hc*, over the superficial layer and activates the branching apical dendrites as well as the internuncial neuron through which the apical dendrites are additionally activated. The active segments of the dendrites are indicated by signs, +, inside and, −, outside. The direction of the generated biocurrents flowing through the dendrites, the cell and the intercellular space is indicated by arrows. These currents cross the synaptic areas, *S*, located on the cell body with the greatest density near the origin of the apical dendrites. Excitation spreading along the superficial cortical layer activates at first one pyramidal neuron, P^1, then the other, P^2. It affects P^2 less than P^1. When flowing outward, electrotonic currents produce an electrotonic block at the level of the synapse. On top and in the middle of each pyramidal neuron a record of the local biocurrent is indicated.

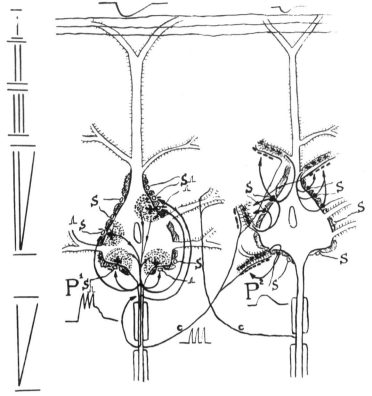

Fig. 90

Diagram of excitation of pyramidal cell and of local inhibition of neighboring pyramidal cells. Symbols the same as in Figure 89. (See text for detailed explanation.)

recorded from the cortex. On the activated synapses (marked by $-$) single spikes are indicated; on the axon of the cell, a slow wave occurs (from the summation of the local electrical cellular potentials) and on top of it, three rapid oscillations from the repeated activation of the axon under the influence of this slow wave. On the horizontal collateral three rapid oscillations caused by excitation spreading from the axon of the pyramidal cell P^1 are indicated. In the pyramidal cell P^2, a negative slow wave is indicated which is caused by the activation of basal dendrites under the influence of the impulses arising from the above-mentioned horizontal collateral. Positive potentials which express the hyperpolarization of the apical dendrites resulting from the block of the axodendritic synapses are represented over the apical dendrites.

Stellate Cells

Morphologic Characteristics

As is known, the cerebral cortex is constituted mainly by stellate and other cells with short axons and by pyramidal and fusiform spindle cells with long axons. The stellate neurons, and other brush-like and spider-like cells, differ from the pyramidal and fusiform cells in that the former lack apical dendrites. They have short dendrites which most often derive from the whole surface of the cell, and because of this the cell appears to be star-shaped. Another important differential characteristic is the absence of the thorn-like spines on their dendrites. The axons of the stellate cells usually form a more or less complex network in the vicinity of the cells. However, there are some stellate cells, the axons of which run in all directions for some distance from the cell, and which form a great number of terminal synapses (Figures 91 and 92).

Stellate cells with short axons constitute most of the cellular mass of the cortex. They are found in all layers of the cortex except the first one. They are particularly numerous in the second, third and fourth layers where they are much more densely represented than in any of the lower layers (Figure 93). Here in the upper layers of the cortex are found most of the typical stellate cells whose densely ramified axons lie in the vicinity of the cell itself. Their relative number increases in animals of a higher phylogenetic development. The stellate neurons with short axons are the main constituents of cells in the phylogenetically newer upper layers, and they represent the cerebral terminals of analyzers.

The stellate cells with short axons can be divided into two groups according to their external characteristics. One group is characterized by more or less dense branching of their processes in the dendritic and axonic nets. In these cases, dendritic and axonic nets are so closely interwoven in the vicinity of the cell body and are made of such fine fibers that they can hardly be differentiated (Poljakov and Sarkisov, 1949). These cells with their dense pericellular reticula are called spider cells or Golgi-type II cells; however, we prefer to call them web-like cells because their reticulum is like a web. These neurons predominate in the third and fourth layers, but are also present in other layers except the first. Some of these cells are characterized by the absence of branches arising from the pericellular net to form at a distance axonal ramifications susceptible to activating other cells (Fig-

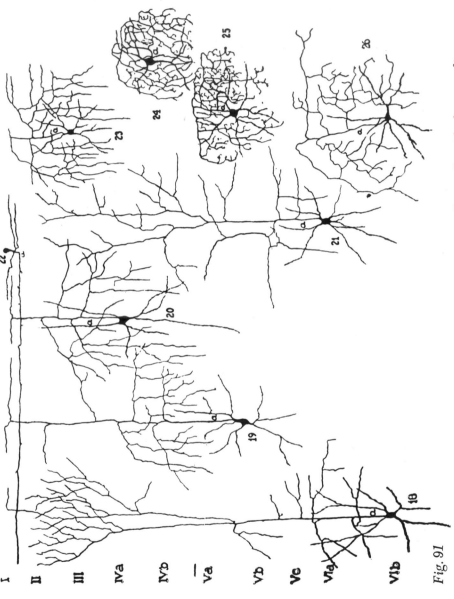

Fig. 91

Three types of neurons with intracortical axons. 18, 19, 20, 21, Stellate cells with the ascending axons; 22, a cell with a horizontal axon; 24, 25, stellate cells, the axons of which form a dense reticulum within the limits of the branching of the dendrites; 23, 26, stellate cells, the axons of which branch in the

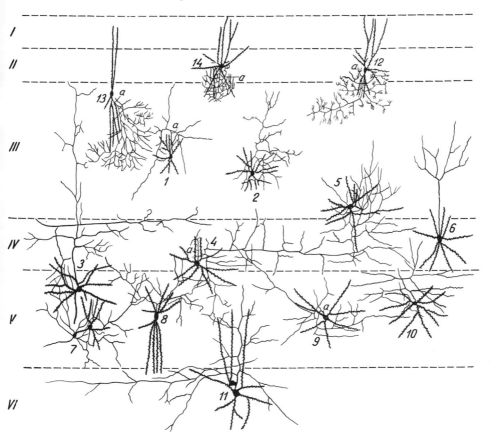

Fig. 92

Cells with short axons in the visual analyzer of the cerebral cortex of rabbit. Many of the cells represented here, *3, 5, 6, 10,* give off axonic ramifications, *a,* in the next layer also. Some of them, *3, 4, 11,* have long axonal branching; axons of certain cells, *12, 13,* form branching ramifications with the basket-like endings. They may, with their axonal ramifications, influence a considerable number of pyramidal cells. According to this figure, the fourth layer is not developed. This is characteristic of the lower mammals. (After O'Leary and Bishop, 1938.)

ure 94: majority of cells; Figure 95: cells 12 and 14). The remaining cells with a pericellular net have axonal ramifications which, after leaving the dendritic field, terminate after a more or less short distance (Figure 92: cells 2, 5, 7 and 9; Figure 95: cells 4, 6, 13 and 15).

Comparing the different forms of stellate cells in man (Poljakov and Sarkisov, 1949) (Figure 94), with lower mammals such as rabbits

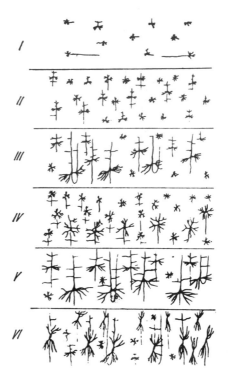

Fig. 93

Schematic representation of the density of cells with short axons and of pyramidal cells in different cortical layers in man. Cells with short axons are represented as small stars. The other cells, with the apical dendrites, belong to the pyramidal neurons of various size. Also fusiform cells are represented in the sixth layer. (After Sarkisov, 1948).

and mice (Lorente de Nó, 1933, O'Leary and Bishop, 1938) (Figures 91 and 92), one may conclude that in man cells with a pericellular reticulum and without any additional axonal net outside of this reticulum predominate; whereas, in mice and rabbits these cells have additional axonal branching outside of the pericellular net. According to O'Leary (1941), area 17 in the cat also has stellate cells with pericellular nets, but without axonal ramifications outside of this reticulum (Figure 95). Apparently, the structure of the visual analyzer in the cat represents a transitional form between the lower mammals and man. Figure 96 points out stellate cells with pericellular nets of dendritic and axonal ramifications in man.

Axonal ramifications around the stellate cells not only repeatedly cross dendrites, but also end upon them in synapses just as they do on

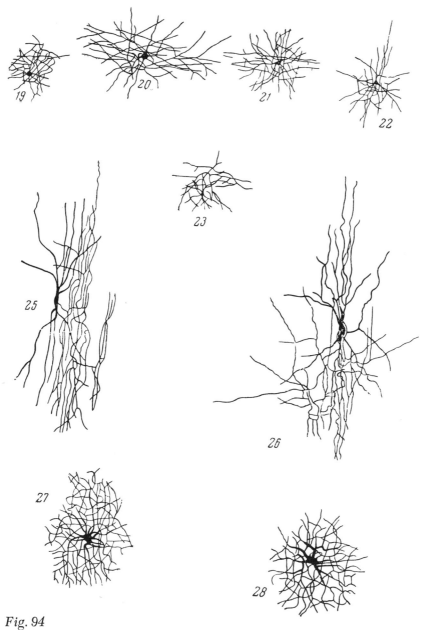

Fig. 94

Stellate cells with the pericellular reticulum made of dendrites and axonal ramifications in man. *22* is from layer II; *21, 25,* from layer III; *23, 27,* from layer IV; *20, 26,* from layer V; *19, 28,* from layer VI. (After Poljakov and Sarkisov, 1949.)

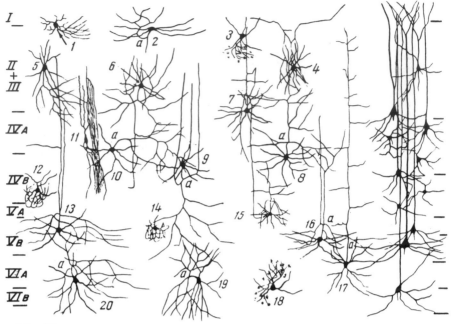

Fig. 95

Distribution of stellate cells with short axons and of pyramidal neurons in the region of the visual analyzer of the cat, from the medial aspect of the area striata. Cell numbers are explained in the text. (After O'Leary, 1941.)

the soma of the cell. This structure offers these neurons the possibility of having closed loops with themselves (Figure 96) (Poljakov, 1953). This must ensure reiterative discharge during each activation of a stellate cell. Characteristically, these stellate cells with a pericellular axonal net, very often do not have any axonal ramification outside of this net. Therefore, these axons serve to produce autoactivation. These structural pecularities of the stellate cells explain the physiologic observation that isolated receptive neurons in the sensorimotor cortex (posterior sigmoid gyrus in the cat) always respond by bursts of discharges; in other words, more or less prolonged series of impulses are evoked by single stimuli applied to the specific nuclei of the thalamus or to an afferent nerve of an extremity. The cortical elements responsible for these discharges discovered by Li and Jasper (1953) are considered by them to be Type I, and they are related to the cortical function of somesthetic perception.

We believe that these Type I neurons with a pericellular axonal net constitute the stellate cells characteristic of all the receptive fields, and

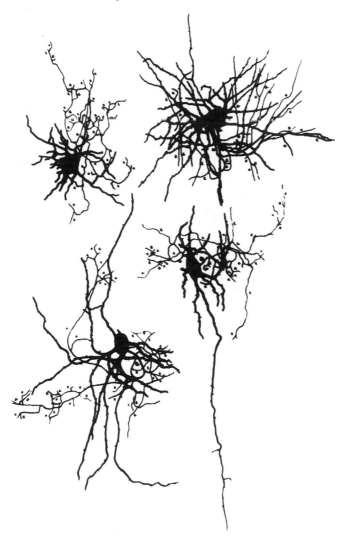

Fig. 96

Stellate cells with axonal reticulum in the cortex of man. Axonal ramifications of each cell form an obvious contact with the dendrites on the same cell. (Courtesy of Prof. Poljakov from his nonpublished drawings.)

not only of the sensorimotor area. They serve, wherever they are distributed, for the perception of impulses conducted from the receptors along a specific thalamic pathway.

The second group of stellate neurons is found in all of the cortical

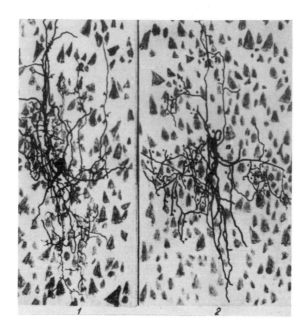

Fig. 97

Axonal ramifications of a single stellate cell terminating upon the cell bodies of a great number of pyramidal cells. The cell bodies of these are represented by lighter shading. Semischematic drawing. (Poljakov, 1958.)

layers. They have few short dendrites and their axons run from the cells into other layers or run horizontally and end by numerous collaterals (Figure 91: cells 18, 19, 20, 21 and 26; Figure 92: cells 3, 6, 12 and 13; Figure 95: cells 8, 10 and 16). Very often the axonal branchings of the stellate cells terminate on the soma of a great number of pyramidal cells. This means that stimulation of each of these cells must generate a state of excitation in a great number of pyramidal cells (Poljakov, 1958). Figure 97 illustrates the connection of a single stellate cell with many pyramidal cells.

Apparently the stellate cells of the second group serve for the transmission of impulses from the afferent thalamic fibers to the associational neurons.

The dendrites of the stellate cells of the second group very often form beads. These are smooth thickenings of a fusiform character, found along the dendrites at different intervals (Figure 98) (Poljakov, 1953; Chang, 1952). They often are found on the dendrites of the stellate cells of the fourth layer (Shkolnik-Yarros, 1954). These

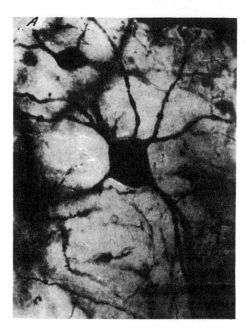
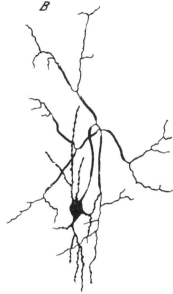

Fig. 98

Stellate neurons. On the left, after Poljakov (microphotograph), and on the right, after Chang (semischematic drawings). A bead-like structure of the dendrites is seen on both illustrations.

protoplasmic thickenings on the dendrites may favor the spread of local excitatory processes that arise under the influence of afferent impulses.

The stellate cells with short axons have synapses present on their cell bodies, as well as on the dendrites. According to the investigations of Entin (1954), these synapses are usually spheroidal, oval, triangular or egg-like in form; and very small in size, not exceeding 2 to 2.5 microns. Often the nerve fiber divides, forming two to three ramifications, each one either ending in a loop or running along the dendrites before forming an ending. All the axodendritic synapses are of the same type as the axosomatic ones. The fibers run over the dendrites for a great distance after their bifurcation (Figure 99). Entin feels that the predominant number of loop-like synapses, particularly large and middle-sized ones, represent the endings of the afferent fibers arising from the subcortical centers.

Furthermore, Entin states that in the fourth layer the synapses are most dense and are distributed on large stellate cells with descending

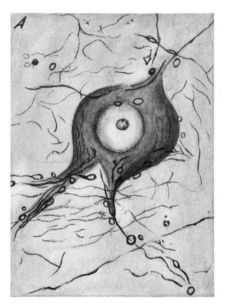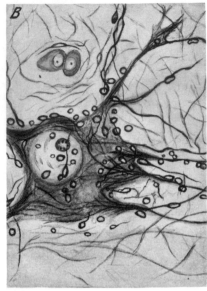

Fig. 99

Synapses. *A*, Synapses on a stellate cell from the fourth layer of area 18.
B, Synapses on a large stellate cell with a long descending axon, from the
fourth layer of area 17. The ring-form and loop-form synapses are seen on
the cell body as well as on the dendrites. The whole cell is covered, in addition, by thin fibers. (Entin, 1954.)

axons, which according to Ramon y Cajal, are specific cellular elements
of the visual area. However, these cells should hardly be considered
as stellate cells; rather they should be considered as specialized neurons derived from the projectional pyramidal neurons, having for
their function the control of the orienting eye movements. Their
axons run down into the white matter and end in the superior colliculi,
where the nuclei of oculomotor mechanisms are located. They are
differentiated from the projectional efferent pyramidal neurons by the
absence of apical dendrites (Figure 103: cells 9 and 12).

A direct activation of stellate cells of the first group, in the fourth
and third layers, probably arises normally through the thalamic afferent neurons of the specific system. As is known, these afferent fibers
terminate mostly in the fourth layer, but a small part of the collaterals
penetrate layer III, as well as layer V. Figure 100 shows the distribution
of thalamic fibers in the same areas of the visual analyzers of a cat.

Characteristically, the ending of a single afferent thalamic fiber

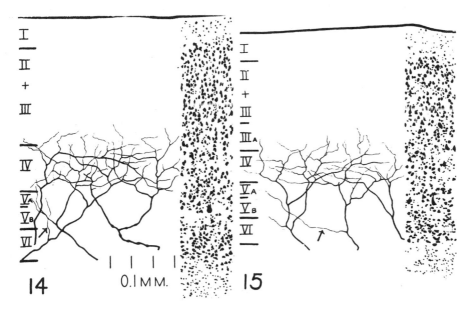

Fig. 100

Specific afferent thalamic fibers in the visual analyzer of the cat. Parts of the area striata are represented. On the right side of each drawing are seen relative widths of the cortical layers; the arrows indicate fine collaterals which run into the fifth layer. (O'Leary, 1941.)

forms such wide ramifications that it may cover several stellate cells of the first group (Figures 78 and 87). However in the third layer one finds the endings of the axons of associational pyramids also contributing to the neural activation of the stellate neurons. The stellate neurons of the second group may also be activated by different fibers; that is, by thalamic specific fibers in the fourth and third layers when they are present, as well as by the associational pyramidal neurons in all other layers. Characteristically the associational fibers from the middle-sized pyramids, connecting different segments of the cortex through the white subcortical matter, terminate mostly in the second and third layers of the cortex and do not end in the fourth layer where the stellate neurons of the first group predominate. Obviously the associational neurons may activate the stellate cells of the fourth layer through the internuncial, pyramidal neurons or the stellate cells with descending axons (O'Leary and Bishop, 1938, Poljakov and Sarkisov, 1949).

FUNCTIONAL CHARACTERISTICS

There are reasons to believe that the subjective reflection of the outside world (feeling, perception, images, mental representation) arises in the primary area of the analyzers under the influence of specific afferent impulses. The observations in man indicate that there is a coincidence between the emergence of primary electrical potentials in this zone of the analyzers and the subjective perceptions of the stimuli which cause these potentials. For example in cases where the subject's attention is distracted by intense intellectual activity such as an attempt to solve a mathematical problem, the amplitude of primary potentials evoked in the cortex by peripheral stimuli or by stimulation of the ascending thalamic tract is lowered. At the same time the subjective feelings arising from these peripheral stimuli are decreased (Hernández-Peón *et al.*, 1959).

Furthermore the observations on humans during surgical operations show that only during electrical stimulation of the primary areas of the analyzers do subjective elementary perceptions arise. The patient perceives light, color, ringing of a bell, feeling of touch, trembling of fingers, etc., depending upon the area stimulated. All these perceptions, however, are very elementary, and are never images of certain definite external events (Penfield, 1952). This is understandable because the emegrence of images implies the participation of a certain complex of cortical neurons spatially disturbed in various areas of the cortex, the simultaneous activation of which cannot be accomplished by electrical stimulation in limited areas of the cortex.

We believe that the web-like cells with pericellular reticulum in the third and fourth layers of the primary areas of analyzers, constitute those neural elements of the cortex which are affected by specific afferent stimulation and which cause a subjective elementary perception during their activation. This is why the stellate cells with a pericellular reticulum could be called sensory cells.

Stellate cells with short axons constitute the greatest number of cells in the cerebral cortex of man. Of the 14 billions of cells, which are presumed to be contained in the human brain, more than half are stellate cells. According to Poljakov (1956), in the fourth layer of the primary areas of the somesthetic analyzer, which is located in the post central gyrus in man and primates, more than half of the total number of cells are stellate cells.

According to Ramon y Cajal, the predominance of stellate cells in the fourth layer is the anatomic correlate for the differentiated functioning of the human brain. Lorente de Nó agrees with the preceding statement (1944). According to Poljakov and Sarkisov (1949), this predominance of neurons with short axons constitutes the main difference between the cerebral cortex of man and that of animals, and these cells account for the greater complexity and structural perfection of the human cerebral cortex.

All this suggests that the stellate cells of the third and fourth layers of the cortex, particularly those which are surrounded by a reticulum of axonal ramifications, bear a direct relationship to the highest function of the cerebral cortex, namely, the subjective perceptions of the outside world. One may assume that a basic characteristic of the stellate cells is the capacity for generating differential perceptions when they are stimulated. From these perceptions, images of the perceived objects are formed and are projected into the environment (Beritoff, 1956b).

As is well known, the high level of excitability in the sensory stellate neurons, which produces the perception of outside objects and their projection into the environment, is influenced by certain regions of the nonspecific reticular formation in the lower brainstem. It is known that after an ablation of the nonspecific system, or after its physiologic elimination through inhibition, the animal ceases to perceive the outside world.

It follows that the readiness or the ability of the sensory stellate cells to be activated by outside stimuli is entirely a function of the reticular system. The level of excitability or sensibility necessary for the perception of the environment, is thus determined by means of nonspecific afferent impulses which affect these stellate neurons.

As was stated earlier, the presence on the stellate neurons of synapses formed between their own recurrent axonal ramifications and their own dendrites, and even with their own cell bodies, results in self-stimulation. Therefore, each time these cells are stimulated their excitatory state reaches maximal intensity. It seems possible that this maximal intensity of stimulation is a prerequisite for this subjective perception of an object and its projection into the environment.

Web-like stellate cells are also found in the fifth and sixth layers of the cortex (Figure 91: cell 26; Figure 95: cell 28), but this should not be surprising because afferent specific fibers may also penetrate these layers. At any rate, in man according to Poljakov (1953) and in cats according to O'Leary (1941) such fibers do terminate in the fifth layer (see Figure 100).

The psychoneural characteristics of the stellate cells of the fourth layer should not be considered merely as a consequence of the external structure of the neurons. These external characteristics, namely, the multiple ramifications of its axons and dendrites constituting a pericellular reticulum, are well adapted for maximal activation of these cells under the influence of afferent impulses. This is why stellate cells, and even web-like cells, may also be found in other divisions of the brain—not just in the cortex. Such functions as the generation of differential subjective perceptions and their projection into the environment, constitute a phylogenetic achievement in neuronal cytoplasm. As Setchenov indicated, mental representations and images constitute the main regulator of behavior of the highest vertebrates; it is the highest form of biologic adaptation (Beritoff, 1948). Without doubt the external forms of sensory neurons may vary a great deal. Probably the web-like form of sensory stellate cells, without connections with other cells, is most characteristic in the highest vertebrates and man.

The observed absence of direct interconnections among many web-like cells must have a profound biologic significance. These cells must enter simultaneously into active states under the influence of the environment in order to create concrete images of it. The spread of excitatory processes within the system of stellate neurons could only prevent the creation of such an image-like perception of the outside world, with rapid changes of such images mirroring the variability of outside events.

The most pertinent fact is that most of the web-like stellate cells do not have axonal connections with pyramidal cells. Only a few such connections are required for the generation of a simple orienting movement of the head. It is therefore suggested that their basic if not sole function is to produce subjective reflections of the outside world and to create images of it.

The images of the outside world, once mentally reproduced, regulate animal behavior in the same way as direct perceptions of the environment. When a hungry animal sees food in a certain place, it runs to this place because of its visual perception and the image which emerged at that time. If after such a perception occurred, the location of food is shielded in such a way that the animal cannot see it, the animal will reach it by going around the obstacle. This can take place because of a projected image of the food location behind the screen. The same kind of psychoneural mechanisms affect a hungry animal when an image of the food location is reproduced under the influence of some object from the environment where the food was previously found (Beritoff, 1956b). Under the influence of such images, the animal will run to the location of the food just as it would if it saw

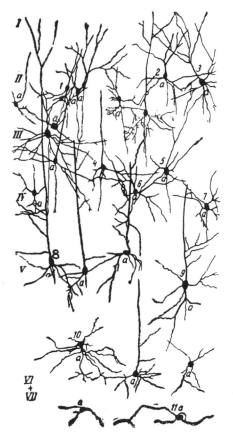

Fig. 101

Neurons of the visual analyzer of the cerebral cortex of hedgehog. *1, 2, 3,* Cells of the second layer; *4,* pyramidal cell of the third layer; *6, 7,* stellate cells of the fourth layer; *8,* pyramidal cell of the fifth layer; *a,* axon. (Shkolnik-Yarros, 1954.)

it there. These instances demonstrate an inborn drive to get food following the image of its location.

The sensory receptive functions of stellate cells of the third and fourth layers can be better understood in terms of the cells' histologic structure as seen when comparing the primary zones of analyzers among various species of mammals and when the primary and secondary areas of the same analyzer are compared. In an animal with poorly developed vision, the hedgehog, the fourth layer in area 17 of the visual analyzer is also poorly developed and the stellate cells are very rare. (Figure 101) (Shkolnik-Yarros, 1954 and 1958a, b). In dogs, which have better vision, the fourth layer is much more developed and contains a considerable number of stellate cells (Figure 102). In lower monkeys, animals with strongly developed visual-orienting and investigating reactions, the fourth layer of area 17 is still thicker; it is divided into three dense cellular layers containing a great number of different stellate cells (Figure 103).

Let us compare the primary area of the visual analyzer area with its secondary regions, areas 18 and 19; the difference in cellular distribution is clearly seen. In areas 18 and 19, where no visual afferents terminate, the stellate cells are rare (Figure 104). Here in the second, third and fourth layers pyramids predominate; whereas, the larger Cajal cells and their smaller forms, serving as we believe for the elicitation of oculomotor reactions, are not seen. These latter cells are characteristically found in area 17.

It is also characteristic in both man and higher mammals that in the cortex of the motor analyzer, where clearly differentiated subjective feelings are not a significant feature, the fourth layer typical for other analyzers is not present. Correspondingly the stellate cells in the motor cortex are very rare; rather they are distributed in all the cortical layers (Zhukova, 1953). This is further reason to believe that subjective perception of the outside world is connected with the presence of stellate cells in the fourth layer.

INHIBITION

We previously considered the mechanisms of inhibition in the case of pyramidal neurons. Now we will take up the question of inhibition in stellate neurons with short axons.

The stellate neurons with short axons are provided in most cases with a relatively small number of dendrites which are also short. In addition the dendrites of stellate neurons do not have the lateral thorny spines, or if they do they are very rare. But in contradistinction to the dendrites of the pyramidal neurons, they have small bead-like swellings all along their dendrites.

We assumed above that the dendrites of the stellate neurons may conduct a local excitatory process up to the cell bodies thus participating in the generation there of conducted impulses. Therefore, in stellate neurons with short axons, axodendritic as well as axosomatic synapses seemingly have excitatory functions.

How then does inhibition of stellate neurons occur? There are many facts which suggest that under certain conditions the excitability

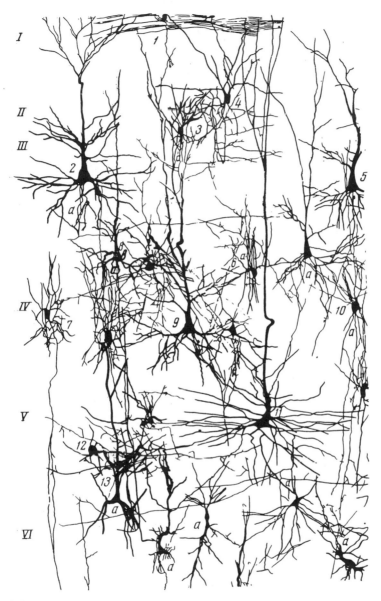

Fig. 102

Neurons of area 17 in the visual analyzer of a dog. *1*, Cell of the first layer; *3*, *4*, stellate cells of the second layer; *2*, *5*, pyramidal cells of the third layer; *8*, *9*, pyramidal cells of the fourth layer; *7*, *10*, stellate cells of the fourth layer; *11*, large pyramidal cell of the fifth layer; *12*, stellate cell of the fifth layer. (Shkolnik-Yarros, 1954.)

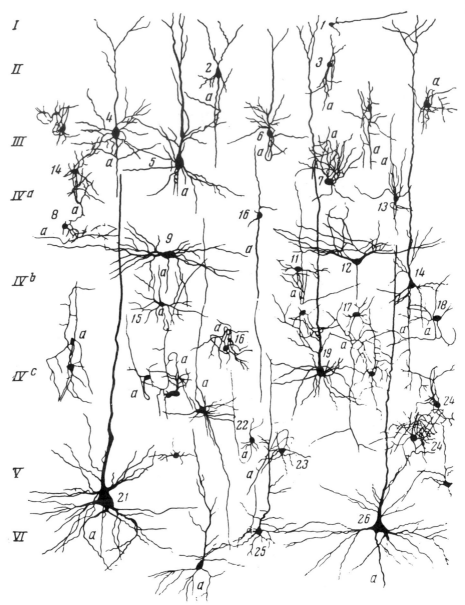

Fig. 103

Neurons of field 17 in visual analyzer of a monkey. *2*, Pyramidal cell of layer
II; *4*, *5*, *6*, pyramidal cells of layer *III*; *10*, small pyramidal cell of sublayer
IVa; *9*, *12*, stellate cells of sublayer *IVb*; *7*, *8*, *13*, stellate cells of sublayer
IVa; *11*, *15*, *17*, *18*, small stellate cells of sublayer *IVc*; *19*, pyramidal cell
of sublayer *IVc*; *21*, *26*, large pyramidal cells of layer V. (Shkolnik-Yarros,
1954.)

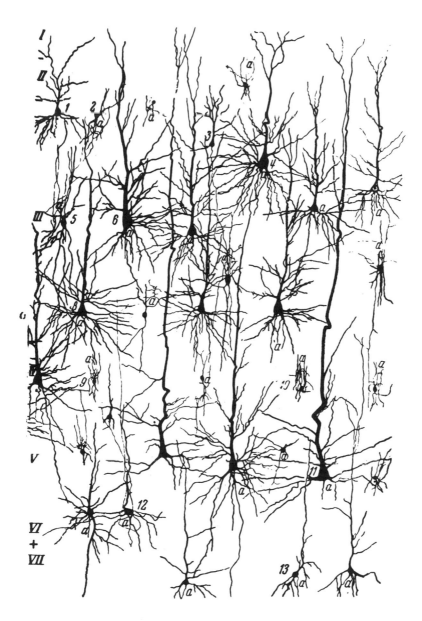

Fig. 104

Neurons of field 19 in visual analyzer of a monkey. *1, 3, 4, 6, 8,* Pyramidal cells of the second and third layers; *5, 7,* bush-like cells of the third layer; *9, 10,* stellate cells of the fourth layer; *11,* pyramidal cell of the fifth layer. (Shkolnik-Yarros, 1954.)

of stellate neurons decreases, leading to a depression of their activity. Thus during stimulation of the cortex, not only is spontaneous electrical activity inhibited, but also inhibited are primary evoked potentials arising, for example, in the primary area of the auditory analyzer as a result of stimulation of the auditory receptor. How could this depression of the primary evoked potentials occur without the primary inhibition of the stellate neurons? This inhibition of the primary potentials to which stellate cells undoubtedly contribute, could be the result of a secondary effect, namely, a depression in the activity of other neurons participating in the generation of primary potentials. In other words, one may assume that the stellate neurons continually receive many impulses from internuncial and associative neurons of the cortex, as well as from the nonspecific thalamic fibers, and in this way maintain their high susceptibility to the stimuli transmitted from the periphery along specific afferent thalamic pathways. A suppression of this intercellular bombardment may bring about, according to our concept, a decrease in the excitability of the stellate neurons and thereby decrease their susceptibility to incoming volleys.

No physiologic facts were discovered which could prove the existence of a primary inhibition of stellate cells receiving specific thalamic volleys. It is true that there is inhibition as well as facilitation of cortical reflex reactions. However, the experiments in man seem to indicate that when we observe the arrest of an external reaction, this is not due to an inhibition of the stellate afferent neurons. For instance during the differentiation or extinction of conditioned reflexes to an external stimulus, the perception of this stimulus persists despite the disappearance of the reflex. Obviously then, at that time the transmitting internuncial and associational neurons as well as the projectional pyramidal neurons themselves, may be inhibited, but not the stellate cells, which are the receptive cells of peripheral stimuli.

Even in animal experiments, during the differentiation or the extinction of a conditioned reflex, it can be shown that there is no inhibition of cortical afferent neurons. It is well known, for example, that in the case of an extinguished reflex, a differential or a conditional stimulation does not generate external reactions, but does depress other conditioned reflexes. This, of course, could not be observed without activation of the stellate cells of the corresponding analyzers.

However, it is generally known that when the cerebral cortex in a man or animal is involved in some important activity, it does not react significantly to many outside stimuli; in fact, they may not even be perceived. And yet even this observation does not indicate that there is inhibition in the stellate cells not directly involved in the important activity under consideration. When stellate neurons stop reacting to external stimuli, this may merely reflect a decrease in their excitability due to the inhibition of the nonspecific activating system and of the internuncial as well as association neurons which ordinarily facilitate and integrate their activity.

Lazarev (1918) assumed and Gerard, Marshall and Saul (1936) confirmed the fact that the facilitating interaction of auditory and visual perceptions takes place in the subcortex. Specifically, in the colliculi and in the geniculates of a cat, an increase in the amplitude of evoked potentials generated by auditory stimuli was observed under the influence of an extraneous visual stimulus (Kravkov, 1950). It is possible that the decrease in visual sensitivities during a very intense auditory stimulation originates in the subcortical regions as a result of central inhibition and depressed state in the subcortical nuclei of the visual system.

During normal sleep the excitability of the cortex in response to peripheral stimuli is significantly decreased. Not only are external reactions in response to the outside stimuli suspended, but also their perception. This can be explained other than on the basis of inhibition in the receptive afferent elements of the cortex, the stellate neurons. It may depend, of course, upon the inhibition of internuncial and associational neurons, as well as on inhibition of the intermediary transmitting nuclei of the subcortex. Particularly important may be the role played by the inhibition of nuclei in the brainstem which transmit peripheral volleys to the cortex, so that at the onset of sleep, afferent bombardment of the cortex may be more or less suppressed. This situation has considerable importance with regard to the level of excitability in the stellate neurons, because as indicated above a high level of cortical excitability depends upon a continuous bombardment from the receptors through the reticular formation.

Thus the stellate cells with short axons, receiving afferent volleys from the receptors and producing subjective feelings, do not have to be subject to direct inhibition. But their sensibility to specific afferent volleys depends upon a certain high level of excitability, which in turn is maintained by a continuous bombardment relayed through the reticular formation, each decrease of this bombardment presumably leading to a cessation of activity in the stellate neurons.

Organization of Cortical Neurons for the Formation of Images of the Outside World

On the basis of the previous analysis of characteristics of the neural elements of the cerebral cortex, we suggested that subjective feelings, such as differentiated perception, are generated by the stellate cells of the third and fourth layers, the terminal points for the afferent thalamic fibers, carrying the peripheral volleys from the receptors. The pyramidal neurons must serve for the integration of cortical neurons between them and for the generation of cortical inhibition. Now the question before us is to conjecture in which way the sensory stellate neurons and pyramidal associative neurons may determine the emergence and reproduction of images of the outside world.

Afferent Systems

The afferent thalamic fibers, originating in the specific nuclei of the thalamus, so-called specific afferent fibers, end exclusively in the third and fourth layers of the primary areas of analyzers. They therefore synapse mainly with the web-like and other stellate neurons with short axons, the pyramidal neurons the axons of which do not leave the limits of the cerebral cortex, so-called internuncial neurons, and with medium-sized pyramids of the third and fourth layers which have associative functions (Figures 78, 95 and 100) (O'Leary and Bishop, 1938; O'Leary, 1941; Lorente de Nó, 1934; Poljakov, 1953). Figure 105 shows these structural relationships. One can see that afferent fibers from the geniculates synapse with stellate cells having short axons, as well as with so-called Cajal cells with long axons, which as will be shown below probably serve for the generation of orienting reactions of the eyes.

Afferent fibers originating in the reticular formation presumably end in all the areas of the cerebral cortex, and probably synapse in all of its layers. Through these so-called nonspecific fibers, the whole cortex may be activated (Lorente de Nó, 1944, Dempsey and Morison, 1943, Moruzzi and Magoun, 1949, Jasper, 1949). Jasper showed that the stimulation of nonspecific nuclei in the thalamus elicits electrical effects in all layers of the cortex, whereas with the stimulation of specific thalamic fibers and nuclei, electrical effects are recorded only in the third and fourth layers.

Stimulation of a part of the ascending thalamic system, the so-called thalamic reticular formation, results in general or partial inhibition of the cortex. This functional particularity of this division of the thalamic afferent system must have a structural basis. We believe that afferent fibers of the nonspecific thalamic system synapse with apical dendrites in the first and second layers. This is illustrated in Figures 88 and 105.

The stimulation of other parts of the nonspecific reticular formation in the brainstem, elicits a general facilitation in the form of a desynchronization of electrical activity, with a decrease in the amplitude of slow waves, and an increase in fast activity. Seemingly, this occurs because these nonspecific fibers synapse with the dendrites of stellate neurons, as well as with the cell bodies of pyramidal neurons in the third and fourth layers of the cortex, thus participating in the formation of the appropriate neuronal circuits (Roitbak, 1955).

However, as Figure 105 shows, in area 19, there are stellate cells which receive the afferent messages from the retina relayed through the pulvinar. What then would be the significance of this neuronal substrate? Experimentally, it is known that after the ablation of the primary areas of the visual analyzers, the conditioned activity to visual stimuli persist. The animal looses object vision, does not differentiate visual patterns, but may form reflexes to light and differentiate it from darkness. This general ability to perceive light probably depends not upon visual fibers relayed in the geniculates, but upon those relayed in the pulvinar synapsing with the stellate cells of the fourth layer in area 19.

As was indicated above, in area 17, there are many Cajal cells with long axons ending in the superior colliculi. As Figure 105 shows, one finds on their cell bodies synapses of afferent thalamic fibers from the lateral geniculate, some of them being relayed by stellate cells. We believe that these Cajal cells, together with the Meynert cells, constitute a "starting mechanism" for orienting oculomotor and cephalogyric movements. When the retina of a man or animal is affected by some object, then the affected visual fibers running in the specific pathway not only activate a certain complex of visual sensory stellate cells, but simultaneously energize the starting mechanism for the eye fixation upon this object for its better perception. One may state that the perception of an object and fixation of the eyes upon it constitute a total process. This important physiologic observation is very well illustrated in Figure 105 as described by Shkolnik-Yarros.

Yet excitation in the reticular formation is conducted more or less selectively. Thus, the stimulation of each receptor generates afferent bombardment through a pathway relayed by the reticular formation of the thalamus, predominantly in the area of the corresponding

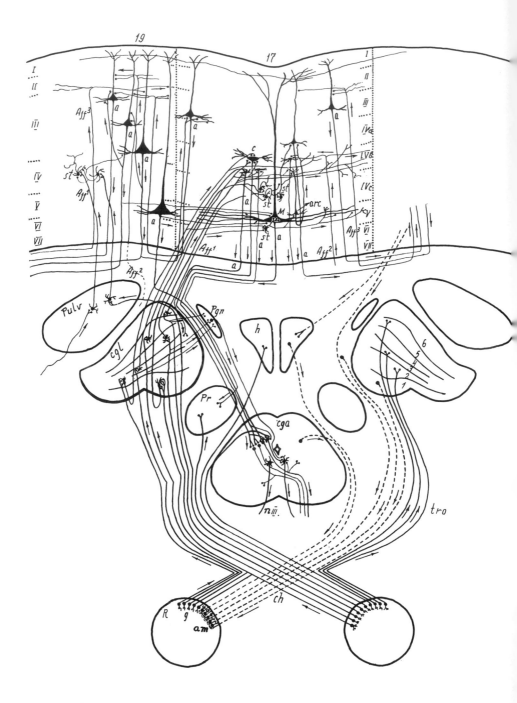

analyzer, in the same locus where the afferent impulses from this receptor arrive via the specific pathway.

In addition, by local electrical stimulation of different parts of the reticular formation of the thalamus, one may predominantly influence corresponding areas of the cortex (Hanbery and Jasper, 1953). With repeated and more intense stimulation, the excitation may spread from a given area of the reticular formation projected predominantly to a certain analyzer, to the whole reticular formation and thus affect other analyzers as well (Roitbak, 1957, 1958a).

ASSOCIATION SYSTEMS AND NERVOUS CIRCUITS

Afferent thalamic fibers of the specific system do not synapse directly with cortical cells of the projectional efferent pyramidal neurons in the fifth and sixth layers. They are connected with them via the internuncial pyramidal neurons and the stellate cells of the second group. Some pyramidal neurons are connected with the projectional pyramids of remote cortical areas in a more complex way, through a chain of internuncial and associational neurons.

Association fibers, running from one area to another, end essentially in the second and third layers and, to a lesser degree, in other layers. Seemingly they also synapse with stellate as well as with pyramidal neurons (Figure 78*e* and *f* and Figure 79).

According to Poljakov (1956), the terminal axonal arborizations of the association neurons in the second and third layers differ essentially from those found in the deeper layers. They branch intensely in the

---

Fig. 105

A schematic representation of neuronic connections in the visual analyzer (areas 17 and 19). Roman numerals indicate the cortical layers; area 19 on the left, area 17 on the right. Limits of the layers are indicated by dotted lines. Area 18 is not represented. The middle of this figure shows subcortical formations; at bottom is the retina. *c*, Stellate cells of Cajal with long axons; *st*, stellate cells with short axons; *Aff¹*, specific afferents from the lateral geniculate; *Aff²*, vertical afferents of unknown origin; *Aff³*, association afferent; *M*, pyramidal cell of Meynert; *arc*, pyramidal cell with an arc-like axon; *a*, axons of pyramidal cells; *Pulv*, pulvinar; *cgl*, lateral geniculate; *Pgn*, anterior genicular nucleus; *h*, hypothalamus; *Pr*, pretectal nucleus; *cga*, superior colliculi; *nIII*, oculomotor nerve; *ch*, chiasma; *R*, retina; *g*, ganglion cells of retina; *am*, amacrine cells; *tro*, optic tract; arabic figures indicate the layers of the lateral geniculate. (By Shkolnik-Yarros based on her own studies and data found in the literature.)

more superficial layers and each arborization forms a fine and dense net covering the cell bodies and dendrites of the local pyramidal internuncial and stellate neurons (1956). These association neurons probably serve for the integration of the activity of the receptive sensory neurons, in other words, for the formation of the images of objects perceived by way of different receptors.

All the small and middle-sized pyramidal neurons with descending and ascending axons, as well as stellate cells with horizontal and vertical axons (group 2), form closed circuits in which each cellular link is connected with the others either directly or through several other neurons. In each given sector of the cortex, these neurons form closed circuits in the vertical direction, ensuring two-way intercellular connections between different layers, as well as in the horizontal direction, between the different areas of the cortex. Two-way connections between the more or less distant sectors of the cortex are represented not only in the cortical layers by means of internuncial neurons, but also in the subcortical white matter through the association neurons. However, the presence of closed neuronal circuits does not yet indicate that excitation of one of the links will generate necessarily a circulating excitatory process in this circuit. It is assumed that a free transmission of the excitation of one segment of this circuit to another is a consequence developed through individual life experiences and it occurs only under certain conditions.

These neuronal circuits involving associative two-way connections are formed in the superficial layers of the cortex, the second, third and fourth layers. Ariens Kappers *et al.* (1936) offer several arguments favoring the view that these layers constitute both the highest receptive as well as the highest associative neuronal substrate. Particularly great is the role played by the second and third layers where the small and middle-sized pyramidal neurons with the descending and ascending axons are preeminent. Characteristically in the primary area of the visual analyzer the axons of many pyramidal neurons run through the fourth layer without giving off collaterals to this layer (O'Leary, 1941). This indicates that in layer four the receptive function is preeminent because of the predominance there of the receptive stellate cells and endings of the afferent thalamic fibers.

Projectional pyramidal neurons may not participate in the formation of these cortical circuits because their collaterals, with the exclusion of those which ascend without branching to the first layer, do not leave the limits of the corresponding fifth layer. Besides, these collaterals essentially synapse with the proximal dendritic formations of the pyramidal neurons. The axons of the projectional pyramidal neurons leaving the cortex seldom give off collaterals (Bechterew, 1898, Lorente de Nó, 1933, 1944, O'Leary and Bishop, 1938). However, efferent projectional pyramidal neurons terminating in the intermediate divisions of the brain participate in the formation of neuronal circuits integrating the cortex and these areas, namely, the thalamus and its specific nuclei as well as its reticular formation. Obviously, extrapyramidal pathways and afferent thalamic fibers constitute the essential segments of these neuronal circuits.

The dendrites of pyramidal neurons with thorny spines may not participate in the formation of the neuronal loops, for as indicated above, they conduct excitation with a considerable decrement, and therefore the impulses may not reach the cell body.

INTEGRATION OF ANALYZERS

The integration of more or less complex neuronal constellations presupposes the presence of a certain integrating center. In order to integrate the receptive elements of one analyzer, this center should be located at its periphery. Thus, for instance, for the visual stellate cells it will be found in areas 18 and 19. For the integration of the receptive elements of different analyzers, this integrating center should be found between them, in so-called associative areas, mainly the frontal and temporal ones. This hypothesis was formulated by Ebbecke (1919), Goldstein (1927), Blumenau (1930) and Beritoff (1932). At the present time it is shared by several other scientists (Penfield, Jasper and others).

The observations of Penfield (1952, 1954) that stimulation of the temporal lobes in man may elicit auditory and visual memory of past events, shows that the temporal lobes constitute mainly a field for the association of auditory and visual perceptions. This belief has a histologic basis in the work of Bechterew (1898), Flechsig (1896a, b) and Poljakov and Sarkisov (1949) related to the ontogenesis of the cerebral cortex of man.

The way in which sensory neurons of the primary area of an analyzer are integrated is schematically represented in Figure 106 which illustrates this integration in the case of the visual analyzer. The afferent visual fibers, *A. vis.*, coming from the thalamus terminate in area 17 on stellate and internuncial neuron cells of layer IV and also on the oculomotor neuron cell. These stellate and internuncial neurons are connected with association neurons, A^3, A^4, and with a Meynert cell, M; the thalamic fiber is also connected with the Meynert cell via stellate cell, S^3. During excitation of the thalamic visual fibers this neuronal system produces perception of the object that caused the stimulation of these fibers, and elicits, on the other hand, an orienting movement of the head and eyes in order to fixate the eyes on the object.

The axons from association neurons A^3 and A^4 of the visual area 17 pass to area 19 and here terminate on cells of internuncial neurons B^3 and B^4, the axons of which converge upon association cell A^2. The axon of this cell passes to area 17 ending here on the cells of intermediate neurons of layer IV and, more frequently, on the intermediate cells of layer II. The axons of the latter terminate on the stellate neurons of layer IV. During visual perception all these nervous connections are excited too and a functionally integrated system is created which is retained for some time serving to reproduce images of the whole object even if only one part of it is perceived by the eye.

In Figure 106, a collateral of the association neuron axon A^2 ends in area 17 on an intermediate cell T, the axon of which enters into contact with the dendrites in the upper layers, in exactly the same manner as the association neuron axons A^3 and A^4, passing to area 19 form collaterals terminating mainly on dendrites of the upper layers. Activation of dendrites of adjacent intermediate and association neurons is elicited through these collaterals and thus causes their general inhibition. This secures a localized excitation in this functional system. The cortical connections with nonspecific thalamic fibers are not represented.

Figure 107 shows diagrammatically the integration of the sensory neurons of two different analyzers. Under the influence of an object certain thalamic fibers, A. *aud.* and A. *vis.*, activate in corresponding analyzers sensorial stellate neurons of layer IV, P^1 to P^4, as well as intermediate neurons B^3 to B^5; B^{12} to B^{14}. Association neurons of analyzers, A^1, A^2, A^5, A^6, are activated via these neurons. Their axons run to the association area, where they converge upon the intermediate neurons B^6 and B^7. The latter activate association cells, A^4, the axons of which pass to acoustic and visual analyzers and terminate there on the intermediate neurons of layers II and IV. In addition, through these neurons, both the sensory neurons, P^1 to P^4, and the motor projection neurons of the eyes and the head, Py, M, C, are activated. Activity of this whole neuronal constellation produces perception and creates the visual-auditory image of the given object. This functional constellation is retained for some time. That is why, if any part of the given object acts upon the auditory or visual organ, the whole neuronal constellation reproducing the image of the perceived object is activated; this is followed by an adequate orienting reaction of the head.

19 field of the visual analyzer | 17 field of the visual analyzer

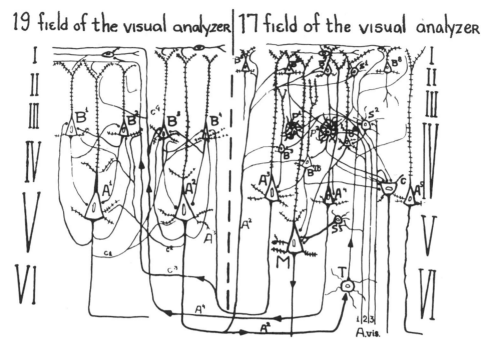

Fig. 106

Schematic representation of neuronal circuits in the visual area producing visual perception and orienting reaction. P^1, P^2, Sensory stellate neurons; S^1, S^2, S^3, transmitting stellate neurons (group II); B^1 to B^{11}, internuncial neurons; A^1 to A^5, association neurons; M, Meynert's pyramid projection neuron; C, Cajal's projection oculomotor neuron; T, Martinotti internuncial neuron; $A.$ $vis.$, afferent visual fibers. (See text for explanation of diagram.)

Sensory stellate neurons, group 1, the axons of which generally branch in the vicinity of their own cells and seemingly having no synapse with the soma of other neurons, do not constitute intermediate links of the neuronal circuits. These cells may be activated by the neuronal circuits, directly through their collaterals or through internuncial neurons, although the axons of the stellate cells do not have connections with these loops. With this functional structure, the system of sensory neurons, as indicated above, is not always able to elicit directly external behavior such as an orienting reaction. We must assume that those afferent visual fibers which will activate a certain complex of sensory neurons generating a perception of the outside world, will at the same time activate the starting mechanism for the

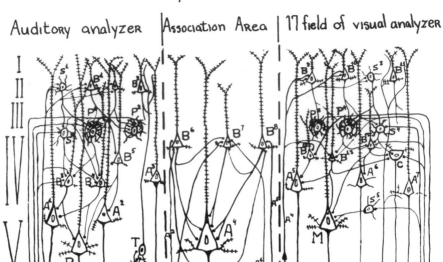

Fig. 107

Schematic representation of nervous circuits integrating acoustic and visual analyzers for reception and creation of image of a sound-eliciting object. Symbols for this figure are the same as for Figure 106. (See text for explanation.)

orienting reaction directly or with the participation of internuncials: see Figure 108, page 290. In other words, we must assume that those neuronal loops which activate a certain complex of sensory neurons, generating an image of some outside object, will at the same time activate in the cortex a corresponding starting mechanism for the orienting reaction (Figures 106 and 107).

Physiologic observations also support the belief that the receptive neuronal elements do not directly constitute a link of a closed neuronal loop. As is known, conditioned reflexes are formed through the cortex. They may be formed to stimuli which are not subjectively perceived, for example, stimuli arriving from the muscle receptors, tendons and viscera as well as those below the threshold, namely, subthreshold extraceptive stimuli, such as studies by Gershuni point out (1947, 1949a, b). In these conditioned reflexes, pyramidal neurons and also stellate neurons with long axons (group 2) which do not generate subjective perceptions, necessarily participate in the formation of the neuronal connections or neuronal circuits. Even during the formation of conditioned reflexes to stimuli that are subjectively perceived, the temporary connections may arise without direct involvement of the sensory stellate cells, as a participant link of these loops. This hypothesis is consistent with the observed behavior following concussion in pigeons, cats and dogs who sustained a blast of moderate intensity. The behavior observed was that psychoncural activity, such as the remembering of where food was located, disappeared. At the same time, the automatized food-getting behavior, learned before the blast and effected according to the principles of a conditioned chain reflex, was preserved without any change (Beritoff, 1945, Bregadze, 1945). This may be explained by an assumption that the blast, as do many other injuring agents, had its most severe effect on the highly developed sensory elements; if these formed an indispensable link in the neuronal loops then the conditioned activity should have also disappeared. One must therefore assume that the neuronal loops are connected with the sensory elements, indirectly, through the collaterals or through an additional system of internuncials.

ELECTRICALLY EVOKED ORIENTING REACTIONS

According to recent investigations of Kaada *et al.* (1954) the orienting reaction could be provoked by stimulation of the marginal zones of analyzers. This reaction proceeds more naturally than that provoked by stimulation of the central zone. Thus, Fingel and Kaada (1960) disclosed that in cats and in monkeys during stimulation of the occipital, temporal and parietal cortical areas, a typical alert reaction is produced (desynchronization of cortical activity, initial depression of cortical and reflex reactions). They also observed the turning of the eyes and of the head to the contralateral side when the marginal zones of the analyzers were stimulated near the corresponding associational fields. The course of this alert reaction is quite the same as during unilateral stimulation of the receptors. It is also accomplished by several autonomic changes, e.g., by mydriasis, alteration of respiration, cardiac rate, blood pressure, etc. In a word, a typical orienting reflex is obviously produced, associated with reproduction of an image projected into the contralateral side of the environment as if the animal perceived from only one side. The same alert reaction, i.e., orienting reflex, is produced during stimulation of the paleocortex. Kaada believes that analogous points are located in the marginal zones of the olfactory and gustatory projection areas.

It is known that the stimulation of the primary projection zone of the analyzer may also provoke the orienting movement of eyes and head. But according to the data of Kaada *et al.,* this reaction is not quite the same as the above-described one; it is elicited by a stronger stimulation. A weaker stimulation is not associated with desynchronization. Usually this reaction has a tonic character and is manifested by a steady deviation of the head to the contralateral side.

We may assume that the orienting reaction in response to the electrical stimulation of the projection area is produced by direct action of the electric current upon the triggering mechanism including the neurons of Cajal and Meynert. Under normal conditions this mechanism is immediately activated by afferent volleys and its activity favors better perception of the stimulating object. During the stimulation of the marginal zones of analyzers, the same mechanism is activated by means of excitation of the neural circuits which connect the marginal zone with the central one. Evidently, the stimulation of the marginal zone produces the reproduction of images and at the same time the alert state occurs followed by searching for the object. Apparently, during the perception of the environment, the stable connections between the triggering mechanism (neurons of Cajal and Meynert) and sensory neurons participating in this perception, become established. Therefore, during artificial stimulation of marginal zones, not only the images of the environment can be reproduced, but the orienting reaction corresponding to these images is also produced. Figure 105 shows that the association neurons of field 19 send their axons to field 17 where they supposedly terminate on the bodies of the neurons of Meynert.

INTEGRATIVE FUNCTION OF THE CORTEX

As to the significance of the receptive as well as the associative field in the general neuropsychologic activity of the cerebral cortex, Herrick (1956) expresses himself essentially in the same way as we did above. He finds that the analytical functions in the cortex are represented by sensory and motor projection fields. Here, the precise localization of specific functions occurs, forming on the surface of the cortex a sort of mosaic. The remaining part of the cortex, consisting of so-called association fields, constitutes an apparatus for integrative functions including conditioned reflexes, the generation and use of symbols and creative processes such as thinking, mental representation and imagination. These synthetic functions are not localized and cannot be represented as a mosaic; they form a constellation of neuronal discharges which spread from moment to moment through different cortical and subcortical regions.

According to Herrick, the contrasts between the above-described systems of cortical neurons become obvious when one compares the particularities of the primary area of the visual projectional area (area 17 of Brodmann) and the nearby associational cortex of the visual area 18. With normal vision, the objects of the external world show a point to point projection in the retina, and from there point to point projection to area 17. However, when these impulses are transferred from area 17 into area 18, then the representative mosaic disappears. This is replaced by a dynamic system of a completely different kind. If area 18 is injured and area 17 is not, then the patient is able to see very clearly, but he cannot recognize what he sees. Therefore, visual perception is conserved, while visual interpretation is lost. This does not mean that visual interpretation, as an act of consciousness, is localized in area 18. This only signifies that area 18 constitutes the first station in a very complex system of neuronal discharges that culminates in a visual picture, to which latent memory traces add meaning, all of this being then converged and projected. The intellectual act of perception is a function of all this complexity and not specific to any special part of it.

Thus, Herrick's concept of the morphologic organization of psychological life or function is very near to ours, as expressed above. The primary area of an analyzer represents that substrate which perceives outside stimuli and generates feelings. The perception of an object and its recognition, the emotions produced by an image, the mental representations and other higher manifestations of the psyche, all these depend upon the integrated activity of the whole remaining part of the brain.

In recent years this statement of Herrick's with which we agree was brilliantly illustrated by the experiments of Penfield, Jasper and their associates. They found that when man receives cortical stimulation in area 17 (calcarine fissure), visual perceptions such as light and shadows and different colors can arise; whereas, the stimulation of areas 18 and 19 elicits reproduction of the contours of an object at rest or in movement which may have characteristics of an elementary image. In view of this, a hypothesis was formulated that the calcarine fissure is a necessary station which generates visual perceptions in response to impulses arriving from the lateral geniculate, and then transmits them to areas 18 and 19 for integration and for the formation of mental images of external objects. Analogous hypotheses are made by them in relation to the auditory and somesthetic analyzers (Penfield and Jasper, 1954).

However, the above-mentioned authors do not indicate what constitutes the essential structural difference between the primary visual area 17 on the one hand, and the associative areas 18 and 19 on the other. Yet it is very probable that area 17 is responsible for visual perception because the stellate neurons are preeminent there and also because of the localization there of the starting mechanism for fixation of the eyes on an external object. In the remaining part of the visual cortex, the stellate neurons are rather poorly represented. However, in these other parts the internuncial and association neurons predominate; these serve to integrate the differential sensation into a perception as a whole, thus forming integrated images of environmental objects.

Therefore the integration of the sensory stellate neurons of an analyzer is carried out through the association neurons which are located around the primary receptive zone. However, the mutual integration of the sensory stellate neurons of the visual and auditory analyzers, occurs by means of association neurons in the associational fields of the parietal and the temporal cortex. In other words, each of these analyzers activated through its afferent fibers may in turn stimulate integrating neurons located in associative areas, so that a visuo-auditory image can be produced by a simultaneous involvement of the visual and auditory fields.

The stimulation of a given integrated complex of neuronal loops must lead at the same time to the activation of basal dendrites in the surrounding pyramidal system, as well as their apical dendrites in the superficial layer; therefore, when a complex of neurons is activated, the effects of its integration being that of a head orientation and the generation of images, such a complex becomes surrounded by a field of inhibition involving all the other neuronal circuits of the cortex. This permits a localization of the process responsible for an emergence of a given visuo-auditory image and for the corresponding orienting movements.

Cerebral Cortex and Orienting Reactions

The primary area of the visual analyzer, area 17, contains a great number of neurons with long axons descending into subcortex areas. These are Cajal "star cells" which, according to my interpretation, are a type of projectional efferent pyramids. They have no apical dendrites. According to Shkolnik-Yarros (1958a, b), the axons of these neurons can be followed to the superior colliculi in the mesencephalon where the coordinating apparatus for oculomotor movements is found. It seems that these neurons serve for the direction and fixation of the eyes upon an external object, including convergence of the eyes, the constriction of the pupils and the contraction of the muscle for accommodation of the lens. As is seen in Figure 105, the afferent thalamic pathways from the lateral geniculate synapse with the stellate cells with short axons as well as with the cells under consideration, namely, those with long axons. Also in area 17 are found the typical pyramidal cells of Meynert. They also are connected with afferent fibers from the lateral geniculates, and their axons also run into the mesencephalon. We believe that these neurons generate the activation of the coordinating apparatus for cephalogyric movement. Because such neuronal formations are not present in areas 18 and 19, it is apparent that these fields, in contradistinction to the area 17, do not serve for the primary perception of external objects. Incidentally, one may say that the absence of apical dendrites in these motor projectional neurons probably has a biologic significance. These neurons, just as the stellate neurons with short axons, must not be subjected to a diffuse inhibition, for visual perceptions require a continual focusing of the eyes upon the objects being perceived. Further argument supporting the idea that the neuronal apparatus in the visual cortex, consisting of cells of Cajal and Meynert, serves for the orienting reaction of the head and eyes is based on experiments in which a stimulation of this cortical area in one hemisphere produced orienting movements of the head and eyes to the opposite side. Such neuronal mechanisms must exist also in other analyzers, particularly in the somesthetic and auditory ones; in other words, in those analyzers which respond to external stimuli by orienting oculocephalogyric movements. According to the investigations of Bechterew and associates (1905), during stimulation of the areas represented in Figure 108 in one hemisphere, for instance in the right one, the head turns to the left; also both eyes move and converge, and at the same time there is a raising of the eyelids, dilatation of the pupils and even a contraction in the accommodation muscles of the lens. Thus, we see that in the analyzers of the cerebral cortex, there are starting mechanisms for generating the orienting of the head and eyes.

The pyramidal pathways of the cortical starting mechanisms for the orienting reactions must end in the superior colliculi and be integrated there, since all the motor nuclei for the eye muscles, eyelids, pupils and muscles of accommodation are located in the mesencephalon. Obviously too, in this integrating mechanism there must origi-

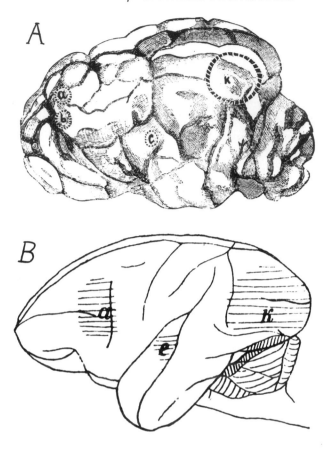

Fig. 108

A, Cerebrum of the dog, showing the areas initiating orienting reactions.
K, visual analyzers; a, b, skin analyzers; c, auditory analyzer. B, Cerebrum
of *Macacus rhesus*. Starting mechanisms of the orienting reactions. K, visual
analyzer; e, auditory analyzer; a, somasthetic analyzer. (Bechterew, 1905.)

nate coordinating volleys transmitted to the motor neurons of the
mesencephalon, the medulla and the spinal cord, effecting the orienting reaction of the head for the purpose of converging the eyes upon
the stimulating object.

As indicated above, the axons of the stellate neurons (group 2), as
well as those of some stellate neurons with pericellular axonal nets
(group 1), have terminal arborizations which synapse with the cell
bodies of a great number of internuncial and associational neurons.
It seems that in this way, the stellate cells manifest a very strong

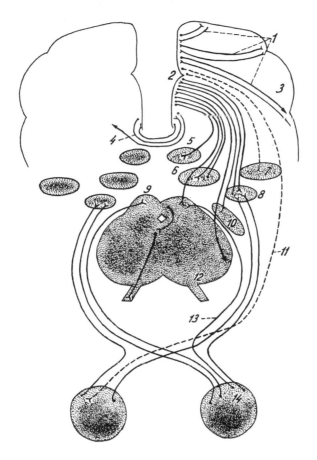

Fig. 109

Schematic representation of the efferent pathways of the visual cortex of carnivora. *1*, Association paths (short, middle, and long); *2*, cortical visual field; *3*, cortical field of other analyzers; *4*, commissural pathways (symmetrical and asymmetrical, marked by an arrow); *5*, pretectal nucleus; *6*, pulvinar; *7*, other nuclei of the thalamus (posterior, ventral and other); *8*, lateral geniculate; *9*, superior colliculus; *10*, internal capsule; *11*, retino-cortical tract; *12*, cerebral peduncle; *13*, visual tracts; *14*, retina. Afferent tracts are included only partially in this schematic representation. (Shkolnik-Yarros.)

excitatory influence upon those nearest internnuncial and associational neurons which generate orienting movements of the head. It follows, that in each analyzer a system of receptive neurons must be firmly connected, through internuncial and associational neurons, with the large efferent pyramids which are present in the same analyzer and which are responsible for effecting orienting movements of the head.

According to histologic investigations by Walberg and Brodal (1953), projectional pyramidal neurons are found not only in the motor area, but also in the temporal and occipital regions of the cortex. They terminate in great numbers in the cervical cord. A good illustration of these connections in relation to the visual analyzer is represented in Figure 109. In this figure, Shkolnik-Yarros gives a schematic representation of a great number of extrapyramidal efferent pathways running toward the pulvinar and other nuclei of the thalamus, namely, pretectal nucleus, lateral geniculate and superior colliculus. These afferent tracts are inborn, but of course they may become more or less developed by experiences during the life of an individual. It is understandable, therefore, that the activation of any analyzer necessarily leads to an orienting movement of the head.

In order to activate an analyzer, and thus elicit any external reaction in addition to the orienting ones, for instance, in order to elicit locomotion, or secretion, or the activation of any other external reaction through another analyzer, one must have several pairings of the activation of this analyzer with the onset of these reactions. Thus, new temporal connections are formed between the receptive stellate neurons of one or another analyzer, on one side and the motor mechanisms of the cortex and subcortex, on the other.

PART IV TEMPORARY CONNECTIONS AND CORTICAL INHIBITION

12 ORIGIN OF THE TEMPORARY CONNECTIONS BETWEEN VARIOUS PERCEPTIONAL NEURONS OF THE CORTEX AND WITH THE MOTOR MECHANISMS

Pavlov, about 1900, created a method for studying temporary connections in the formation of the conditioned salivary reaction in a sound-proof room; Bechterew, about 1906, used this method to investigate such connections in the establishment of a conditioned defensive reaction (leg withdrawal) when the animal was immobilized in a stand. Starting in 1916 we studied temporary connections in the formation of defensive motor reflexes, just as Bechterew did using the conditions of a restricted environment in the experimental chamber. But later, beginning in 1926, we studied the automatization of food-getting behavior by observation of free movements. All the considerable material which has been accumulated by such methods, and by those in the more recent studies made by electrophysiologists and morphologists investigating the cerebral cortex, will be used in explaining the mechanism involved in the formation of temporary connections.

The idea of temporary connections was presented by Pavlov more than 50 years ago, and it had reference to the possibility that new functional connections are formed between neuronal complexes in the cerebral cortex when they are activated simultaneously or consecutively. In the higher animals such temporary connections underlie all kinds of individually acquired reactions. The work of Pavlov and his students for more than 50 years has been concerned with a careful and complex investigation of the conditions under which temporary connections originate, their variability and their role in behavior. However, the very nature of temporary connections, that is, the physiologic and structural basis for their establishment and variability, has not been the object of continuous and minute analysis. Kupalov (1948) and Asratyan (1952) devoted special articles to the origin of temporary connections, but without up-to-date physiologic and structural knowledge of the cerebral cortex. In addition to the investigations by Pavlov and his school, studies of the formation of functional connections in the cerebral cortex were made by Bechterew as long ago as 1898 and by myself in 1926 and 1927. Later, such work was done again by myself in 1940 and 1948, by Sarkisov in 1948 and by Sepp in 1949. Our most recent attempt to elucidate the nature of temporary connections was published in an article entitled "Newest Data Concerning the Structure of the Cerebral Cortex in Relation to Individually Acquired Reflex Activity" (1940); it was reprinted in the second volume of "General Physiology of Muscle and Nervous Systems" (1948). We there considered temporary connections and their function from the point of view of the structure of the cerebral cortex as given us by Ramon y Cajal and Lorente de Nó, and other such physiologic information concerning the cerebral cortex which was known at that time. But even this attempt was schematic and deprived of specific formulations because we were using morphologic notions without considering their concrete content in each particular case. This was also true with regard to the physiologic basis for the temporary connections, inasmuch as many theoretical statements derived from research on the spinal cord were automatically applied to the cortex without adequate proof.

In the present attempt to elucidate the nature of temporary connections, we have used new factual material concerning the physiology and morphology of the cerebral cortex. While this present explanation expresses a further development of the concept we expressed during our first attempt, we offer new theoretical statements supported by experiments and which therefore seem to be more convincing.

Physiology of the Formation of Temporary Connections

As was shown before, and will be further discussed below, new temporary connections are formed at once between receptive stellate cells at the occurrence of the first simultaneous or consecutive stimulation. This does not happen for the simultaneous and consecutive stimulation involving the receptive cells and efferent neurons of the cortex; that is, during the formation of a conditioned reflex, temporary connections between them are formed and reinforced as a result of the repeated coincidence of their activation. Pavlov and Bechterew, as well as their pupils, studied this kind of temporary connection exclusively. Obviously when a conditioned defensive withdrawal of an extremity is formed to a sound by its association with electrical stimulation of the leg, temporary connections are found at first between the afferent neuronal structures of the auditory and somesthetic analyzers. But then, the unconditional stimulation elicits motor reactions (expressed by orienting movements of the head, as well as by more or less complex defense reactions related to the lifting of the leg and general escape behavior, such as yelping and increased respiration), so that, as a direct result of the stimulation of proprioceptors, an activation of the motor analyzer takes place. It is because of this process that the analyzer of the conditional stimulation becomes associated with the motor analyzer.

Ordinarily, with the first associations of the conditional stimulus with the unconditional one, one may observe only an orienting reaction of the head and a change in respiration in response to the conditional stimulus. For instance, in the case of a conditional stimulus of food-getting behavior, the dog turns its head toward the location of food, and in the case of painful stimulation, to the site of the stimulated skin. This reaction is elicited presumably because during the conditional stimulus there is a reproduction of the image either of the food location, or of the stimulated area, and this in turn produces a corresponding orienting reaction of the head.

As to the conditioned motor reaction of the extremities or a conditioned salivary reaction, such behavior occurs after several or many associations of conditional stimuli with unconditional ones. When the temporary connections between the analyzer of the conditional stimuli and the analyzer of the unconditional excitation reach an optimum development, activation of the efferent system of pyramidal neurons and the emergence of an external reaction, either secretion or leg withdrawal, will occur.

We believe that neuronal elements of the motor analyzer which receive proprioceptive stimuli, are connected with efferent pyramidal neurons by innate pathways involving internuncials. Such connections in postembryonal life are further developed by training.

It is quite possible that stimulation of the skin elicits simple leg withdrawal through the somesthetic analyzer because of the presence of developed neuronal pathways between this analyzer and the motor one. In other words, stimulation of the skin analyzer of any extremity activates the efferent system of pyramidal pathways of that extremity through the motor analyzer. However, a general defensive reaction, such as a movement of escape or attempts by the animal to free itself from the stand, must be elicited by other pathways as will be discussed below.

During the formation of a food-getting conditioned reflex to sound, temporary connections must be formed between the afferent elements of the auditory, olfactory and interoceptive analyzers. One must assume that if interoceptive stimuli may form temporary connections in the cerebral cortex, then there must be an analyzer corresponding to these interoceptive stimuli. It must be activated each time that there is a visceral reaction, and because of this it may enter into temporary connections with all sorts of coincident stimuli. In this way the reaction in the inner organs will be reinforced and prolonged just as the motor reaction is by the activity of proprioceptors.

According to recent oscillographic investigations, interoceptive analyzer in mammals over-laps with the skin analyzer. It was found that with electrical stimulation of the splanchnic nerve and mechanical stimulation of the viscera, both slow and rapid electrical potentials can be recorded in the gyrus sigmoideus posterior and in the anterior part of the gyrus ectosylvius anterior. Their highest amplitude is then observed in the opposite hemisphere in the area of projections for afferent impulses arising from skin receptors in the trunk. To a lesser degree, they are present in the homolateral hemisphere (Amassian, 1951). Stimulation of the vagus produces an increase of electrical activity in the cerebral cortex orbital surface (Bailey and Bremer, 1939).

It is quite possible that the premotor area, so termed by Fulton, is an additional associative field for the interoceptive analyzer which, however, is essentially located in the gyrus sigmoideus posterior and gyrus ectosylvius anterior. This is completely in agreement with the results of the experiments of Bykoff (1947) and associates who disclosed that an ablation of the premotor area changes to some extent the conditioned regulation of the visceral organs.

It seems, therefore, that the formation of a salivary conditioned reflex is related to the establishment of temporary connections of the analyzer of the conditional stimulation with not only the taste analyzer but also the interoceptive analyzer. One must assume that secretion in response to the conditional stimulus cannot occur without the participation of this analyzer. The fact that a conditioned salivary reflex requires a considerably greater number of associations with the unconditional stimulus in order to be formed than the defensive reflex does, seems to indicate that the interoceptive analyzer is less able to form temporary connections than is the motor analyzer.

Therefore, we may assume that when temporary connections between the analyzer activated by the conditional stimulation and the motor or interoceptive analyzer, activated by the unconditional stimulation, reach a certain level of development, they become able to stimulate the efferent system of pyramidal neurons and elicit external reactions as expressed by leg withdrawal or by salivary secretion.

When afferent structures of the motor or proprioceptive analyzer are connected by well-developed neuronal pathways with a certain efferent system, and thus the excitability of this neuronal complex is significantly increased as a result of daily conditioning activity, new temporary connections with this afferent-efferent system may be formed immediately following the first association with new stimuli. These then become capable of eliciting external reactions. For instance, we first formed a conditioned reflex in the right foreleg of a dog to the sound of a bell; then when this reflex became stable, we started to form a conditioned reflex in the right hindleg to a scratching of the left thigh. The first trials with a slight electrical stimulation of the hindleg would already elicit the lifting of the foreleg, either at the time or after the withdrawal of the hindleg (Figure 110; see also Figure 5). Several associations of the scratching of the left thigh with electrical stimulation of the right hindleg were necessary before the scratching would regularly elicit lifting of the hindleg (Beritoff, 1924c). According to recent oscillographic investigation (Makarov, 1960, Kogan, 1960) the neuronal structures receiving unconditional and conditional stimuli show an increased excitability and lability during the formation of conditioned reflexes.

Morphologic Changes of Cortical Cells and Synapses

The formation of temporary connections implies not only a high excitability in cortical cells, but also morphologic changes in these elements, as well as in the synapses. According to the data of Agduhr (1920), after brief training there is an increase in the number of large nerve cells in the spinal ganglia and also in the number of large nerve fibers in the spinal roots. In addition, there is a significant increase in the neurofibrillar reticulum of the nerve elements. Conversely after isolation of the spinal cord from peripheral influences as a result of the section of all dorsal roots and all descending pathways, there is a thinning of the axons and a decrease in the size of nerve cells and dendritic mass in the spinal cord. There are similar changes in the peripheral nerves and nerve endings (Tower, 1937).

According to the principle of neurobiotaxis of Ariens Kappers (1927), with increased activity of a neuronal chain axons grow in the direction of their own nerve impulses, that is, in the direction away

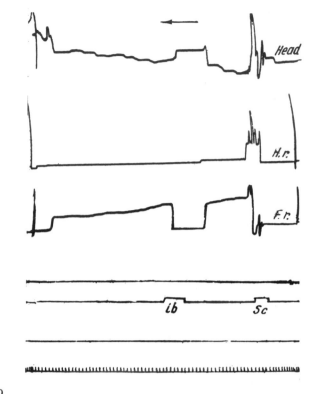

Fig. 110

Reflexes in response to electrical stimulation and scratching. Following the
formation of a conditioned flexion of the right foreleg to sound (bell), a
new conditioned reflex was formed to scratching of the left thigh. The
initial testing of scratching elicited a general movement of escape, then a
flexion of the right foreleg; repeated scratching elicited lifting of the foreleg
from the onset of the stimulus. *H.r.*, Right hindleg; *F.r.*, right foreleg; *ib*,
electric stimulus; *sc*, scratching; bottom trace, time in seconds; read from
right to left. (Beritoff, 1924c.)

from the cell, whereas the dendrites and cell bodies of neighboring
cells move toward the growing structures. Therefore, one may assume
that in a chain of active neurons, narrow synaptic spaces will become
still narrower, because of the mutual attraction of the nervous elements. This decrease of the synaptic space will lead to an increase of
electrical conduction and, therefore, to facilitation of the transmission
of excitation in a given chain of neurons. Ariens Kappers often considered the genesis of neuronal connections as analogous to the development of associative (temporary) connections in the individual life

of the animal (1927). The same phenomenon was mentioned by Ramon y Cajal (1893) in relation to the embryonal development of the nervous system; when the axons approach a nucleus, the dendrites move from there to meet the axons. The same is seen as far as the body of the cell is concerned; in this case, a growing axon plays the role of an active nerve element.

Permeability of the nerve fibers is also increased as a result of excitation; it persists sometime after excitation and becomes pronounced following repeated excitation (Ebbecke, 1922).

A particularly important role may be assigned to functional changes in synaptic endings. According to the newest investigations, the prolonged increase in excitability of the central nervous system following tetanizing stimulation, the so-called post-tetanic potentiation, is determined by functional changes. Namely, it is assumed that an increase in the magnitude of post-tetanic discharges results from increased synaptic activity (Granit, 1956, Eccles, 1957).

Eccles (1955) even thinks that during this post-tetanic potentiation there is a change in the synapse volume consisting of an increased concentration of intracellular electrolytes and an osmotic penetration of water into the synapse.

Based on the foregoing, one may assume that repeated activity in a neuronal chain results in an increase in the proximity between successive links at the locus of the transmission of stimulation from one neuron to another. The cell membrane, the synaptic area, becomes more permeable to ions, with a notable increase in the neurofibrillary substance of the cell and synapses and an enhancement of the processes of excitation, inasmuch as the degree of excitability and the intensity of excitation are directly correlated with the amount of neurofibrillary substance. This situation not only should quicken the transmission of excitation in the reflex arc in general, but should also facilitate the spread of excitation across the synapse.

These physiologic and morphologic changes seem to arise in connection with excitation in all divisions of the central nervous system, including in particular the cerebral cortex during the formation of conditioned reflexes. However, these changes may occur much quicker in cortical neurons and may persist for a longer time, sometimes the entire life span; whereas in other divisions of the brain they are usually only short lived and disappear very quickly following the excitation.

Thus, the formation of temporary connections leading to the conditioned reflex of a defensive or secretory nature, is based on the functional and morphologic development of nerve elements, mainly, the synapses of the cell bodies participating in the formation of these connections.

Structures Taking Part in Formation of Temporary Connections

Asratyan (1941, 1952), as well as Sperry and Miner (1955), investigated the effects of transections of the cortex upon conditioning. They sectioned the whole cortex leaving the subcortical white matter intact. In this way, Asratyan dissociated the analyzers in a dog, while Sperry and Miner performed multiple sections of the cortex in the visual analyzer, cutting all its horizontal pathways. Conditioned activity was not impaired by the operation, since the existing conditioned reflexes were completely reestablished in 2 or 3 weeks following the surgery, together with their fine differentiation. But when transection of the cortex is associated with that of the subcorical white matter, the effect is entirely different. In his experiments, Dzidzishvili (1956) sectioned the whole cortex with the subcortical white matter. He disconnected the analyzers in a dog by means of a section of the cortex to a depth of 7 to 8 mm. involving all the subcortical white matter. After such an isolation of the motor analyzer from the auditory and visual analyzers, the existing conditioned reflex, a simple lifting of the leg, could not be elicited by the auditory or optic stimulus for a long time. It reappeared only in a weakened and unstable form 5 to 6 months after operation. This reestablishment of the reduced conditioned defense reflex must be due to the reestablishment of temporary connections with the motor analyzer. It seems that this reestablishment or restoration, takes place because of the regeneration of certain axons of the internuncial and association neurons in the area of the section.

Just as with the conditional stimulation, the unconditional one activates primarily the stellate and other neurons with short axons in the cortex. The unconditional stimulation by its primary activation of the stellate neurons seems to determine the perception of the outside world and its subjective expression; whereas the conditioned stimulation, through its temporary connections, probably elicits a secondary activation of these neurons, determining, we believe, the reproduction of the same environment as mental images. The efferent projectional system which generates external conditional reactions, mainly the orienting reaction, is probably activated through the same stellate neurons.

And yet, as is obvious from histologic investigations, small and middle-sized pyramids are found in great number in the third and fourth layers, in the immediate vicinity of the stellate cells. Therefore, the afferent fibers from the midbrain may also terminate directly upon cell bodies of these neurons. It follows that the transmission of excitation from the afferent fibers takes place not only through the stellate neurons with their short axons, but also through the small and middle-sized pyramids; in other words, directly through the internuncial and associational neurons. Therefore one may assume that temporary connections may be established not only through the stellate neurons, but without them directly through the small and middle-sized pyramids of the third and fourth layers. Probably this explains why many unconditioned and conditioned reflexes elicited through the cortex are not associated with subjective feelings. For example some reflexes evoked through proprioceptive and interoceptive stimuli may be activated without the participation of the stellate neurons. It will be recalled that the fourth layer of the motor analyzer contains very few stellate cells with short axons.

Since external stimulation activates the stellate neurons directly, as well as with participation of a facilitating bombardment from the reticular formation through the nonspecific pathways, one must assume that during a somewhat weaker excitation of the receptors, when the reticular formation is not activated to such a degree as to influence the stellate system by a facilitating action, the afferent bombardment from these receptors conducted along specific pathways may not activate the stellate system, but only the internuncial neurons. Because of this, the receptive internuncial neurons of the cortex receiving the afferent impulses may form temporary connections without the participation of sensory stellate neurons. As we indicated above, the formation of the skin galvanic and other autonomic conditioned reflexes to subthreshold visual or auditory stimulation according to Gershuni (1947, 1949a, b), must occur with the participation of only internuncial and associational neurons. It seems that normally temporary connections are formed with the internuncial and associational neurons either through their activation by the sensory stellate neurons or directly via thalamic afferent fibers. However, temporary connections without participation of sensory stellate neurons, that is, without subjective perceptions, are established with much more difficulty and after a prolonged latency period.

Therefore, as regards the formation of conditioned reflexes, the participation of the stellate neurons with short axons, that is, the psychoneuronal substrate of the cerebral cortex, is not necessary; such conditioning may occur without their participation.

We indicated above that the Betz cells and other pyramidal cells initiating the pyramidal and extrapyramidal pathways, possess collaterals which synapse only on dendrites. This is why their antidromic excitation could not activate neuronal circuits of the cortex. It follows that those temporary circuits of the conditioned reflex which are newly established in adult animals cannot directly comprise these efferent projectional neurons. Obviously, internuncial and associational neurons of newly formed temporary connections of defensive conditioned reflexes do not directly affect the efferent system consisting of Betz cells and other large pyramids of the deep layers of the cortex. Just as with a conditional stimulation, an unconditional stimulation must activate this projectional efferent system through the motor analyzer by means of the same neurons which receive musculo-articular stimuli. These kinesthetic neurons are connected with the efferent pyramidal neurons by means of well-developed neuronal connections established between this group of receptive and efferent pyramidal neurons during the past life of the individual.

In 1934 Pavlov had already arrived at the same conclusion. In an article concerning voluntary movements, he considered the question of the connections of kinesthetic neurons with the corresponding projectional motor cells. He concluded that these connections are established during the individual's entire life each time a man or any higher vertebrate learns to master the primary movements of a behavioral act. Later on, Pavlov (1949b) formulated this thought in the following way: "Kinesthetic cells of the cortex may be connected, and in reality are connected, with all the cortical cells representing the external influences as well as all sorts of inner processes of the organism." He also stated that the same kinesthetic neurons "are necessarily connected with the efferent element, in other words, with certain movements."

Recently, Burns, Grafstein, and Olszewski (1957), on the basis of an oscillographic investigation, concluded that the largest pyramidal cells of the fifth layer, the secondary type B cells, do not participate in the formation of the neuronal loops. Their main function consists of the transmission of stimuli received from other cells, namely, primary type B cells, which form neuronal loops. These primary B-type cells are, according to our terminology, associational and internuncial pyramidal cells, while the secondary type B cells are, according to our terminology, projectional efferent pyramids forming pyramidal and extrapyramidal pathways.

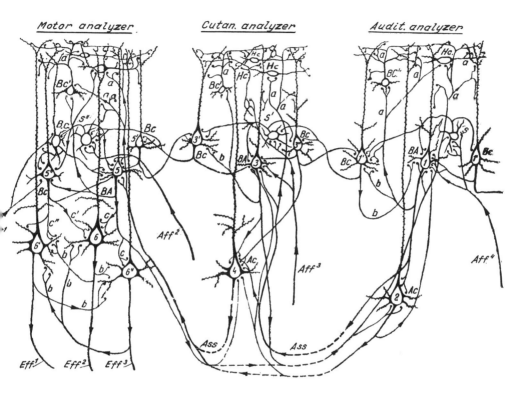

Fig. 111

Schematic representation of neuronal cortical connections relative to a conditioned defensive reflex of the hindleg in response to auditory stimulation and their interaction with receptive neuronal elements, efferent pyramidal system and dendritic mass. *Hc*, Horizontal neurons of the first and second layers; *Bc*, Internuncial cells, neurons of the fourth layer, their descending axons synapting with the projection and association neurons; *Bc¹*, internuncial neurons of the second and third layers, their ascending axons terminating in the first layer; *Ac*, pyramidal association neurons of the fifth and sixth layers, the axons of which run in the white matter and serve for integration of different sectors of the cortex; *BA*, complex of the internuncial and association neurons of the fourth layer; *S*, stellate neurons with short axons; *Eff¹*, large pyramidal cells giving origin to pyramidal pathways toward the foreleg; *Eff²*, same to the head; *Eff³*, same to the hindleg; *Ass*, association fibers in the white subcortical matter; *1* to *5*, cellular complexes; *a*, collaterals ending at the apical dendrites; *b*, collaterals ending in the basal dendrites; *c*, axons activating efferent pyramidal cells. (From histological data of Lorente de Nó, Poljakoff and Chang as well as recent oscillographic investigations.) (See text for detailed explanation.)

Figure 111 shows a suggested diagram of temporary connections of defensive reflexes in response to an auditory stimulus. Also indicated are all those neurons (stellate, internuncial and associational) that participate in the formation of a given temporary connection.

Thus, the stellate and internuncial neurons of the motor analyzer serve for interconnection of various cortical areas, for formation of new forward and reverse connections and to elicit motor reactions through efferent pyramids.

This diagram represents not only the direction of the excitatory processes in some cell elements, but also the presence of inhibition in the others. On the figure are given temporary neuronal connections through internuncial neurons alone as well as by means of internuncial and association neurons. The neuronal connections S, $1'$, $3''$, 3, represent temporary forward pathways with participation of some internuncial neurons. Excitation starts in the complex of neurons receiving sounds and terminates in the somesthetic analyzer; S', 3, $3'$, $5'$, 5 is a similar forward path from the somesthetic receptive complex of neurons to the motor analyzer. The neuronal connections $3''$, $1'$, and also $5'$, $3'$, represent reverse pathways made of internuncial neurons, correspondingly from the skin analyzer to the auditory and from the motor to the somesthetic. Neuronal connections, including cellular complexes 1, 2, 3, 4, 5, represent a long temporary forward pathway from the internuncial and association neurons through the somesthetic analyzer. Neuronal connections, including cells 1, 2, 5, constitute a short forward path made of association neurons without participation of the somesthetic analyzer. Neuronal connections 3, 2, 1, represent the reverse temporary connections from the association neurons of the somesthetic analyzer toward the auditory one and 5, 2, 1, the same reverse connections from the motor analyzer to the auditory one.

13 ORIGIN OF CORTICAL INHIBITION

Basic Experimental Data and Concepts

We observed the phenomenon of general cortical inhibition as stimulation of the cortex modified motor reactions ordinarily elicited by the stimulation of afferent nerves (Beritoff and Gedevani, 1941). We studied general inhibition in cats during barbiturate narcosis, when the inhibition was elicited by a tetanizing electrical stimulation of a segment of the motor cortex and of other areas as well. Even if the stimulation of the cortex elicited no motor effects, the inhibition of motor reactions ordinarily resulting from the stimulation of the afferent nerves was observed. The thresholds for cortical inhibition were much lower than the level of excitation at which motor effects were produced. Inhibition was obtained during the first second of stimulation. It was a widespread inhibition, evidenced by the fact that motor effects elicited by stimulation of the afferent nerves of the ipsilateral hindleg as well as the contralateral hindleg were arrested. After the cessation of cortical stimulation, the inhibition lasted several minutes; this was much longer than in the spinal preparation, where the general inhibition of the spinal reflex lasts only a few seconds after the cessation of stimulation (Figure 112) (Beritoff and Gogava, 1937, Beritoff and Chichinadze, 1937, Beritoff and Gedevani, 1941).

A similar general inhibition of the motor effects, elicited by the stimulation of the motor cortex, was obtained from cortical stimulation of parietal and occipital cortices (Figure 113) (Gedevani, 1943, Beritoff and Ordzhonikidze, 1958).

The general inhibition of motor reactions, during stimulation of the cortex, was also described by Dusser de Barenne and McCulloch (1941a). However, they obtained it only during the stimulation of certain strips in the sensory area. Also the latent period of the suppression reaction they described was several minutes and was obtained only under deep anesthesia. They came to the conclusion that this depression takes place not in the cortex, but in the subcortex. They considered it as being due to the participation of such structures

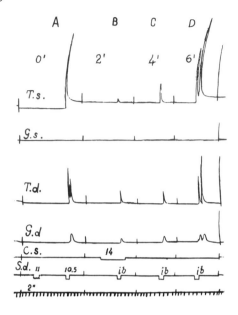

Fig. 112

General inhibition during stimulation of the cerebral cortex (cat). Contractions of the ankle flexors are recorded; gastrocnemius, *G.d.*, right, and *G.s.*, left; anterior tibial, *T.d.*, right, and *T.s.*, left; *C.s.*, stimulation of the right parietal lobe; *S.d.*, right saphenous nerve; bottom trace, time in seconds. Numbers over tracings *C.s.* and *S.d.* indicate the intensity of stimulation expressed in centimeters of intercoil distance (inductorium). *A*, Stimulation of the right saphenous nerve elicits strong contraction in the flexors and a slight contraction of the right extensor; *B*, same stimulation is applied during the stimulation of the ipsilateral parietal lobe (right); it now produces only a slight effect; *C*, 2 minutes later, again a slight effect is produced, but after additional 2 minutes the stimulation of the same nerve elicits an usually strong contraction. (Beritoff and Gedevani, 1941.)

as nucleus caudatus, putamen, globus pallidus, thalamus, substantia nigra and cerebellum; in other words, all those structures the stimulation of which may indeed elicit a widespread inhibition. (See also Clark, Kao, Gillaspy, and Klotz, 1949.)

In our experiments general inhibition following cortical stimulation began in the very first second and spread very quickly over the whole cortex; it was observed under superficial narcosis, that is, at a time when a general movement of the animal could be elicited by stimulation of the motor zone of the cortex or of an afferent nerve. In addition, it could be observed with a subthreshold stimulation of

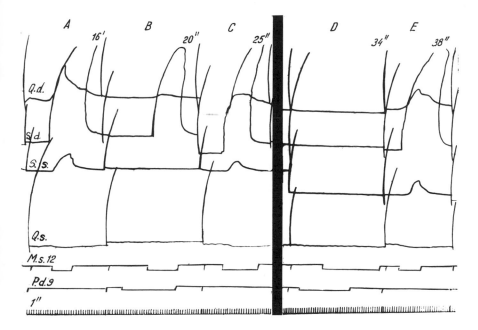

Fig. 113

General inhibition during cortical stimulation (cat). Contractions of quadriceps and semitendinosus on both sides recorded. *Q.d.*, right quadriceps; *S.d.*, right semitendinosus; *S.s.*, left semitendinosus; *Q.s.*, left quadriceps; *M.s.*, stimulation of the left motor cortex; *P.d.*, same, right parietal cortex; bottom trace, time in seconds. *A, C, E,* Stimulation of the left motor cortex alone; a strong contraction of the contralateral flexor is observed as well as a slight contraction of the ipsilateral flexor and contralateral extensor. *B, D,* Same stimulation during activation of the contralateral parietal lobe (sensory). In the first instance a slight motor effect was observed on the right flexor, while in the second trial no effect was obtained. (Beritoff and Ordzhonikidze, 1958.)

the motor cortex not sufficient to elicit a motor effect. All of this suggests that widespread inhibition elicited by us during stimulation of the cortex actually originated in the cortex itself.

The oscillographic investigations also seem to favor the belief that inhibition resulting from stimulation of the cortex originates in the cortex itself. When Roitbak (1953) investigated the changes of the spontaneous electrical activity during stimulation of any cortical area, he found that they occur over the entire cortex. It is noteworthy that electrical reactions elicited at a short distance, no more than 10 mm.

from the stimulated area, were expressed by negative electrical potentials, while in the distant areas they were positive, although the negative potential followed the positive potentials. This suggests that the direct effect of the stimulation spreads over the proximal segments of the cortex in the area of the negative potentials, while the activation of the distant areas is due to the participation of associative subcortical pathways. Furthermore, the positive potentials express the activity of dendrites in the third and fourth layers, followed by the negative potentials expressing activity in the superficial layers. If one takes into consideration the observation that during the negative slow potentials elicited by stimulation of the cortex there is a depression of spontaneous electrical activity, then one should assume that in our experiments the depression of the motor effects, as well as of the spontaneous electrical activity, was of a cortical origin elicited through activation of the apical dendrites in the entire cortex. This widespread activation of the cortex may occur through the spread of these impulses along the associative fibers running in the white subcortical matter, as well as by means of the participation of the thalamic ascending system, as may occur during stimulation of the anteromedial nucleus of the thalamus shown in studies of Hanbery and Jasper (1953). In both cases, inhibition actually takes place in the cortex. It is quite possible that a prolonged inhibitory after effect, which may last minutes, is determined by the activity of corticothalamo-cortical closed neuronal circuits.

Now let us consider how the associative pathways generate inhibition in the distant areas of the cortex. Associational neurons transmit excitation toward the more or less distant neurons, but at the same time they activate the neurons of the same sector where their cell bodies are located, so that by their collaterals they may influence the numerous neurons located nearby. It is quite possible that they depress the soma of these neurons through activation of basal dendrites. By this mechanism the localization of excitation at its point of origin and its specific transmission are secured.

In the areas of their distant termination the associational neurons must have both axosomatic and axodendritic synapses, so that they must generate in these end regions processes of excitation in some cells and of inhibition in others. In this way, during the excitation of the associational fibers, the circumscribing of the resulting reaction may be achieved due to the fact that the terminal arborizations of the associational neurons excite certain neuronal circuits while others in the same vicinity are inhibited.

As is known, during excitation of afferent fibers, certain external reactions occur associated with a simultaneous general inhibition of the cortex. It follows that the afferent impulses produce excitation of stellate and other neurons with short axons, as well as of certain internuncial and association neurons, and at the same time elicit inhibition of all the other pyramidal neurons by activating their dendrites in the superficial layers of the cortex. As a result, an environmental stimulus first elicits excitation of neuronal circuits in the cortex, in which complexes of stellate neurons participate. Then during the subsequent spread of excitation along the internuncial and association neurons, with a final involvement of the projectional pyramidal cells, the effect becomes more or less circumscribed in some neurons due to the inhibition of others. The resulting localization of the cortical reaction corresponds precisely with the environmental situation.

The apical dendrites constitute the main dendritic mass in the superficial layers of the cortex, and are surrounded by all kinds of nerve fibers of cortical and thalamic origin which form synapses with the thorny spines densely covering these dendrites. By their activation one may assume that they generate widespread cortical inhibition.

Excitation spreading through the superficial layers along the axonal fibers from the internuncial and association neurons affects the apical dendrites of almost all pyramidal neurons in the fourth to sixth layers, and because of this almost the entire associative and efferent systems of the cortex must be inhibited. Probably the basic function of the first layer, consisting essentially of the apical dendrites, is the generation of inhibition in all those association and projectional efferent neurons of the cortex to which these dendrites belong.

However, association and efferent neurons of the cortex are also submitted to a focal inhibition. During intense excitation of certain cortical areas, for instance after a local application of strychnine, the background electrical activity around this segment is depressed and the excitability significantly decreased (Beritoff and Gedevani, 1945). We believe that the local inhibition around this focal area, affected by the strychnine, is due to the activation of basal dendrites of pyramidal neurons under the influence of the nervous impulses from the neuronal circuits influenced by this drug. Numerous short basal dendrites of pyramidal neurons are seemingly able to generate, during their activation, such strong anelectrotonic action upon the cell synapses that the cell cannot be stimulated through these synapses. Therefore, we believe that the basic function of the basal dendrites consists in a focal suppression, resulting in a local functional isolation of certain pyramidal cells.

Probably the general inhibition of the whole cortex through the apical dendrites of pyramidal neurons and the local inhibition of certain neurons through the basal dendrites constitute a necessary reaction of the cortex in response to bombardment from the receptors. It is because of such cortical reactions that an adequate differentiated adaptation of the organism to changes in the external and internal milieu is achieved.

Origin of External Inhibition

Every external stimulus is able to elicit an orienting reaction and depress a conditioned reflex. This depression of the reflex, according to Pavlovian terminology, is called "external" inhibition. Figure 114 illustrates inhibition of a conditioned defensive reflex in the right foreleg under the influence of an extraneous sound. This sound suppresses the conditioned reflex when it occurs during the presentation of the positive conditional signal (experiment 1) as well as when it occurs during the conditioned reflex itself (experiment 2).

It is also easy to elicit a depression of a conditioned defensive reflex by other extraneous stimuli. If the same extraneous stimulus is repeated several times, it will finally cease to elicit the orienting reactions, and then its negative action upon conditioned reflexes will be decreased.

We are faced with this question of how inhibition of conditioned reflexes is achieved under the influence of extraneous stimuli. One may assume that the conditioned reflexes are suppressed through the inhibition of their temporary connections located in the cortex. Pavlov himself came to this conclusion. He formulated a hypothesis according to which when any center of the central nervous system enters into an active state, under the influences of external or internal stimuli, there is an immediate decrease of excitability, or a complete depression in other centers, because of the "attraction" of the excitatory process by the newly activated center. Later on Pavlov explained the phenomenon of external inhibition by a negative induction from the primary activated focus; in other words, he assumed that the focus of excitation in the cortex conjointly generates inhibition of all other foci of excitation in the cortex. In this way, according to Pavlov, all the inhibiting action of the extraneous stimulus takes place in the cerebral cortex.

For a long time we shared this opinion that the inhibition of conditioned reflexes expresses the inhibition of the cortical segment of

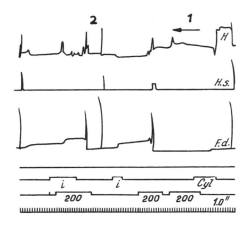

Fig. 114

Influence of an unusual extraneous stimulus upon a conditioned reflex (dog). Movements of the head, *H*, the left hindleg, *H.s.*, and right foreleg, *F.d.*, recorded. A stable conditioned reflex is present on the right foreleg to the tone of 200 c./sec. In experiment *1*, an unusual sound is elicited, *Cyl*, percussion of a metallic cylinder. At this time, the dog was dozing. At the sound, it woke up and raised its head (depression of the curve, *H*). For a few seconds the conditional tone of 200 c./sec. was added to this sound; then the extraneous sound was suppressed and the conditional sound continued for 17 seconds. There was no conditioned reflex. However it could be elicited by the conditional signal after an interruption of 5 seconds. In experiment *2*, at first the reflex was elicited; during this time the extraneous sound was produced and the conditioned reflex was somewhat decreased. (Beritoff, 1927.)

this reflex arc. We initially explained external inhibition as being due to the general increase of excitability in the cerebral cortex under the influence of the extraneous stimulus. We assumed that because of this general increase of excitability, the initial excitation set up in the cortex by a conditional signal spreads from the focus of the conditioned activation and, in general, from the cortical elements of the reflex arc, over all of the cortex. According to the principle of a conjoint spread of excitation, we assumed that the latter does not activate temporary connections to a degree necessary to elicit external effects. The increase of excitability in the cortex was explained as being mostly a result of secondary proprioceptive stimulation originating in the neck and other structures involved in the orienting reaction, as well as a result of the spread of excitation from the corresponding cortical centers (Beritoff, 1927, 1932).

More recently, when it was established that widespread inhibition also occurs in the cortex and that this inhibition is conditioned by slow potentials of dendritic origin, we assumed that the negative action of an extraneous stimulus upon a conditioned reflex results mainly from the general inhibition in the cortex. We suggested that any action in the external environment elicits excitation of certain neuronal loops of the cortex and simultaneously a widespread inhibition through the activation of apical and basal dendrites (Beritoff, 1948, 1956a).

However, this concept of the cortical origin of inhibition of conditioned reflexes by more or less intense extraneous stimuli cannot be completely justified. We know that an extraneous stimulus elicits widespread inhibition of reflex activity in almost the entire central nervous system. This inhibition involves the nuclei of the cerebrum as well as those of the spinal cord. For instance, in puppies as was discussed earlier, pinching the skin of the head produces some slight head movement along with widespread inhibition of the whole musculature, associated with the depression of clonic as well as tonic reflexes. The same effect can be observed during feeding of the animal, stretching and pinching its tail, etc.; all these stimuli elicit certain reflex movements, but at the same time there is a depression of other reflexes, as well as of respiration, vocalitation and spontaneous twitching. Generally, all these effects are equally observed in normal and decorticate animals (Beritoff, 1928, 1930). Thus, Figure 115 illustrates a diffuse depression of innate behavioral reactions in decorticate puppies during feeding, and Figure 116 during pinching of the skin of the head.

Inhibition of conditioned reflexes under the influence of extraneous stimuli in normal animals thus may be due entirely to subcortical effects, namely, widespread inhibition in the spinal cord and brainstem. Since we believe that inhibition is achieved through the reticular formation and substantia gelatinosa of the spinal cord, we conclude that the observed inhibition of conditioned reflexes in normal animals is also due to the involvement of these structures.

Recently, this assumption was proved by oscillographic investigations. When an electrical stimulation of the leg of a cat was used to elicit a defensive reaction, the cortex manifested a general increase of activity which oscillographically was expressed by the suppression of slow waves and an increased production of beta waves, in other words, by desynchonization. At the same time, afferent impulses from other receptors did not reach the cortex. In response to these latter stimuli, no primary potentials followed by fast activity could be elicited. For instance Roitbak (1958a) showed that during electrical stimulation

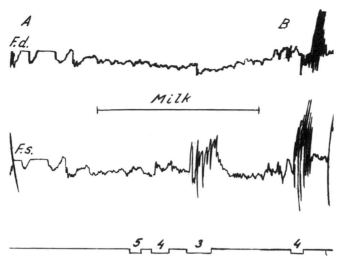

Fig. 115

Influence of feeding upon the defensive reflex of the left foreleg to electrical stimulation. A decorticate puppy on the eighth day after operation. The puppy was suspended by a towel with legs stretched downward through holes in it. *F.d.*, right foreleg; *F.s.*, left foreleg. The left foreleg was stimulated. In experiment A, stimulation of the leg (4 to 5 cm. between the primary and secondary coils of the inductorium) while the puppy was licking milk did not elicit any significant reaction. A stronger current (3 cm.) elicited a slight reaction involving only the stimulated leg. In experiment B, in the absence of feeding, stimulation (4 cm.) produced a general and strong reaction of the stimulated as well as of the opposite leg. (Beritoff, 1929a.)

of the skin, and sometimes several scores of seconds afterward, primary potentials do not occur in the auditory area in response to sounds (Figure 117).

Hernández-Peón *et al.* (1956) showed that evoked potentials elicited by visual stimuli in the cortex, in the lateral geniculate body and in the reticular formation of the mesencephalon, disappear partially or completely during auditory and olfactory stimulion that elicits orienting reactions which the authors called "the reactions of attention."

It was then established that following a direct stimulation of the reticular formation of the brainstem, or during its activation by strong electrical stimuli applied to the skin, there is, along with the inhibition of the external reactions to other stimuli, depression of afferent impulses running in the ascending pathways which persists for several scores of seconds after the cessation of stimulation

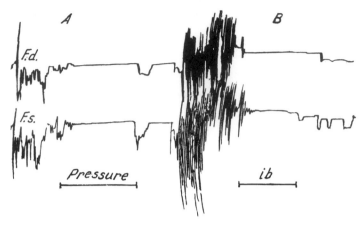

Fig. 116

Same animal and apparatus. *A*, During a general movement of escape and yelping the skin of the head was pinched. Immediately, the movements as well as the yelp were suppressed; *B*, during spontaneous phasic movements of the running type the same pinching caused their cessation; the dog also stopped yelping. (Beritoff, 1929a.)

(Hernández-Peón *et al.*, 1956). This inhibition occurs in the nuclei of the spinal cord and medulla. Hagbarth and Kerr (1954), Roitback (1958) and Gershuni (1958–1959) showed that in the cat during feeding or strong mechanical stimulation the stream of afferent impulses at different levels of the auditory system is depressed.

On the basis of all these observations, one may conclude that the depression of conditioned reflexes under the influence of external stimuli is not due to cortical inhibition, but rather to the blockade of afferent volleys in the nuclei of the brainstem. It is assumed that there is, in the reticular formation of the brainstem, a mechanism which regulates the afferent bombardment (Hernández-Peón *et al.*, 1956, Gershuni, 1959). This regulation must be carried out through transmission of impulses from the cells of this formation along their axons to the nuclei of the afferent systems. There they may activate the dendritic mass, eliciting slow potentials which may cause an anelectrotonic depression of synapses on the corresponding cells and thus block the transmission of excitation from these nuclei to the cortex.

The activation of the reticular formation primarily occurs as a result of afferent bombardment from the receptors. However, it may also be activated secondarily under the influence of corticofugal impulses.

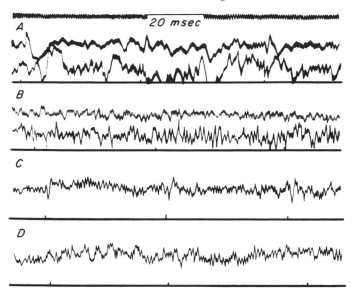

Fig. 117

Suppression of primary evoked potentials in the auditory analyzer during electrical stimulation of the skin (dog). The recording electrodes were applied to the auditory (upper tracings) and somesthetic cortical areas (lower tracings). A, Effects of three auditory stimuli in a resting stage; B, effects of the same auditory stimuli during an electrical stimulation of the foreleg skin, eliciting strong movements; C, potentials recorded only in the auditory area (effects of three auditory stimuli); D, effects of the same auditory stimuli when the dog was eating meat. (Roitbak, 1958a.)

This is revealed during stimulation of the cortex; the resulting impulses run along the extrapyramidal pathways and affect the reticular formation, producing there both a blockade and a facilitation for the conduction of afferent impulses (Hernández-Peón and Hagbarth, 1954). Therefore, one may assume that during stimulation of the cortex by afferent impulses through specific pathways, the extra pyramidal system may be activated in the cortex and in turn affect the reticular formation producing either an inhibition or a facilitation for the conduction of afferent impulses. Even the spinal cord, and particularly the substantia gelatinosa of Rolando, may participate in the inhibition of conditioned reflexes in the muscles of the extremities. Thus an external inhibition of conditioned reflexes is elicited by external stimulation through a mechanism of diffuse inhibition of the whole central nervous system from the spinal cord to the cortex.

Origin of Internal Inhibition

In the theory of conditioned activity the concept of internal inhibition has a central significance. It occurs in all cases when the conditional stimulation is applied for more or less prolonged periods of time without being associated with an unconditioned reflex; the conditioned reflex is then no longer elicited because of the onset of internal inhibition. Loss of conditioned reflexes as a result of differentiation, apparent nonactive state during delayed and trace conditioning, the extinction of conditioned reflexes and the experimental sleep, are all considered manifestations of internal inhibition. In his last article on conditioned reflexes, Pavlov (1949a) characterized internal inhibition in the following way:

In these cases . . . we deal with a special inhibition of the cerebral hemispheres, a cortical inhibition. It arises, under certain conditions, in a situation when previously it was not present. It can be trained, varies in its intensity, disappears under certain other conditions, and by this it differs from more or less stable inhibition in the lower division of the central nervous system, and because of this was called internal inhibition in contradistinction to the latter (external). Inhibition participates in all activity as constantly, complexly and subtly as does the excitatory process.

Therefore, according to Pavlov, internal inhibition is, first, a specific cortical inhibition. Second, it is a trainable conditioned inhibition; in other words, it is generated in the cortex not immediately, but through the transformation of an excitatory signal into an inhibitory one as a result of training during repeated occurrences.

Despite the fact that the phenomenon of internal inhibition plays an essential role in the dynamics of conditioned activity, Pavlov did not consider it possible to suggest a theoretical explanation of the nature of internal inhibition. In 1927 in his lectures on the work of the cerebral hemispheres, Pavlov made some hypothetical formulations, namely, that "cortical cells become inhibited in connection with a functional disturbance of the cell during activity elicited by their stimulation," which may spread over the nonactive cells that were not "injured functionally." But this hypothetical view did not satisfy Pavlov. Even then he repeatedly stated his reluctance to adhere to any definite theory of inhibition. The above statement was made in 1927, but according to Mayorov's, "History of Studies of Conditioned Reflexes," 1946, Pavlov until his death considered the problem of inhibition and its relationship to excitation an unsolved problem; he referred to it as a "curse."

The pupils of Pavlov, during his life as well as after his death, could not give any new theoretical explanation for internal inhibition. Only recently, Anokhin (1958), on the basis of the teaching of Wedensky in regard to the pessimal effects in neuromuscular preparations that result from a high frequency and intensity of stimulation, found it possible to treat central inhibition, in particular internal inhibition, as being the equivalent of a "pessimum" phenomenon. He assumed that each time "when in the central nervous system one integrated activity is followed by another, in other words, when there is a conflict of two systems representing two states of excitation, mechanism of inhibition of one of them is related to the intensity and frequency of the more intense neuronal activity." It is true that during the interaction of two reflexes or behavioral acts, the more intensive one takes over, while the other act cannot be carried through because of the inhibiting action of the activated neuronal loops upon the remaining nervous system. However, there is no basis for assuming that this inhibitory action is a function of the intensity or frequency of nerve impulses.

Together with the level of intensity and frequency of impulses, Anokhin also borrows another theoretical idea from the teachings of Wedensky, namely, that of perielectrotonus which may operationally be defined as follows: In the area of polariazation of a nerve the excitability in the vicinity of the cathode is increased, and catelectrotonus is present; beyond the limits of this segment at a distance of approximately 20 mm. or more the excitability is decreased. An analogous phenomenon is found in the area of the anode, in the vicinity of which the excitability is decreased while at a distance from it, there is an increase of excitability (Wedensky, 1920). However, Anokhin does not give any experimental basis for the application of the notions of pessimum and catelectrotonus in specific cases of internal inhibition. One cannot deny that under certain circumstances the frequency of stimulation and electrotonic changes may cause depression of neuronal elements in the central nervous system. But the author does not give any experimental or theoretical analysis of these phenomena in order to clarify the role of the frequency of stimuli, or of electrotonus in conditioned activity.

Some pupils of Wedensky and Uchtomsky prefer to explain central inhibition as a parabiotic phenomenon which is created in the nerve cells under the influence of nerve impulses. Such a parabiosis is customarily referred to as functional (Golikov, 1956). Here again, the hypothetical explanation is based only on analogy.

Our theoretical consideration of internal inhibition stems from the previously mentioned concept regarding the formation of special neuronal loops during the establishment of each conditioned reflex, and from our hypothesis as to the nature of inhibition being due to dendritic slow potentials. More specific considerations will be formulated in the following section.

Origin of Delayed Conditioned Reflexes

Internal inhibition is elicited during the formation of delayed or trace defensive reflexes (Pavlov). These may be formed by pairing an unconditional electrical stimulus with a conditional signal, provided that the former occurs not at the beginning of the conditional stimulus, but at the end of it or sometime afterward. Then in the initial trials, the conditioned reflex occurs at the very beginning of the conditional signal. However, later on, after a great number of associations, the reflex starts to occur after a greater delay, and finally it is elicited only at the time when the electrical stimulation is usually applied. Figure 118 gives an example of a delayed conditioned reflex which occurs at the end of the conditional stimulation. In other words, the figure shows that when the delayed or trace conditioned reflex had not yet become stable enough, during the first experimental trials, it

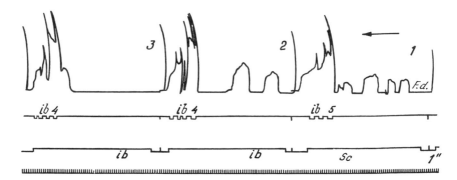

Fig. 118

Delayed conditioned reflex of the right foreleg in response to scratching of the back (dog). Electrical stimulation applied 60 sec. after the beginning of scratching; the eleventh day of the formation of this reflex. In experiments *1* and *2* the paw was lifted several times before the signal and in experiment *3* only a few seconds before the onset of stimulation. The downward deflexion of the upper marker line indicates the electrical stimulation, while the upward deflexion of the lower line indicates the scratching; bottom trace, time in seconds. (Beritoff, 1924.)

occurred substantially before the time of the unconditional stimulus, but with repetition it began to occur almost at the time of the unconditional stimulation. Thus, Figure 118 shows a delayed conditioned reflex occurring one minute after the onset of the conditional stimulus.

Very often a fairly stabilized delayed (trace or consecutive) conditioned reflex is changed into a simultaneous reflex, in other words, one that starts at the very beginning of the conditional signal. This occurs, for instance, after a strong electric reinforcement. Thus, in Figure 119 experiment *1* shows a consecutive conditioned reflex occurring after the conditional visual stimulus, as in the usual delayed conditioning. This reflex was then reinforced by an electric stimulus. In the following trails, the same signal at first elicited a simultaneous reflex and then a consecutive one. This obviously was a result of the increased excitability of the motor cortex. In other cases also, when for some reason the excitability of the motor cortex is increased, as generally occurs when a strong external stimulus elicits a pronounced orienting reaction, the inactive phase disappears. It is this inactive phase of the delayed or consecutive conditioned reflex which is considered to be an expression of internal inhibition, and it can be elicited and developed by delaying the unconditional electric stimulus.

When delayed or consecutive conditioned reflexes are formed and when therefore the conditional stimulation operates a relatively long time before the unconditional stimulus is initiated, the reverse connec-

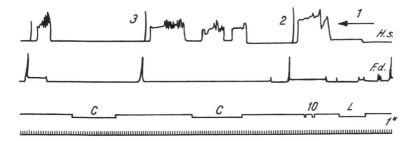

Fig. 119

Formation of the consecutive defensive reflex over the left hindleg to the light of an electric bulb. Unconditional electrical stimulation applied 10 sec. after the signal, sixth day of the experiment. In experiment *1* the light elicited a consecutive reflex of the left paw; the electrical stimulation to the leg was applied during this trial (10 cm. between the primary and secondary coils of the inductorium). In trial 2, 3 minutes afterward, the reflex occurred at the signal and then after it (consecutive reflex). During this trial electrical stimulation was not applied. In trial 3, still 3 minutes later, the light elicited only consecutive reflex. (Beritoff, 1924.)

tions are developed much more firmly than when the conditional and the unconditional stimuli occur at the same time. This situation must increase considerably the activation of dendrites in the region where the reverse connections originate, that is the area of the motor analyzer, which is energized by the unconditional stimulus. Since the efferent pyramids responsible for the defensive reaction are located in the motor analyzer, it is easy to see that the dendrites of these pyramids must be particularly subject to activation via collaterals of the activated reverse neuronal connections.

As mentioned above, initially the conditional signal elicits a coincident conditioned reflex through the initial activating action of the forward connections upon the cells of the efferent pyramids. This action is more intense at that time than the inhibiting action of the reverse connection upon their dendrites. Later on, the latter will predominate. As is known, the total surface of dendrites and the total number of synapses upon the dendrites of a spinal or a cortical neuron is always much larger than the total surface of the cell bodies and the number of the adjacent synapses (Cholokashvili, 1953). Therefore, with full activation of the dendrites of a cell, the sum of all the electrical potentials thus developed will be larger than the potential which acts upon the cell body by way of axosomatic synapses. As a result, the cell and all the adjacent synapses will be depressed by the action of dendritic potentials during the period of delay.

After a certain time, however, the activity of reverse connections decreases as a result of fatigue, the effect of better-developed forward connections becomes relatively stronger, and the conditional response emerges.

ORIGIN OF NEGATIVE CONDITIONED REFLEXES

Following several associations of the defensive conditioned reflex with any indifferent stimulus without reinforcement (by electrical stimulation of the leg) several behavioral events may be observed. At first this indifferent stimulus becomes a positive conditional signal which if used separately elicits the conditioned withdrawal of the leg. Therefore, a new conditioned reflex is formed on the basis of the existing conditioned reflex.

However, during the following trials the dog will stop withdrawing its leg, and on the contrary will become tranquilized, lower its head or even doze. If then this new stimulus is presented along with another otherwise effective conditional stimulus, the conditioned reflex will not occur and the animal will put its leg down (Figure 120). The new

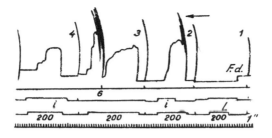

Fig. 120

The negative conditioned reflex to light (L) and its action upon the positive conditioned reflexes of the foreleg to the tone of 200 c./sec. (dog). In experiment 1 the positive signal produced while the light was on did not elicit a reflex. In experiment 2, on the contrary, the influence of the light was tested while the positive reflex was effective; the light suspended it. In experiment 3, the positive reflex was elicited and reinforced by an electrical stimulus (upper marker line). After this, experiment 4, the positive signal tested while the light was on, elicited a slight positive reflex. (Beritoff, 1924.)

stimulus, with its learned negative effect, is called in the Pavlovian school a conditional inhibitor; we prefer to call it a conditioned negative reflex. This negative conditioned reflex is caused by internal inhibition according to the studies of Pavlov. We explain this phenomena in the following way.

During the formation of a negative conditioned reflex, the forward and reverse temporary connections arise between the neuronal complexes activated by the newly applied stimulus and those which are activated during the associated conditioned reflex. At first, the forward connections are developed so strongly that the newly applied stimulation becomes a positive signal and elicits a conditioned reaction.

Seemingly the cell bodies and their synapses are subject at first to a more intense activation by the forward connections, than to the anelectrotonic effects originating in the dendrites activated by the reverse connections. However, when the reverse temporary connections are significantly developed, the impulsation from the temporary circuits of a new conditioned reflex in the motor analyzer, where the reverse temporary connections begin, is increased. This is why during action of a new conditional stimulus, the activation of the dendrites of the efferent pyramidal neurons is increased to such a level that there is a blockade of the pyramidal cell synapses. Because of this the stimulation ceases to produce the conditioned reaction; in other words, the positive stimulus becomes a negative one. It seems that this lasts as long as fatigue of the reverse connections does not result from a continuous circulation of excitation in a particular neuronal circuit.

ORIGIN OF THE EXTINCTION OF A CONDITIONED REFLEX

One of the characteristics of conditioned activity is its ability to be extinguished. The conditioned reflex will no longer be evoked if the corresponding conditional stimulus is applied several times consecutively, without being reinforced by the unconditional stimulus. Different types of extinction may be considered. An acute extinction results from a prolonged application of the conditional stimulus, or a rapid repetition of the conditional stimulus; while a persistent extinction is one that develops during several days of trials without reinforcement. In the first case, extinction disappears after a period of rest, without leaving any significant trace in the animal's behavior; whereas, in case the second, extinction does not entirely disappear even after a period of rest.

The acute type is shown in Figure 121, which illustrates the extinc-

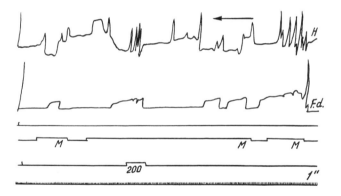

Fig. 121

Influence of extinction of the conditioned defense reflex upon another analogous reflex (dog). *H*, Movement of the head; *F.d.*, movement of the right foreleg; *M*, prolonged (2 min.) action of the conditional signal (metronome) produced an extinction of the conditioned reflex on the right foreleg. Approximately 1 min. after the beginning of this signal, this reflex was extinguished. At that time the other conditional signal, tone of 200 c./sec., elicited a significant conditioned reflex. After a second interruption of the metronome for only 12 sec. the extinguished reflex to the metronome was reestablished, but it was still weak. (Beritoff, 1927.)

tion of a defensive conditioned flexion of the right foreleg by a prolonged application of the conditional stimulus, namely, the sound of a
metronome. In the case of this dog, there was another defensive reflex
in the same leg conditioned to a tone of 200 c./sec. The figure shows
that after the extinction of the reflex to the sound of the metronome
the 200 c./sec. tone would still evoke it. This indicates that the
extinction of the reflex in this case was not due to fatigue or inhibition of motor cortical elements common to both of these reflexes.

The same results can be obtained if the conditioned reflex is extinguished by several repetitions with short intervals; in this case, the
reflex becomes progressively weakened and finally extinguished. Again,
in this case, other analogous reflexes do not manifest extinction (Figure 122). In this dog, conditioned withdrawal of the right foreleg was
established to several conditional stimuli, a tone of 200 c./sec., the
sound of a metronome and a light from an electric light bulb. When
the reflex to the 200 c./sec. tone was extinguished, the metronome
and light could still elicit reflexes. When the reflex to the light was
extinguished, the reflex to the tone was reestablished despite the fact
that prior to this the reflex to light was repeatedly tested. This clearly
indicates that the extinction of the conditioned reflex did not depend
upon fatigue or inhibition of those motor elements of the cortex which
are common to the same group of reflexes.*

One might think that the extinction under discussion depends upon
the fatigue of the initial neuronal structure of forward temporary
connections, in other words, elements which perceive conditional
stimulation. We proved by a special experiment that the extinction
cannot be due to this. Indeed, we showed that a new prolonged sound,
initially eliciting an orienting reaction, does not lose its negative
effect upon the conditioned defensive reflex even after it has lost the
ability to evoke the orienting reaction. If such a negative stimulus,

---

*We showed the universality of the conditional extinction by the results
of the following experiment (Liberson, W. T., and Marques, P., Le Travail
Humain 1:204, 1933). A subject was asked to exercise daily on an electric
bicycle for several months and the increase of his pulse was recorded. One
day the current was not turned on in the bicycle and the subject had to
pedal without resistance. This was repeated daily for a week. The first day
with no "reinforcement" the pulse increased during the first minute as much
as during the actual work done previously. However, 3 days later, the pulse
decreased during the first minute of exercise *below* the resting level, as a
result of an active process of inhibition. Finally, the pulse stabilized at a
level slightly above the resting cardiac rate. This experiment reveals a direct
conditioned inhibition of the heart rate, probably through the vagus nerve,
as a result of an extinction of the conditioned cardiac reflex.

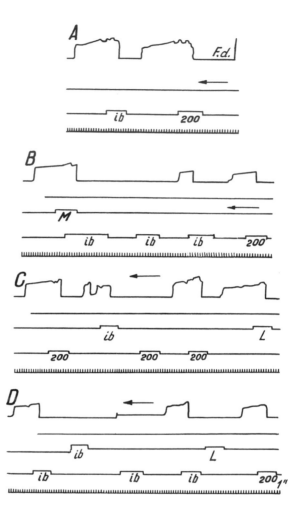

Fig. 122

Interaction of the conditioned analogous reflexes after extinction of one of
them by means of several repetitions (dog). The same conditioned reflexes
of the right foreleg were established to a tone of 200 c./sec., sounding of
a metronome and light of an electric bulb. Each time the conditional signal
lasted 10 sec. and was repeated 10 sec. after cessation of the preceding
reflex. A, Beginning of extinction to the tone of 200 c./sec.; B, fifteenth to
eighteenth repetition of the tone when the reflex was already extinguished.
At that time, another condition signal, M, (metronome) produced a considerable reflex. After this experiment, the effect of the light, L, was tested
five times in a row and it also elicited a reflex; C, the fifth trial with light
elicited a reflex and after 10 sec. the tone also elicited a reflex; D, at the
end of a prolonged series of trials of different signals recorded 3.5 min.
after tracings C; the 200 c./sec. tone elicited the reflex only with a prolonged
interval of 37 to 48 sec. At the same time, light did not elicit a reflex even
with an interval of 1.5 min. (Beritoff, 1927.)

326

bell or metronome, is kept in action for scores of minutes, and a conditioned sound, for example, a 600 c./sec. tone, is presented, the latter will still fail to elicit the conditioned reflex. It was concluded from this that during an acute extinction of a reflex, when the conditional sound is continued no more than a few minutes, the cortical elements receiving this sound should not be fatigued or inhibited. Therefore, during an acute extinction, neither the terminal neuronal elements of the forward temporary connections (the efferent projectional pyramids) nor their initial structure (the stellate cells and other receiving elements) are fatigued or inhibited; the temporary connections themselves are obviously involved (Beritoff, 1927, 1932).

Yet, by means of other experiments we found that when a dog has two analogous reflexes on the same leg, extinction of the older and the stronger reflex by repeating nonreinforced trials in succession, at intervals of 10 to 20 seconds, will also affect the other relatively weak and more recently established reflex. This so-called secondary extinction does not last long. It can be revealed only in cases when the second reflex is tried during the conditional stimulation corresponding to the extinguished reflex, or within some seconds afterward. Since for all these reflexes the final points of the temporary connections and entire descending nervous path are common, whereas the temporary connections consist of different pathways, it follows that the depressant action of one reflex upon another may take place in the efferent apparatus. But we know that even after the absolute extinction of a conditioned flexion of the leg, electrical stimulation of the skin of this leg elicits an intense unconditioned flexion. It follows then that in this case fatigue or inhibition occurs at the end of the cortical pathway, but still not in the subcortical motor effector mechanism (Beritoff, 1927, 1932).

Such has been our experimental basis for the localization of extinction in the cortical substrate of the conditioned reflex. Recent electroencephalographic investigations of the conditioned reflex confirm many of the above-discussed theoretical assumptions. Roitbak (1956, 1958a, b) found that after the extinction of the orienting reflex to auditory stimuli, the latter continues to have an effect upon the cortex for many minutes. Primary potentials continue to be elicited in the auditory zone of the cortex, with an initial positive oscillation followed by an alpha-like negative potential. This observation proves that the receptive stellate cells in the auditory zone continue to be activated without fatigue or inhibition for a long time after the extinction of the orienting reaction.

It was also found that even during the extinction of a conditioned food-getting reflex elicited by auditory stimuli the primary responses evoked by these stimuli not only are not decreased, but on the contrary are increased. The positive as well as the negative potentials become higher in amplitude, although fast activity and the beta waves activated during the formation of the conditioned reflex are now decreased (Figure 123). As the increased activation of the beta activity was associated with the formation of the temporary connections, the decrease of this activity during extinction suggests the presence of either fatigue or inhibition of the temporary connections.

Furthermore, Roitbak showed that during a prolonged presentation of the conditional stimuli to which the conditioned food-getting reflex was extinguished, the animal would show a transition to the sleep state; simultaneously slow negative potentials would arise in other cortical areas, and the amplitude of the beta activity would be decreased (Figure 124). Therefore, during extinction of the food-get-

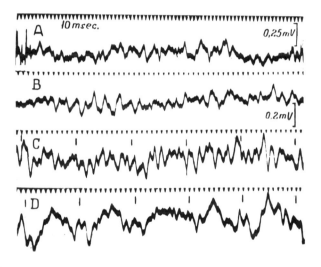

Fig. 123

Electrical activity of the cortical analyzer during extinction of the conditioned reflex. A cat with electrode implanted in the auditory region after the establishment of the conditioned alimentary reflex to the auditory stimuli (10 c./sec.). *A*, Electrical activity of the auditory area during feeding; *B*, electrical activity, the same area in the absence of eating or conditional signals; *C*, reaction to the auditory conditional stimuli 5 sec. after their onset during the occurrence of the conditioned reflex; *D*, sixth application of the conditional stimuli without reinforcement (intervals between auditory trials were 1 min.); the tracing was taken a few seconds after the beginning of this trial during which the conditioned reflex did not occur. (Roitbak, 1958a.)

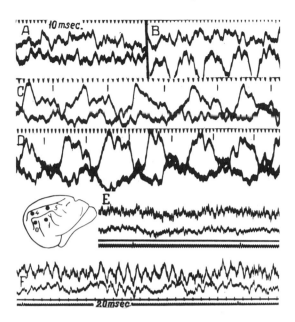

Fig. 124

Same cat, after extinction of the alimentary orienting reflex to the conditional auditory stimuli (10 per sec.). Potentials recorded from points 1 and 0 (upper tracings) and 4 and 5 (lower tracings). *A*, Spontaneous activity (cat did not sleep); *B*, cat started to doze; *C*, cat had been sitting calmly for 1 sec. from the beginning of the auditory stimuli; *D*, a few seconds after the onset of auditory stimuli; *E*, *F*, another cat; *E*, before stimulation; *F*, 25 sec. after onset of conditional auditory stimuli, when they cease to evoke an alimentary orienting reflex. (Roitbak, 1958a.)

ting conditioned reflex, we observe a widespread inhibition of the neuronal circuits responsible for the beta activity. Since slow potentials are generated presumably by activation of pyramidal dendrites, one may assume, according to our dendritic hypothesis of inhibition, that the widespread inhibition of fast potentials is due to the electrotonic spread of currents generated in the dendrites to the cell bodies of pyramidal neurons and their anelectrotonic action upon adjacent synapses.

During the extinction of the food-getting orienting conditioned reflex to auditory stimuli, slow potentials occur not only in the auditory cortex, where the peripheral impulses arrive via the specific system, but also all over the cortex; therefore, one cannot assume that the activation of the whole dendritic mass occurs by way of collaterals of the neuronal loops participating in the conditioned reflex. Rather, one should think that the collaterals of the temporary connections depress through the activation of the basal dendrites of these pyramids only the connections with the efferent projectional pyramids responsible for the peripheral motor reaction. This activation must be significantly increased as a result of the development of reverse connections. This could be expressed in the EEG by an increase of positive potentials.

The emergence of the slow potentials and the depression of the fast activity beyond the auditory area all over the cortical surface may be due, as Roitbak believes, to the involvement of the activity of inhibiting diencephalic mechanisms. The impulses from this area through a nonspecific system reach the apical dendrites of the pyramidal neurons all over the cortex and elicit there a local excitation which is expressed on the cortical surface by slow negative potentials.

The activation of the diencephalic-inhibiting mechanisms may be due to the bombardment from the cortex through the extrapyramidal pathways. This may be assumed because in cats without neocortex, orienting reactions to sound are not completely extinguished even after repeated auditory stimulation. In the normal cat, however, these reactions are extinguished after only a brief repetition of the stimulation. Therefore, the inhibiting diencephalic mechanisms of the orienting reaction are not activated directly through the ascending pathways. The motor centers of the orienting reaction of the head and eyes are located in the mesencephalon; during peripheral stimulation they are activated initially. The fact that in normal animals the orienting reaction is extinguished very rapidly, whereas decorticate animals do not show extinction, seems to signify that the activity of these motor mechanisms is regulated from the cortex. Probably during extinction this regulation is secured through the diencephalic-inhibiting mechanisms which seem to inhibit the cortex simultaneously with the inhibition of the motor mechanisms in the brainstem.

The reason for the lasting extinction of the conditioned reflex must be found in the structural changes of the temporary connections. Under conditions of repeated trials in which the conditional stimulus is not associated with the unconditional stimulus, the forward temporary connections will undergo a regression of their morphologic development. This must take place particularly in the synapses as we mentioned before.

The reverse connections from the analyzer of the unconditional stimulation, as well as from the motor analyzer to the analyzer of the conditional stimulation, probably develop further during extinction because of the frequent repetition of the conditional stimulus and the very slight fatigability of the stellate system receiving such stimulation. During each trial with the conditional stimulation, excitation of the motor analyzer, as well as the analyzer of the unconditional stimulation, must occur through the forward connections; from there the excitation must spread along the existing reverse connections toward the analyzer of the conditional stimulation, namely, to those of its receiving elements where excitability is increased by the conditional stimulus. Correspondingly the inhibiting action of the collaterals of these connections upon the neighboring pyramidal neurons is increased, particularly in the case of those which are responsible for the conditioned reaction.

It is probable that during the repeated application of a conditional stimulation there is also a morphologic development in certain cortico-thalamic pathways leading to the diencephalic-inhibiting mechanisms. Because of this, conditioned stimulation will more strongly activate these inhibiting mechanisms and elicit through them a pronounced inhibition upon the cortex as a lasting after effect.

ORIGIN OF RECEPTIVE DIFFERENTIATION IN CONDITIONED REFLEXES

During the formation of food-getting or defensive conditioned reflexes, the reaction at first occurs in response not only to the conditional stimulus, but also to other stimuli of the same kind. This phenomenon of signal or receptive generalization is undoubtedly related, in part, to an increase in the excitability of the conditional stimulus analyzer, the auditory analyzer, for example, if the conditional stimulus is a sound. The increase in excitability arises first because of the spread of excitatory events from the neuronal elements activated by the sound, and second because of the activation of elements in the analyzer by impulses spreading from neuronal complexes involved in the unconditional stimulation. But the unconditional stimuli also intensely activate the reticular formation of the brainstem, especially the alerting centers which maintain the excitability of the cortex at a high level. In addition, the unconditional stimulation activates the limbic system through which emotional reactions are mediated, those of fear in the case of painful unconditional stimulus, and those of alimentary excitement in the case of reinforcement for a hungry animal. The limbic system in turn activates somatovegetative centers in the hypothalamus and other divisions of the subcortex. These processes result in a general increase of excitability throughout the central nervous system and in the cerebral cortex in particular.

Electrophysiologically this generalization which occurs in the forming of conditioned reflexes is characterized by an increase in fast activity (beta rhythm) and a decrease in relatively slow potentials; this change involves almost the entire cortex (Kogan, 1949, Sakhiulina, 1955). During the stabilization of the reflex, the above effects are limited to the foci of the conditional and unconditional stimulation (Rabinovich and Trofimov, 1957). One must assume that the increase of fast activity in the entire cortex is determined mostly by the activating influence of nonspecific afferent bombardment arising in the reticular formation of the brainstem.

However, if the newly applied stimulus, which has some characteristics in common with the usual conditional stimulus is repeatedly presented, but is not associated with feeding, this stimulus not only will cease to elicit the conditioned reflex, but moreover will also affect the conditioned reflex in a negative way and inhibit it. This latter occurrence is demonstrated in Figure 125, where it is shown as occurring not only when the conditional sound is presented during the time of application of the newly introduced sound (experiment 3), but also when the conditional sound is presented soon after the cessation of the other sound (experiment 1). This depressing action of the second sound upon the conditioned reflex is a learned effect, and one must consider it as an expression of internal inhibition. The latter occurs essentially as a result of the same processes as those considered above, namely, because of the over development of reverse connections due to a lack of reinforcement.

According to the observation of Kogan (1949), the transition from generalization to differentiation is associated with the occurrence of slow potentials and the suppression of fast ones in the analyzer which perceives the conditional stimulation. It follows that the differentiated stimulus may elicit an inhibiting action in the analyzer; in other words, it may develop such a degree of internal inhibition that not only will it be unable to elicit the reflex, but also the usual conditional stimulus will be ineffective if both occur simultaneously or if the conditional signal is given soon after the differentiated stimulus.

It is known that a differentiation (differential inhibition) of the reflex by a new nonreinforced stimulus resembling the conditioned one leads to the simultaneous differentiation of other stimuli that are less similar to the original conditional signal; it therefore becomes easier to differentiate additional new stimuli.

New stimuli, more or less resembling the conditional stimulus, do not elicit the conditioned reflex after a few scores of reinforcements of the conditional signal. However, in order to differentiate a new stimu-

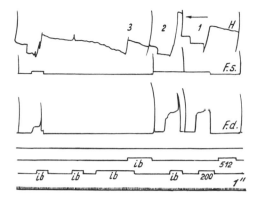

Fig. 125

Interaction of a differentiated stimulation and the conditioned reflex (dog).
H, Head; F.s., left foreleg; F.d., right foreleg. The right foreleg reflex was
formed to the 200 c./sec. tone. In experiment *1* differentiated stimulation
was applied (tone of 512 c./sec.), which did not produce any effects. Three
seconds later a conditional signal was tried. It elicited effects, but weaker
than in experiment 2, when it was not preceded by a differentiated stimulation. In experiment 3, a 512 c./sec. tone was given first and then a 200
c./sec. tone added and continued for another 25 sec. after the differentiated
sound. The conditional signal elicited only a slight raising of the head; after
that the dog put its head down and started to doze. The conditional tone
was interrupted for 11 sec. and then resumed, but the reflex was not present.
Then, the conditional sound was interrupted for 25 seconds and after this
interruption it again elicited the usual but rather slight reflex, weaker than
in experiment 2. Between experiments 2 and 3, the conditional tone was
associated with electrical stimulation. (Beritoff, 1927.)

lus that closely resembles the conditional signal, several hundred
reinforcements are necessary (Macharashvili, 1955). This differentiation must be related to a decrease of excitability in the internuncial
and associative pyramidal neurons around the temporary connections
of the conditioned reflex.

This hypothesis should be considered in the light of recent experiments of Jasper *et al.* (1958). They formed a defensive conditioned
reflex in monkeys by associating a flickering light with electrical stimulation of the paw. Simultaneously, they studied electrical activity of
the cortex by means of microelectrode recordings from the cells. During the formation of the conditioned defensive reflex, they recorded an
increase in the frequency of cell discharges in the corresponding cortical neurons of the sensory motor cortex. At the same time there was a
partial decrease in the frequency of discharges of cortical neurons in

the frontal and parietal areas, although the amplitude of the discharges in the parietal area increased.

The decrease of excitability, and of activity in general, around the temporary connections must have occurred mainly because of inhibition resulting from the spread of excitation along the collaterals of the temporary circuits of the conditioned reflex. In this way then, widespread inhibition must occur in the nearby internuncial and associative pyramidal neurons. But it is also quite probable that in this differentiation of the generalized reflex, an important role is played by the involvement of the corticothalamic neuronal pathways eliciting inhibition of the cortex through afferent bombardment from the reticular formation of the thalamus. The disappearance of the initially increased beta activity, first outside of the cortical focus of the conditional stimulation, and then in this focus itself, as well as the onset of the slow potentials spreading beyond the corresponding analyzer during the time of the differentiated stimulation, suggests first of all a participation of the reticular formation of the thalamus which, as mentioned above, must play a role in the general inhibition of cortical activity.

In a previous chapter, we considered the observation of a particular type of differentiation with regard to conditioned reflexes; namely, when a complex conditional stimulation elicits a reflex while its components do not, as a result of not being associated separately with the unconditional stimulus. Or conversely, the components will elicit the reflex because they have been associated with the unconditional stimulus while their combination, not reinforced, would not elicit the reflex. At that time, it was shown that when the complex or the components stop eliciting the reflex, they acquire a negative character. We came to the conclusion that this characteristic peculiarity of the complex stimulation is explained by the fact that, along with the formation of temporary connections to the components, there is a formation of forward and reverse temporary connections between the additional neuronal elements subjected to (1) subthreshold action of the components and (2) the effects of the neuronal complexes activated by the unconditional stimulus. We may assume from the above-formulated explanation of the mechanism of differentiation of conditioned reflexes, that the observed reflex effects result from the interaction of the exciting influence of forward temporary connections upon the pyramidal cells, which elicits the external response, and the inhibiting action of the reverse connections upon the same cellular elements through the activation of their dendrites.

Analogous results are obtained if a component with a negative action is applied first, and a positive-acting complex stimulus is presented immediately afterward. The latter may last several seconds without eliciting a positive reaction. One may assume that under the influence of the negative component, the excitability in the corresponding temporary connections is increased to such a degree that even after its withdrawal, these paths continue to be activated under the influence of the complex stimulus and thus the positive action of the latter is cancelled.

These negative after effects may last scores of seconds. However, if the positive stimulus is arrested for a few seconds, thus inducing a lowering of the excitability in the temporary connections of the negative reflex, then after a resumption of the positive stimulus, the reflex will take place. This interaction is typical for each case of an association of a negative with a positive reflex. For example, if the positive signal is tested a few seconds after the negative one, the reflex will take place. If, however, both are produced simultaneously and then only the positive one is presented, no reflex is observed; the latter signal must be discontinued for a while to lower the excitability in the pathways of the negative reflex, and then a reapplication of the stimulus will become effective.

ORIGIN OF THE EFFECTOR DIFFERENTIATION OF CONDITIONED MOTOR REFLEXES

In the formation of conditioned motor reflexes, the development of temporary connections is associated with an effector differentiation. For example, in the case of a defensive conditioned reflex, instead of a pronounced orienting reaction and a complex movement of escape with increased respiration and yelping, a limited head movement develops together with a localized contraction of the leg muscles responsible for its withdrawal. We have ascribed this phenomenon to the development of more stable temporary short connections between the analyzer for conditional stimuli and the motor analyzer. As we stated in 1920–1922, temporary connections may be of different degrees of complexity, especially when initially formed. For example, during the establishment of a conditioned defensive reflex to a sound, by pairing the latter with the electric stimulation of the right foreleg, temporary connections are formed through the somesthetic analyzer. as well as directly from the auditory analyzer to the motor one. However, at first, temporary connections through the somesthetic analyzer are preeminent. This is revealed by the appearance of the complex reaction so characteristic of a painful stimulus; namely, forced orienting movements with the head, general escape reactions, yelping, increased frequency of respiratory movements, etc. This must result from the activation of subcortical motor mechanism through the extrapyramidal pathways from the somesthetic analyzer. But later on the direct connections between the auditory and motor analyzers take over; this results in the much more limited reaction described above (Beritoff, 1922a). This latter simplified reaction results from the preferential development of the temporary connections with those neuronal complexes of the motor analyzer that are responsible for leg withdrawal.

One must assume that electric stimulation of the skin of a leg increases excitability most of all in the corresponding complex of neurons of the motor analyzer, and this excitability is further sustained by the proprioceptive stimuli, arising from the moving leg. Because of this the neuronal complex begins to react to all kinds of stimuli, including the conditional stimulus. This seems to involve the same phenomenon as the one revealed by the experiments of Roitbak (1953). He showed in the cat that during a tetanizing stimulation of the cortex or of the subcortical white matter there is at first an appearance of electrical activity to the rhythm of the stimulation in the more or less wide area around the stimulated point. But later on, not far from the stimulated point, a different kind of electrical activity appears in a limited area of the cortex. This activity shows a different rhythm which is obviously due to the excitation of new circuits made of different intermediary and associational neurons (Figures 126 and 127). These figures show that this complex of neurons becomes the focus of a heightened excitability easily responding to the influence of other stimuli.

Electrographic investigations showed that during the formation of a conditioned defensive reflex, the electrical activity of the cortex is subject to a progressive change. At first, during the period of formation of the reflex, when the animal reacts to the conditional stimulus more or less violently, electrographic activity of the cortex is characterized by an increased desynchronization and by a disappearance of relatively slow waves over a large surface of the cortex (Kogan, 1949, Roitbak, 1958a, b). However, with the formation of a stable defense reflex, the normal background electrical activity is reestablished with the exception of those cortical foci which are activated by the conditional and unconditional stimuli.

The conditioned activity of the cortex affects the electrical activity, as is shown by several electroencephaloscopic investigations. Livanov (1958) noted in rabbits that in the initial period of the formation of

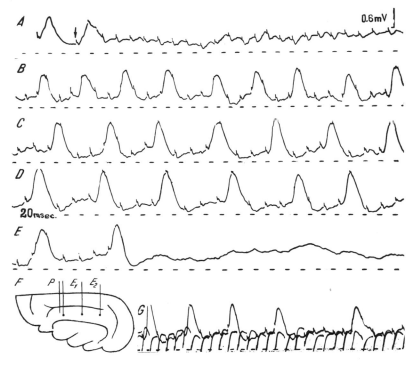

Fig. 126

Rhythmic responses of the cortex of the cat during tetanizing stimulation.
Sleep induced by pentobarbital (Nembutal). A pair of stimulating electrodes, P, and the recording electrode, E_1, were applied to the surface of
the gyrus suprasylvius. The distance between them was 6 mm. Intensity of
stimulation was 30 volts. A, At the beginning the effects of a single stimulus
is shown; then indicated by the arrow, stimulation at 40 c./sec. was applied.
B, 8 sec. after the beginning of stimulation; C, 9 sec. later; D, 10 sec. later;
E, end of stimulation. After this, a second recording electrode, E_2, was
applied 10 mm. from the stimulating electrode. The diagram indicates the
position of these electrodes. G, Biopotentials recorded simultaneously from
point E_1 (upper tracing) and from point E_2 (lower tracing); the tracing
was taken 15 sec. after the beginning of the tetanizing stimulation (40
c./sec., 30 volts). (Roitbak, 1953.)

a conditioned defensive reflex, foci of negativity, projected over the
screen of the electroencephaloscope, arise for very short periods of
time in different parts of the cortex. During this time, the conditioned
reflex appears as a general movement of escape. But later on more
stable foci of electronegativity are formed in the cortex, at first in
the frontal area affected by the unconditional electrical stimulation

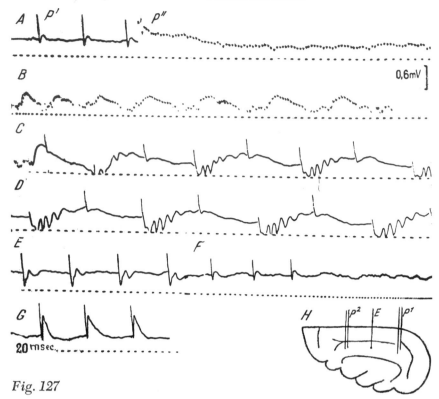

Fig. 127

Rhythmic responses of a focus of heightened excitability in the cortex of the cat as a result of intercurrent stimuli. Superficial Nembutal narcosis. Stimulating electrodes, P^1, P^2, and a recording electrode, E, applied to gyrus suprasylvius, (diagram H). A, Threshold stimulation (4 volts) via electrode P^1 at 8 c./sec. and then additional strong, 40 volt, stimulation through electrode P^2 at 100 c./sec.; B, continuation of combination P^1 and P^2, resulting in occurrence of slow low frequency waves; C, end of stimulation via P^2 while stimulation via P^1 continued; D, direct continuation of record C; E, 10 sec. after D.; F, 40 sec. after suspension of stimulation through P^1; G, effect of strong stimulation (25 volts) via P^1. (Roitbak, 1953.)

of the skin, and then in the occipital area where the conditional visual stimulation is projected. Still later, additional focus is formed in the motor area, that which corresponds to the activated leg. It is characteristic that these foci move over the surface of the cortex in a certain direction, from the occipital areas to the somesthetic or the motor areas. All this indicates the onset of well-developed temporary connections between these foci.

Finally, according to Livanov (1958), after a great number of reinforcements, when the conditional reaction is limited to a simple movement of the leg, a focus of excitation may not appear at all in the somesthetic area during the conditional stimulation.

This progressive change in cortical electrical activity is quite consistent with the theoretical concept developed by us concerning the formation of a conditioned defensive reflex. It seems that at the beginning of the formation of a conditioned reflex, when it is associated with a considerable emotional component, this reflex occurs with the participation of the limbic system. This is why this initial defensive reaction does not find expression in the electrical activity of the neocortex. As a result of repeated conditioning trials stable foci of excitation arise in the somesthetic, visual and motor areas with a path of negativity between these areas (represented by a row of luminous points on the screen of the oscilloscope). We therefore witness the generation of temporary connections, long ones through the somesthetic area, as well as short ones from the occipital area directly to the motor one. Still later the fact that the focus in the somesthetic area often fails to occur when the conditional signal is given, supports our basic contention that with strengthening of the short temporary connections, the long path through the somesthetic area becomes inactive. Such stable, active foci have been observed in rabbits, even in the absence of a conditional signal. This may be due to conditional stimulation from the total experimental environment.*

*A changing degree of participation of the hippocampus in different phases of conditioning was demonstrated by the following experiment (Liberson, W. T., and Ellen, P., in *Recent Advances in Biological Psychiatry*, Grune & Stratton, Inc., pp. 158–171, 1960). An avoidance reaction of the rat was conditioned by a presentation of a 3 c./sec. flicker. During the early phases of conditioning, there was a progressive incidence of this rhythm in the resting electroencephalogram (between the periods of actual presentation of the flicker). However, when the efficiency of the conditional stimulus approached its maximum, the incidence of the induced 3 c./sec. activity progressively decreased. It disappeared in the hippocampus when the conditioned avoidance behavior became stable. Analogous observations were made during the actual presentation of the flicker, which resulted in a driven 3 c./sec. rhythm. Here again the participation of the hippocampus, as expressed by electrical manifestations of the rhythm perceived by the animal, was evident during the formation of the conditioned behavior; it progressively disappeared when this behavior became stable.

That the hippocampus participates in the higher processes of integration of significant stimuli is illustrated by another experiment (Liberson, W. T., and Cadilhac, J., EEG Clin. Neurophysiol. 6:710–711, 1954; Liberson, W. T., Amer. J. Physchiat. 112:91–106, 1955; Liberson, W. T., in *Rhinencephale et Comportement*, Semaine Neurophysiol. Salpetriere, Paris, 1956). When flashes of light were regularly alternated with clicks, the hippocampal

Recently, the same kind of switching from the long temporary connections to the short pathways, without participation of the somesthetic analyzer, was confirmed by Jasper *et al.* (1958) with oscillographic techniques. They found that during the formation of a conditioned defensive reflex in monkeys, evoked potentials may be initially observed in the somesthetic analyzer, but that later on they stop occurring there. At the same time, they may still be present in the motor zone. This is explained by Jasper as a shift in the central activating mechanisms, from the sensory link of the conditioned reflex to the motor one.

In the case of the formation of a conditioned food-getting reflex, at first a long path to the olfactory analyzer or the taste analyzer is formed; thus feeding motor and secretory effects are generated. As was discussed previously, the interoceptive analyzer may be responsible for the unconditioned and conditioned secretory reactions. Impulses arising from the taste analyzer reach the efferent secretory pyramidal system through the interoceptive analyzer. It follows that interoceptive cortical neurons must also enter into temporary connections with the analyzer of the conditional stimulus. These shorter temporary connections are developed later, but when they develop sufficiently they may independently elicit a conditioned salivary reaction. This appears to have occurred in an experiment by Rozhanski. He observed that a dog, while in a dozing state, may salivate in response to the conditional stimulus without exhibiting an orienting reaction, even without opening its eyes or being awakened (Rozhanski, 1913). This reaction must, therefore, be carried out over a short pathway, from the focus of the conditional stimulation toward the cortical secretory neurons, directly through the interoceptive analyzer.

---

evoked potentials responding to auditory stimuli became quite irregular and those responding to the flashes of light completely disappeared. However, when, instead of the regular alternation of flashes and clicks, consecutive flashes were presented to the animal, the evoked potentials reappeared and followed each flash for a brief period of time. Thus effects of "surprise" could be recorded in the hippocampus. (Editor.)

14 SUMMARY AND CONCLUSIONS

We call behavior those complex motor acts of animals and men which permit the organism to adapt to different environmental conditions for the purpose of satisfying natural needs. There are two types of behavior of higher vertebrates. One type is conditioned by heredity or an inborn organization of the nervous system. In this kind of behavior, each of its segments is an unconditional reflex elicited by the stimulation of exteroceptors or interoceptors. This type also comprises the instinctual behavior in which an important role is played by activation of the central nervous system by various active substances manufactured by either endocrine glands or the nervous system itself. If an inborn or instinctual behavior is repeated under the same conditions several times, it is modified because of the additions of individually acquired conditioned reflexes.

The second type of behavior involves activities of the central nervous system which is reorganized on the basis of previous experiences. This type of behavior is guided by an image or a concrete representation of vitally important objects. The creation of such an image may take place immediately following a single perception of an object at the time it directly influences the organism. The image of any environmental object is always created under some specific conditions and is so closely related to these conditions that it is reproduced and projected to the environment not only when a part of it is present but also when any component of the environmental situation under which it was perceived initially, is present. The image of such an object is created immediately on the basis of perceptions elicited with participation of different types of receptors such as visual, auditory, olfactory, or those located in the skin and muscles. However, this image is perfected by each new perception of the object. This is why the appearance of an image of a vitally important object may elicit the same kind of goal-directed behavior as the perception of the object itself.

Individual behavior directed by such images constitutes the highest form of behavior of vertebrates. Both types of behavior—that which

341

is regulated by the principle of stimulus-response, and that which is directed by the images from the outside world—are also characteristic of human behavior. In early childhood, these are the only two types of behavior known to man. However, adults may exhibit a still higher form of behavior which is planned and industrious. This behavior is characterized by the fact that prior to the beginning of the behavioral act, its plan may be verbalized and also mental representation of the end results is present in the mind. It is essentially based not only on the experience of a given individual but also on the historical background of the society to which the individual belongs.

Image-driven behavior of animals and men is further characterized by the observation that the individual establishes spatial relationships between images and between the images and himself. These spatial relationships are created with the participation of the visual and vestibular analyzers. When the visual and labyrinthine perceptions are lacking, animals and men are unable to orient themselves in a given environment with only the other senses to aid them.

The neural substrate responsible for the generation of images of different objects seems to be located in the cerebral cortex, and its principal elements are believed to be the stellate cells with a pericellular axonal network located in the third and fourth layers of the primary areas of each analyzer. The threshold of excitability of these sensory stellate neurons, which has to be reached for their activation, with a resulting subjective feeling, is a function of a continuous bombardment via a nonspecific activating system originating in the reticular formation.

In order to generate a concrete image of an object, a certain number of the stellate cells of one or several analyzers stimulated by this object are integrated in a certain functional system with the help of a great number of internuncial and associational pyramidal neurons. The cells of these neurons are located at the periphery of the analyzers, or between different analyzers in the so-called association areas, and are found mostly in the intermediary layers of the cortex.

The perception of an external object as well as the reproduction of the image of this object elicits an orienting movement in the direction of the image projected into the environment. This reflex is entirely due to the presence, in the visual, auditory and somesthetic analyzers, of the projectional pyramidal neurons responsible for generating movements of the head and eyes. These neurons are closely associated with the afferent thalamic system, which activates them either directly or through the internuncials as well as via the stellate sensory neurons. This is why the orienting reaction takes place not only during the perception of the object but also during the reproduction of its image. Following the orienting movement of the head, one observes the running of the animal either toward the location of the projected image if the corresponding object is needed, or away from the location if the image is related to a noxious object. This movement of the animal takes place either through inborn or through individually acquired reflexes.

In the goal-directed movement of the animal, which takes place after the orienting movement of the head, an essential role is played by the associated stimulation of the labyrinthine, visual, skin, muscle, and other receptors. These stimuli become conditional signals of certain movements and turns of the animal which occur during the repetition of the same image-driven individual behavior arising in the same situation. Because of this repetition, any image-driven individual behavior may be transformed into an automatic behavior. Each segment of the latter behavior is conditioned by concurrent or preceding stimulation of a conditional character. Here again, a representation of the vitally important object takes place; however, this mental representation directs behavior only when the automatic conditioned performance of behavior cannot be carried out in view of an unusual modification of a standard situation.

The formation of a conditioned reflex as well as of the image of an external object is based on the establishment of temporary connections. During the perception of the outside world, temporary connections between perceiving sensory neurons of the neocortex are formed immediately during the very first concurrent or consecutive stimulation of these neurons. In the neocortex this event is responsible for the creation of the integrated images of the outside world capable of being reproduced in the future.

The temporary connections in the paleocortex, that is, the limbic system, between the perceiving neuronal elements and those that generate emotional feelings, are also established immediately.

The formation of the temporary connections between the perceiving stellate neurons of the neocortex and the projectional pyramidal neurons necessitate, however, a repetition of the association of stimuli. This is how various conditioned defensive and salivatory reflexes are formed. The establishment of these temporary connections is based not only on the functional and morphological development of neuronal circuits, made of internuncial and associational neurons, but also on their synaptic endings on the projectional pyramidal neurons.

Each behavioral reaction results from a stimulation of a certain complex of neurons in the cortex and other divisions of the brain, as well as from the inhibition of the remaining cerebrum. We believe that inhibition in the cerebral cortex, just as in the brainstem and the spinal cord, is due to an activation of the dendrites of certain types of neurons. We formulated a hypothesis according to which the inhibition of nervous cells in the central nervous system is due to an anelectrotonic blockade of their synapses by the slow currents electrotonically spreading from their dendrites. However, inhibition does not result from such a process in all nervous cells. It is assumed, for example, that the sensory stellate cells of the cerebral cortex are not inhibited through their dendrites. Nevertheless, they may cease to be activated because of the inhibition of the pyramidal neurons which integrate their activity as well as that of the neurons of the nonspecific thalamic nuclei in which the facilitating bombardment of the cortical stellate cells originates.

During the performance of each behavioral act, there is a reciprocal stimulation and inhibition of certain cerebrospinal systems of neurons and generation of coordinated movements for the purpose of adaptation to the environment. Moreover, there is a more or less widespread general inhibition of the remaining cerebrospinal system of neurons. The mechanisms of this general inhibition are believed to be localized in the first layer of the cerebral cortex and in the reticular formation. In the spinal cord this mechanism is represented by the substantia gelatinosa of Rolando. General inhibition, as in the case of reciprocal inhibition, must result from the activation of the dendritic mass.

The general inhibition is responsible for the fact that the behavior reaction takes place as a whole. It is because of inhibition that there is localization of excitation in a certain system of neurons, in response to each external or internal stimulation. This constitutes a mechanism by which the central nervous system is protected from being stimulated by unrelated stimuli. However, it is significant that certain weak stimuli may elicit general inhibition without any outward reaction. In such a case, the biological meaning of the general inhibition seems to be the protection of the organism from unnecessary expenditure of energy in response to weak, unusual or indifferent stimuli.

Any behavioral act takes place for the satisfaction of a certain organic need. Behavior aimed at the satisfaction of the alimentary needs triggers an emotional feeling of hunger, while a complete satisfaction of this need is associated with an emotional sense of satiation. Satisfaction of the alimentary needs is associated with different emotional feelings depending on the type and amount of food involved.

Emotional feelings are believed to be elicited by the activation of a certain type of the cellular elements of the paleocortex. These sensory elements seem to be the stellate cells with short axons as in the case of the neocortex. The animal without neocortex may manifest full emotional reactions: feelings of hunger and satiation, fear and rage, as well as the corresponding external expressive reactions. However, the cerebral cortex is able to regulate the emotional reactions in such a way that they are integrated into the behavioral act aimed at the adaptation of the organism to the conditions of the environment. Animals deprived of the neocortex are unable to exhibit an alimentary behavior that is directed by the spatial images of food; in general, they are unable to orient themselves in the environment on the basis of visual, auditory and labyrinthine perceptions. In such animals, conditioned alimentary reflexes may be formed, such as leaving the cage to feed themselves following auditory and optic stimuli. Such reflexes are established with considerable difficulty and are irregular as well as being scarcely differentiated. However, in animals without the neocortex, fear reactions to indifferent stimulus associated with painful electrical stimulation of the skin may be established as easily as in normal animals.

The paleocortex is activated by peripheral stimuli transmitted through the brainstem as well as by the stimulation arising in the neocortex. It is probable that somewhere in the cortex or in the subcortex there is a nervous substrate that integrates the activities of both the neocortex and the paleocortex. Nevertheless, apparently an external stimulation may activate the paleocortex through this integrating center as well as via the neocortex and elicit directly a corresponding emotional excitation and the associated generation of a psychoneural process responsible for the formation of some images.

Thus, the behavioral act always results from the total activity of the central nervous system from the cortex to the spinal cord inclusively. It is directed toward the satisfaction of a certain organic need. In this act, the neocortex participates by formation of images of the outside world, the paleocortex by the generation of emotional excitation, and all other divisions of the cerebrum and the spinal cord by the processes of excitation in certain nuclei and nervous pathways and an inhibition of the remaining mass of the central nervous system.

REFERENCES AND INDEX

REFERENCES

Adrian, E. D., 1924. Some recent work on inhibition. Brain, 47, 399.

Adrian, E. D., 1936. The spread of activity in the cerebral cortex. J. Physiol. 88, 127–161.

Adrian, E. D., and Buytendijk, F. J. J., 1931. Potential changes in the isolated brain stem of the goldfish. J. Physiol. 71, 121–135.

Agduhr, E., 1920. Studien über die postembryonale Entwickelung der Neuronen und die Verteilung der Neuriten in den Wurzeln der Spinalnerven. J. Psychol. u. Neurol. 25, 463.

Akert, K. M., and Anderson, B., 1951. Experimentaler Beitrag zur Physiologie des Nucleus caudatus. Acta Physiol. Scandinav. 22, 281–298.

Aladjalova, N., 1960. Slow Electric Processes in the Brain. 128 pp. Moscow, Gosisdat.

Almeida, M. O. de, Moussatché, H., and Dias, M. A., 1938. Recherches sur l'inhibition de Ch. Richet. Arch. internat. physiol. 47, 277–288.

Amassian, V. E., 1951. Cortical representation of visceral afferents. J. Neurophysiol. 14, 433–460.

Anderson, S., and Gernandt, B. E., 1954. Cortical projection of vestibular nerve in cat. Acta oto-laryng. Suppl. 116, 10.

Anokhin, P. K., 1949. Main problems of a study of higher nervous activity. In: Problems of Higher Nervous Activity. Moscow, Gosisdat, pp. 9–128.

Anokhin, P. K., 1958. Internal Inhibition as a Problem of Physiology. Gosisdat, Moscow.

Ariens Kappers, C., 1927. On neurobiotaxis. A psychical low in structure of the nervous system. Acta psychiat. et neurol. 2, 118.

Ariens Kappers, C., Huber, G. C., and Crosby, E. C., 1936. The Comparative Anatomy of the Nervous System of Vertebrates. New York, Macmillan.

Asratyan, E. A., 1937. Anatomico-histological base of conditioned reflective activities of the higher animals. Nature, Leningrad, 12, 74–88.

Asratyan, E. A., 1941. Das "Schaltungsprinzip" bei der bedingt-reflektorischen Tätigkeit. J. Physiol. U.S.S.R. 30, 13–18.

Asratyan, E. A., 1952. Contribution to the study of the physiology of temporary connextions. Transaction of the 15th Conference on "Problems of Higher Nervous Activity"; dedicated to 50 years of Pavlov's study on conditioned reflexes. Moscow-Leningrad, Gosisdat, 68–99.

Bailey, P., and Bremer, F., 1939. A sensory cortical representation of the vagus nerve. J. Neurophysiol. 1, 405–412.

Bajandurov, B., 1926. Physiology of conditioned inhibition in birds. J. Exper. Biol. & Med., Moscow *4*, 10/11, 210–212.

Bakuradze, A., 1943. General inhibition in the central nervous system from mechanical stimulations of the skin. Trans. Beritashvili Physiol. Inst., Tbilisi *5*, 105–124.

Barron, D. H., and Matthews, B. H. C., 1935. Intermittent conduction in the spinal cord. J. Physiol. *85*, 73–103.

Barron, D. H., and Matthews, B. H. C., 1938. The interpretation of potential changes in the spinal cord. J. Physiol. *92*, 276–321.

Beburishvili, N., 1937. Über die Einwirkung der optischen und akustischen Reizungen auf die Bewegungsreaktion beim Frosche. Trans. Beritashvili Physiol. Inst., Tbilisi *3*, 345–360.

Bechterew, W. M., 1898. Spinal and Cerebral Conducting Pathways. Part 2. Petersburg.

Bechterew, W. M., 1905. The Basis of the Study of Brain Function. Petersburg.

Bechterew, W. M., 1926. Spinal and Cerebral Conducting Pathways. 3rd ed., Moscow-Leningrad, Gosisdat.

Beck, A., 1914. Über elektrische erscheinungen im Zentral-nervensystem des Frosches. Pflügers Arch. ges. Physiol. *155*, 461–470.

Belenkov, N., 1950. Conditioned reflexes in cats devoid of cerebral cortex. I, II. Bull. Exper. Biol. & Med., Moscow *29*, 100–103, 182–185.

Belenkov, N. 1957. Function of some analyzers in animals devoid of cerebral cortex. J. Higher Nervous Activity, Moscow *7*, 291–298.

Beritoff, J. S., 1911. Ueber die reziproke Innervation der Skelettmuskeln bei der lokalen Strychninvergiftung der Rückenmarkes. I. Mitt, Trav. Soc. Natural. St. Pétersbourg, Bd. 41, fasc. 2, 245–302.

Beritoff, J. 1912. Über die reflektorische Nachwirkung der Skelettmuskeln des Rückenmarkfrosches. Arch. Anat. u. Physiol., Physiol. Abt. S. 1–22.

Beritoff, J., 1913. Zur Kenntnis der spinalen Koordination der rhythmischen Reflexe vom Ortsbewegungstypus. Pflügers Arch. ges. Physiol. *151*, 171–225.

Beritoff, J., 1914. Ueber die zentrale reziproke Hemmung auf Grund d. elektrischen Erscheinungen am Muskel. I, II, III Mitt. Ztschr. Biol. *65*, S. 75, 285, 307.

Beritoff, J., 1915a. On the mode of origination of labyrinthine and cervical tonic reflexes and on their part in the reflex reactions of the decerebrate preparation. Quart. J. Exper. Physiol. *9*, 199–229.

Beritoff, J., 1915b. To the study of labyrinth and neck tonic reflexes. II. The role of labyrinth and neck reflexes in reflex reactions of extremities of decerebrate preparations. Bull. Acad. Impér. Sci., Petrograd *2*, 853–882.

Beritoff, J., 1917. Upon the variability of the cortical reflex motor reaction under artificial augmentation of cortical excitability. J. Physiol. U.S.S.R. *1*, 12–34.

Beritoff, J., 1920. Textbook of Physiology (in Georgian), Tbilisi, Gosisdat.

Beritoff, J., 1922a. Allgemeine Charakteristik der Tätigkeit des Zentral-nervensystems. Ergebn. Physiol. *20*, 407–432.

Beritoff, J., 1922b. General Physiology of Nervous and Muscle Systems, Tbilisi, Georgian Gosisdat.

Beritoff, J., 1923. Über die reziproken Innervationen der Skelettmuskeln bei Reizung der hinteren Wurzeln. Pflügers Arch. ges. Physiol. *198*, 604–614.

Beritoff, J., 1924. Ueber den Rhythmus der reciproken Innervation der antagonistischen Muskeln bei Warmblütern. Ztschr. Biol. *80*, 171–192.

Beritoff, J., 1924a. Über den Übergang der Erregung von den sensiblen auf die motorischen Neurons. Pflügers Arch. ges. Physiol. *202*, 265–273.

Beritoff, J., 1924b. Über die neuro-psychische Tätigkeit der Grosshirnrinde. I Mitt. J. Psychol. u. Neurol. *30*, 217–256.

Beritoff, J., 1924c. On the fundamental nervous processes in the cortex of the cerebral hemispheres. I. Brain *47*, 109.

Beritoff, J., 1924d. On the fundamental nervous processes in the cortex of the cerebral hemispheres. II Brain *47*, 358.

Beritoff, J., 1926. Über die individuell-erworbene Tätigkeit des Zentral-nervensystems bei Tauben. Pflügers Arch. ges. Physiol. *213*, 370–406.

Beritoff, J., 1927. Über die individuell-erworbene Tätigkeitt des Zentral-nervensystems. J. Psychol. u. Neurol. *33*, 113–335.

Beritoff, J., 1928. Charakteristik und gegenseitige Wirkung der angeborenen Reflexakte des Verhaltens der Tiere. I, II Mitt. J. Exper. Biol. & Med., Moscow *20*, 106–116, 117–130.

Beritoff, J., 1929a. Ueber die angeborenen Reflexakte im Verhalten der Tiere. Ztschr. Biol. *89*, 59–76.

Beritoff, J., 1929b. Ueber die Entstehung der tierischen Hypnose. Ztschr. Biol. *89*, 77–82.

Beritoff, J., 1930. Science about behavior as reflexology. Uspekhi exper. Biol., Moscow, ser. 15, fasc. 3.

Beritoff, J., 1932. Individually Acquired Activity of the Central Nervous System. Tbilisi, Georgian Gosisdat, 350 pp.

Beritoff, J., 1934a. On the psychonervous foundations of individual behavior. Acad. Sc. U.S.S.R. Filiale Transc. Section Georgienne. Trav. Biol. T.I. 21-32.

Beritoff, J, 1934b. On the psychonervous principles of labor behavior of man. Acad. Sc. U.S.S.R. Filiale Transc. Section Georgienne. Trav. Biol. T.I. 41–76.

Beritoff, J., 1934c. Studies of individual behavior of dogs. I, VI, VII. J. Physiol. U.S.S.R. *17*, 176–183, 912–920, 1186–1197.

Beritoff, J., 1935. Studies of individual behavior of dogs. IX, X. J. Physiol. U.S.S.R. *19*, 496–507, 43–51.

Beritoff, J., 1937a. Excitation and inhibition in the central nervous system recorded from the point of view of its neuroneuropil structure. Trans. Beritashvili Physiol. Inst., Tbilisi *3*, 21–86.

Beritoff, J., 1937b. The neuropil of the brain stem and its physiological function. J. Physiol. U.S.S.R. *22*, 755–765.

Beritoff, J., 1938. Neuropil of the spinal cord and its physiological function. J. Physiol. U.S.S.R. *24*, 63–77.

Beritoff, J., 1941. On the excitation, inhibition and facilitation of the spinal cord. Trans. Beritashvili Physiol. Inst., Tbilisi *4*, 1–38.

Beritoff, J., 1945. On changes in psychonervous activity in pigeons after blast trauma. Trans. Beritashvili Physiol. Inst., Tbilisi *6*, 175–190.

Beritoff, J., 1947a. On the psychonervous mechanisms of attitude in individual behavior. J. Physiol. U.S.S.R. *33*, 301–312.

Beritoff, J., 1947b. The Main Forms of Nervous and Psychonervous Activity. Moscow-Leningrad, Acad. Sc. U.S.S.R.

Beritoff, J., 1948. General Physiology of Nervous and Muscle Systems. Vol. 2, Moscow, Acad. Sc. U.S.S.R., 130.

Beritoff, J., 1949. On the origin of slow potentials of the spinal cord. Gagra Colloquium, Vol. 1. Bioelectrical Potentials, Tbilisi, 209–251.

Beritoff, J., 1953. The role of vestibular and kinesthetic stimuli in the spatial orientation of animals. Trans. Physiol. Inst. Acad. Sc., Georgian S.S.R. *9*, 3–24.

Beritoff, J., 1956a. On the mechanism of external and internal inhibition. Gagra Colloquium, Vol. 2. Problem of the Nature of Central Inhibition, Tbilisi, 201–215.

Beritoff, J., 1956b. On the spatial orientation of man and animals in environment. Problems of Psychology, Moscow *4*, 54–65.

Beritoff, J., 1957a. On physiological mechanisms of behavior of higher vertebrates. Bull. Acad. Sc. U.S.S.R. ser. Biol. *2*, 137–153.

Beritoff, J., 1957b. On the spatial projection of perceived objects in the external environment by means of labyrinthine receptors J. Physiol. U.S.S.R. *43*, 600–610.

Beritoff, J., 1958a. On the perception of objects at a distance in higher vertebrates. Bull. Acad. Sc. U.S.S.R. ser Biol. *5*, 513–532.

Beritoff, J., 1958b. The role of the cerebral cortex in the spatial orientation of animals J. Physiol. U.S.S.R. *44*, 1017–1025.

Beritoff, J., 1959a. On the mechanism of spatial orientation in man. J. Higher Nervous Activity *9*, 3–13.

Beritoff, J., 1959b. Nervous mechanisms of Spatial Orientation of Mammals. Tbilisi, Acad. Sc. Georgian S.S.R., 346 pp.

Beritoff, J., 1959c. The role of emotional excitation in individual food-getting behavior. Trans. Physiol. Inst. Acad. Sc. Georgian S.S.R. *12*, 19–53.

Beritoff, J., and Bakuradze, A., 1939a. On the action of acetylcholine upon the central nervous processes of the spinal cord. Acta med. U.S.S.R. *2*, 371–383.

Beritoff, J., and Bakuradze, A., 1939b. On the nervous processes in the spinal cord resulting from stimulation of the posterior roots. J. Physiol. U.S.S.R. *27*, 387–406.

Beritoff, J., and Bakuradze, A., 1940a. On inhibition in the spinal cord. Doklady Acad. Sc. U.S.S.R. *26*, 961–964.

Beritoff, J., and Bakuradze, A., 1940b. Spinal cord inhibition as dependent on intensity, frequency and duration of stimulation. Doklady Acad. Sc. U.S.S.R. *26*, 965–968.

Beritoff, J., and Bakuradze, A., 1940c. On the action of acetylcholine upon the spinal cord. J. Physiol. U.S.S.R. *28*, 3–17.

Beritoff, J., and Bakuradze, A., 1940d. On the action of mechanical stimulation upon the spinal cord. J. Physiol. U.S.S.R. *28*, 18–24

Beritoff, J., and Bakuradze, A., 1941. General inhibition upon stimulation of the ventral roots. J. Physiol. U.S.S.R. *30*, 45–54.

Beritoff, J., and Bakuradze, A., 1943a. On the nature of the reflex responses elicited by electrical stimulation of the spinal cord. Trans. Beritashvili Physiol. Inst., Tbilisi 5, 1–38.

Beritoff, J., and Bakuradze, A., 1943b. General inhibition evoked by the stimulation of the receptors and sensory nerves of the visceral organs. Trans. Beritashvili Physiol. Inst., Tbilisi 5, 125–142.

Beritoff, J., and Bakuradze, A., 1943c. On the afferent pathways of the vegetative nervous system. Trans. Beritashvili Physiol. Inst., Tbilisi 5, 143–159.

Beritoff, J., Bakuradze, A., and Narikashvili, S., 1937. On the phenomenon of excitation and inhibition in the central nervous system. I, II. Trans. Beritashvili Physiol. Inst., Tbilisi 3, 147–171, 173–195.

Beritoff, J., Bakuradze, A., and Roitbak, A., 1948. On the electrical activities of the spinal cord of the cat. Trans. Beritashvili Physiol. Inst., Tbilisi 7, 89–128.

Beritoff, J., Beburishvili, N., and Tsereteli, M., 1934. Studies of the individual behavior of dogs. IV. J. Physiol. U.S.S.R. *17*, 688–697.

Beritoff, J., and Bregadze, A., 1929. Zur Physiologie des Verhaltens der Tiere auf eine Komplexreizung. III. J. méd.-biol., Moscow-Leningrad, *4*, 83–101.

Beritoff, J., and Bregadze, A., 1930. On the physiology of behavior in response to complicated stimuli. IV. J. méd.-biol., Moscow-Leningrad *1–2*, 104–126.

Beritoff, J., and Chichinadze, N., 1937. On the localization of cortical processes evoked by visual stimulations. Trans. Beritashvili Physiol. Inst., Tbilisi 3, 361–372.

Beritoff, J., and Dzidzishvili, N., 1934a. On the studies of microcephalic behavior. Acad. Sc. U.S.S.R. Section Georgienne. Trav. Biol., Tbilisi *1*, 75–104.

Beritoff, J., and Dzidzishvili, N., 1934b. Ueber die Beziehungen zwischen angeborene, individuall envorbener und bewusster Tätigkeit des Menschen. Acad. Sc. U.S.S.R. Section Georgienne. Trav. Biol. T.I., Tbilisi 1–73.

Beritoff, J., and Gedevani, D., 1941. Allgemeine Hemmung in der Grosshirnrinde. Mitt. Akad. Wiss. Georg. S.S.R. *2*, 157–168.

Beritoff, J., and Gedevani, D., 1945. On the electrical activity of the cerebral cortex in Monkeys (Macacus rhesus). Trans. Beritashvili Physiol. Inst., Tbilisi 6, 279–317.

Beritoff, J., and Gogava, M., 1937. The general inhibition of reflex activity. Trans. Beritashvili Physiol. Inst., Tbilisi 3, 265–274.

Beritoff, J., and Gogava, M., 1958. Electrotonic interaction of A and B nerve fibers. Unpublished observations.

Beritoff, J., and Kalabegashvili, S., 1944. Salivary secretion while imagining food. Trans. Tbilisi State Univ. 26a, 41–60.

Beritoff, J., and Khechinashvili, S., 1958. Vestibular function in space orientation. Bull. Acad. Sc., Georgian S.S.R. 13, 482.

Bertioff, J., and Kherkheulidze, N., 1958a. On the origin of spatial orientation in man. Bull. Acad. Sc., Georgian S.S.R. 20, 481–488.

Beritoff, J., and Kherkheulidze, N., 1958b. On spatial orientation in blind men. Bull. Acad. Sc. Georgian S.S.R. 20, 707–714.

Beritoff, J., Kvavilashvili, S., and Roitbak, A., 1950. Distortions produced by the transitional condenser in the resistance coupled amplifier at low frequency. Trans. Beritashvili Physiol. Inst., Tbilisi 8, 1–16.

Beritoff, J., and Ordzhonikidze, Z., 1958. General inhibition of the cerebral cortex. Unpublished observations.

Beritoff, J., and Roitbak, A., 1948. The electrical potentials of the spinal cord during inhibition. Trans. Beritashvili Physiol. Inst., Tbilisi 7, 69–88.

Beritoff, J., and Roitbak, A., 1950a. On the change of electrical potentials of the spinal cord during long stimulation. Utchenie zapiski L.G.U., Leningrad (Scientific papers of the Leningrad State University) 123, 185–201.

Beritoff, J., and Roitbak, A., 1950b. Oscillographic study of reflex activity of the spinal cord at strychnine poisoning. Trans. Beritashvili Physiol. Inst., Tbilisi 8, 43–92.

Beritoff, J., and Roitbak, A., 1953. Steady cortical potentials. Unpublished observations (cf. Beritoff, J., and Roitbak, A., Gagra Colloquium 1956).

Beritoff, J., and Roitbak, A., 1955. On the nature of central inhibition. J. Higher Nervous Activity, Moscow 5, 173–186.

Beritoff, J., and Roitbak, A., 1956. Oscillographic study of physical electrotonus. Gagra Colloquium 2, 228–266. Discussion – On the mechanism of external and internal inhibition. Tbilisi.

Beritoff, J., and Tsereteli, M., 1934. Studies of individual behavior of dogs. II, V. J. Physiol. U.S.S.R. 17, 184–195, 698–706.

Beritoff, J., Tsereteli, M., and Akhmeteli, M., 1934. Studies of individual behavior of dogs. III. J. Physiol. U.S.S.R. 17, 457–463.

Bethe, A., 1903. Allegemeine Anatomie und Physiologie des Nervensystems. Leipzig, G. Thieme.

Bishop, G., and Clare, M., 1953. Responses of cortex to direct electrical stimuli applied at different depths. J. Neurophysiol. 16, 1–19.

Bjalava, I., 1953. The fixing attitude and system work of brain hemispheres. Bull. Acad. Sc. Georgian S.S.R. 14, 635–642.

Blumenau, A., 1930. Data of the First All-Union Congress on studying the behavior of a man, Leningrad, 361.

Bregadze, A., 1930. The study of food-motor behavior on a complex figure. J. méd.-biol., Moscow-Leningrad, fasc. 6, 483–498.

Bregadze, A., 1945. The influence of the blast wave on the behavior of animals. Trans. Beritashvili Physiol. Inst., 6, 157–171.

Bregadze, A., 1950. Behavioral effects of frontal lobectomy in the cat. Tbilisi, Trans. Beritashvili Physiol. Inst. 8, 241.

Bregadze, A., 1953. Elaboration of a defensive conditioned reflex in dogs. Trans. Physiol. Inst. Georgian Acad. Sc., Tbilisi 9, 43–59.

Bregadze, A., 1956. The formation of temporary connections in dogs in response to indifferent stimuli. In: Problems of Modern Physiology of the Nervous and Muscle Systems. Symposium dedicated to J. Beritoff, Tbilisi, 279–284.

Bremer, F., 1936. Facilitation centrale par influences antidromiques. C. r. Soc. Biol., Paris, 121, 1374.

Bremer, F., 1949. Considérations sur l'origine et la nature des "ondes" cérébrales. EEG Clin. Neurophysiol. 1, 177–193.

Brown, T., 1911. Studies in the physiology of the nervous system. IX. Quart. J. Exper. Physiol. 4, 331.

Brown, T., 1912. Studies in the physiology of the nervous system. XI. Quart. J. Exper. Physiol. 5, 237–307.

Burns, B., 1951. Some properties of isolated cerebral cortex in the unanaesthetized cat. J. Physiol. 112, 156–175.

Burns, B., 1954. The production of after-bursts in isolated unanaesthetized cerebral cortex. J. Physiol. 125, 427–446.

Burns, B., and Grafstein, B., 1952. The function and structure of some neurons in the cat's cerebral cortex. J. Physiol. 118, 412–433.

Burns, B., Grafstein, B., and Olszewski, G., 1957. Identification of neurons giving burst responses in isolated cerebral cortex. J. Neurophysiol. 20, 200–210.

Buytendijk, F., 1936. Mind of the Dog. Boston, Houghton-Mifflin.

Bykoff, K. M., 1947. Cerebral Cortex and Internal Organs. Chapter XIX. Effect of removing different regions of the cerebral cortex upon the cortical regulation of the activity of internal organs. Moscow, Gosisdat, pp. 248–258.

Cannon, W., 1929. Bodily Changes in Pain, Hunger, Fear and Rage. An Account of Recent Research into the Function of Emotional Experiment, ed. 2. New York, Appleton.

Chang, H., 1951. Dendritic potential of cortical neurons produced by direct electrical stimulation of the cerebral cortex. J. Neurophysiol. 14, 1–21.

Chang, H., 1952. The cortical neurons with particular reference to the apical dendrites. Cold Spring Harbor Symposium. Quant. Biol., 17, 189.

Chang, H., 1953a. Cortical response to activity of callosal neurons. J. Neurophysiol. 16, 117–131.

Chang, H., 1953b. Interaction of evoked cortical potentials. J. Neurophysiol. 16, 133–144.

Chichinadze, N., 1939. On the localization of cortical processes originated by visual stimuli. J. Physiol. U.S.S.R. *26*, 213–218.

Chichinadze, N., 1940. Das Problem der Localization kortikaler Prozesse, welche durch optische Reize hervorgerufen werden. Mitt. Akad. Wiss. Georg. S.S.R., Tbilisi *1*, 609–614.

Chichinadze, N., 1946. On the duration of central inhibition. Bull. Acad. Sc. Georgian S.S.R. Tbilisi 7, 387–396.

Cholokashvili, E., 1953. Quantitative distribution of synapses on the cell body and dendritic branches of the spinal cord. Trans. Physiol. Inst. Acad. Sc. Georgian S.S.R., Tbilisi *9*, 161–169.

Cholokashvili, E., 1958. Some data concerning the dendrite pyramidal neurons of the cerebral cortex. Trans. Inst. Physiol. Acad. Sc. Georgian S.S.R. *11*, 207–230.

Clark, G., Kao, Liang Chow, Gillaspy, C., and Klotz, D., 1949. Stimulation of anterior limbic region in dogs. J. Neurophysiol. *12*, 459–464.

Coghill, G., 1929. Anatomy and the Problem of Behavior. Cambridge, Cambridge University Press.

Coghill, G., 1936. Integration and motivation of behavior as a problem of growth. J. Genet. Psychol. *48*, 3–19.

Cowan, W., and Powell, T., 1955. The projection of the midline and intralaminar nuclei of the thalamus of the rabbit. J. Neurol. Neurosurg. & Psychiat. *18*, 266–279.

Danilewsky, B., 1881. Ueber die Hemmung der Reflex- und Willkürbewegungen. Pflügers Arch. ges. Physiol. *24*, 489–525.

De Castro, F., 1951. Anatomical aspects of the ganglionic synaptic transmission in mammalians. Arch. internat. physiol. *59*, 479–525.

Dempsey, E., and Morison, R., 1943. The electrical activity of a thalamocortical relay system. Am. J. Physiol. *138*, 283–296.

De Robertis,   , 1959. Histopathology of the synapse. XXI International Congress of Physiological Sciences. Special lectures, 213–216.

Djavrishvili, T., 1956. On two-way temporary connections. Trans. Beritashvili Physiol. Inst. *10*, 163–187.

Djavrishvili, T., 1959. An oscillographic study of the interaction between nerve fibers. J. Physiol. U.S.S.R. *45*, 186–193.

Dunlop, C. W., 1958. Viscero-sensory and somato-sensory representation in the rhinencephalon. Electroenceph. Clin. Neurophysiol. 10, 297.

Dusser de Barenne, J., 1933. Welche Elemente der Grosshirnrinde bringen bei ihrer elektrischen Reizung die motorischen Reaktionen hervor? Pflügers Arch. ges. Physiol. *233*, 529–536.

Dusser de Barenne, J., and McCulloch, W., 1936. Extinction as a cortical phenomenon. In: Problems of Nervous Physiology and Behavior. Symposium dedicated to J. Beritoff, Tbilisi, 15–18.

Dusser de Barenne, J., and McCulloch, W., 1938. The direct functional interrelation of sensory cortex and opticthalamus. J. Neurophysiol. *7*, 176–186.

Dusser de Barenne, J., and McCulloch, W., 1939. Factors for facilitation and extinction in the central nervous system. J. Neurophysiol. *2*, 319–355.

Dusser de Barenne, J., and McCulloch, W., 1941a. Suppression of motor responses obtained from area 4 by stimulation of area 4s. J. Neurophysiol. *4*, 311–323.

Dusser de Barenne, J., and McCulloch, W., 1941b. Functional organization of sensory and adjacent cortex of the monkey. J. Neurophysiol *4*, 324–330.

Dzidzishvili, N., 1939. On the interaction of excitation and inhibition in the effect of skin stimulation. J. Physiol. U.S.S.R. *26*, 354–368.

Dzidzishvili, N., 1940a. On the general inhibition and facilitation caused by thermal stimulation of the skin. Mitt. Akad. Wiss. Georg. S.S.R. *1*, 217–224.

Dzidzishvili, N., 1940b. On the influence of acoustic and optic stimuli on reflex motor reactions. Mitt. Akad. Wiss. Georg. S.S.R. *1*, 461–468.

Dzidzishvili, N., 1956. Some experiments on the physiology of the cerebral cortex. In: Problems of Modern Physiology of the Nervous and Muscle Systems. Symposium dedicated to J. Beritoff, Tbilisi, 99–114.

Dzidzishvili, N., and Nutsubidze M. 1954. The effect of disconnection of different cortical areas upon reflex activity. Fifth Scientific Conference of Aspirants and Young Scientists of the Academy of Sciences of the Georgian S.S.R., Tbilisi, 117–119.

Dzidzishvili, N., and Nutsubidze, M., 1956. Conditioned reflex on increasing of the intensity of sound. J. Higher Nervous Activity, *6*, 726–731.

Earle, K., 1952. The tract of Lissauer and its possible relation to the pain pathway. J. Comp. Neurol. *96*, 93–108.

Ebbecke, U., 1919. Die kortikalen Erregungen. Leipzig.

Ebbecke, U., 1922. Membranänderung und Nervenerregung. Pflügers. Arch. ges. Physiol. *195*, 555–587.

Ebbinghaus, H., 1911-1912. Grundzüge der Psychologie. Leipzig.

Eccles, J., 1955. The Neurophysiological Basis of Mind. Oxford, Oxford University Press, 328 pp.

Eccles, J., 1957. The Physiology of Nerve Cells. Baltimore, Johns Hopkins Press.

Eckstein, A., 1919. Weitere Untersuchungen Zur tierischen Hypnose. Pflügers Arch. ges. Physiol., *177*, 38–55.

Entin, T., 1954. A study of synapses in the visual area of the cerebral cortex. Arch. Anat. Histol. & Embryol. Leningrad, *31*, f. 4, 25.

Fingel, C., and Kaada, B., 1960. Behavior "attention" and "fear" by cortical stimulation in the cat. Electroencephalog. & Clin. Neurophysiol. *12*, 575–588.

Flechsig, P., 1896a. Gehirn und Seele. Leipzig, Veit & Co.

Flechsig, P., 1896b. Lokalisation der geistigen Vorgänge. Leipzig, Veit & Co.

Forman, D., and Ward, J., 1957. Responses to electrical stimulation of the caudate nucleus in cats in chronic experiments. J. Neurophysiol. *20*, 230–244.

Förster, O., 1927. Die Leitungbahnen des Schmerzgefühls. Berlin. Urban u. Schwarzenberg.

Förster, O., Altenberg, H., and Kroll, F., 1929. Über die Beziehungen des vegetativen Nervensystems zur Sensibilität. Ztschr. ges. Neurol. u. Psychiat. *121*, 139–185.

Frank, K., and Sprague, J., 1959. Direct contralateral inhibition in the lower sacral spinal cord. Exper. Neurol. *1*, 28–44.

Fröhlich, A., and Meyer, H., 1922. Zur Frage der visceralen Sensibilität. Ztschr. ges. exper. Med. *29*, 87–113.

Fulton, J., 1926. Muscular Contraction and the Reflex Control of Movement. Baltimore, Williams and Wilkins, 318–320.

Gastaut, H., 1957. The neurophysiological basis of conditioned reflexes and behavior. In: Neurobiological Basis of Behavior. London, Ciba Symposium.

Gastaut, H., Naquet, R., Roger, A., Dongier, S., Regis, H., Morell, F., Jus, A., Jus, C., 1957. Neurophysiological interrelation of conditioned electroencephalographic reactions. Moscow, J. Higher Nervous Activity 7, 203–213.

Gastaut, H., and Roger, A., 1958. Neurophysiological basis of higher nervous activity. Moscow, International Colloquium of the Electroencephalographic Society, 6–71.

Gedevani, D., 1939a. The localization of the processes of general inhibition of antagonistic muscles and of isolated facilitation of the synergist in the neuronic elements of the spinal cord. J. Physiol. U.S.S.R. *26*, 374–383.

Gedevani, D., 1939b. On the conditions for the arising of general facilitation without preliminary inhibition. J. Physiol. U.S.S.R *26*, 384–388

Gedevani, D., 1941. On the inhibitory influence of the stimulation of n. vagus upon the central nervous system. Symposium dedicated to V. V. Voronin, Tbilisi, 110–117.

Gedevani, D., 1943. Research on cortical inhibition. Trans. Beritashvili Physiol. Inst., Tbilisi 5, 39–106.

Gedevani, D., 1947. Motor effects produced by stimulation of the cortical "pain center." Georgian S.S.R. Acad. Sc., Trans. Inst. Physiol. 7, 317–339.

Gellhorn, E., 1953. The physiological basis of emotion. Physiologic Foundation of Neurology and Psychiatry, Minneapolis, University of Minnesota Press.

Gerard, R., Marshall, W., and Saul, L., 1936. Electrical activity of the cat's brain. Arch. Neurol. & Psychiat. *36*, 675–738.

Gerebtzoff, M., 1940. Recherches sur la projection corticale du labyrinthe. I. Des effets de la stimulation labyrinthique sur l'activité électrique de l'écorce cérébrale. Arch. internat. physiol. *50*, 59–99.

Gerebtzoff, M., 1949. Recherches sur l'inhibition généralisée de Richet. Arch. internat. phsyiol. *56*, 286–310.

Gershuni, G., 1947. A study of subsensory reactions during the activity of the sense organs. J. Physiol. U.S.S.R. *33*, 393–412.

Gershuni, G., 1949a. Reflex reactions during the influence of external stimulations upon the sense organs of a man in connection with sensation. J. Physiol. U.S.S.R. *35*, 542–550.

Gershuni, G., 1949b. A study of auditory perception and conditioned reactions in man. Trans. Pavlov Physiol. Inst. *4*, 19–24.

Gershuni, G., 1958–1959. Regulation of the afferent flow in the auditory system. Gagra Colloquium, vol. 3. Tenth All Union Congress of Physiological Society *1*, 149.

Gershuni, G., Kozhevnikov, V., Maruseva, A., Chistovich, L., 1948. On peculiarities of formation of temporal connections to subliminal sound stimuli in man. Moscow, Bull. Biol. & Méd. exper. *26*, 205–209.

Glees, P., 1944. The anatomical basis of cortico-striate connections. J. Anat. *78*, 47–51.

Glees, P., and Wall, P., 1946. Fiber connections of the subthalamic region and the centro-median nucleus of the thalamus. Brain *69*, 195–208.

Gogava, M., 1939. A contribution to the problem of general inhibition and facilitation. Moscow, Bull. Biol. & Méd. exper. *7*, 75–77.

Goldstein, K., 1927. Die Lokalisation in die Grosshirnzinde nach den Erfahrungen am Kranken Menschen. In Handbuch d. normalen Pathologie und Physiologie, Vol. 10. Berlin, J. Springer, p. 600.

Golgi, C., 1883. Recherches sur l'histologie des centres nerveux. Arch. ital. biol. *3*, 285; *4*, 92. Quoted by Lenhossek, 1895.

Golikov, N., 1956. On the theory of central inhibition. Gagra Colloquium, Tbilisi *2*, 307–343.

Goltz, F., 1892. Der Hund ohne Grosshirn. Pflügers Arch. ges. Physiol. *51*, 570–614.

Gonzalez, A., 1932. The prenatal development of behavior in the albino rat. J. Comp. Neurol. *55*, 395–442.

Gottschik, J., 1955. Die Leistungen des Nervensystems, Jena, G. Fischer.

Granit, R., Leksell, L., and Skoglund, C., 1944. Fibre interaction in injured or compressed region of nerve. Brain *67*, 125–140.

Granit, R., 1956. Post-tetanic potentation, spasticity, myanesin. Problems of Modern Physiology of the Nervous and Muscle Systems. Tbilisi, Dedicated to J. Beritoff, 61–66.

Granit, R., and Skoglund, C., 1945a. Facilitation, inhibition and depression of the "artificial synapse" formed by the cut end of a mammalian nerve. J. Physiol. (London) *103*, 435–448.

Granit, R., and Skoglund, C., 1945b. The effect of temperature on the artificial synapse formed by the cut end of the mammalian nerve. J. Neurophysiol. U.S.S.R. *8*, 211–217.

Grastyán, E., Lissack, K., and Molnar, L., 1953. The functional relation between gyrus cinguli and caudate nucleus in the cat. Acta Physiol. Hung. *4*, 261–270.

Green, J. D., and Arduini, A. A., 1954, Hippocampal electrical activity in arousal. J. Neurophysiol. *17*, 533.

Hagbarth, K., and Kerr, D., 1954. Central influences on spinal afferent conduction. J. Neurophysiol. *17*, 295–307.

Hanbery, J., and Jasper, H., 1953 Independence of diffuse thalamo-cortical projection system shown by specific nuclear destructions. J. Neurophysiol. *16*, 252–271.

Hebb, D., 1946. On the nature of fear. Psychol. Rev. *53*, 259.

Henneman, E., Cooke, P., and Snider, R., 1948. Cerebellar projections to the cerebral cortex in cat and monkey. Am. J. Physiol. *155*, 443–443.

Henneman, E., and Snider, R., 1949. Electroanatomical studies on cerebellar projections to the cerebral cortex in cats and monkeys. Anat. Rec. *103*, 68.

Hernández-Péon, R., 1955. Central mechanisms controlling conduction along central sensory pathways. Acta neurol. latino-amer., *1*, 256–264. (Quoted by Magoun, H., The Waking Brain, Springfield, Charles C Thomas, 1958.)

Hernández-Péon, R., Dittborn, L., Borlone, M., and Davidovish, A., 1959. Changes of spinal excitability during hypnotically induced anaesthesia and hyperesthesia. Abstracts of XXI International Congress of Physiological Sciences, Buenos-Aires, p. 124.

Hernández-Péon, R., Gusman-Flores, C., Alcaras, M., and Fernandez-Guardiola, A., 1956. Photic potentials in the visual pathway during "attention" and photic "habituation." Fed. Proc. *15*, 91.

Hernández-Péon, R., and Hagbarth, K., 1954. Interaction between afferent and cortically induced reticular responses. J. Neurophysiol. *18*, 44–55.

Hernández-Péon, R., Scherrer, H., and Jouvet, M., 1956. Modification of electric activity in cochlear nucleus during "attention" in unanesthetized cats. Science *123*, 331–332.

Herrick, C., 1930. The medulla oblongata of necturus. J. Comp. Neurol. *50*, 1–96.

Herrick, C., 1933a. The amphibian fore-brain. VI. Necturus. J. Comp. Neurol. *58*, 1–288.

Herrick, C., 1933b. The amphibian fore-brain. VIII. Cerebral hemispheres and pallial primordia. J. Comp. Neurol. *58*, 737–759.

Herrick, C., 1934. The amphibian fore-brain. IX. J. Comp. Neurol. *59*, 93–116.

Herrick, C., 1956. Analytic and integrative nervous function. In: Problems of Modern Physiology of the Nervous and Muscle Systems, Symposium dedicated to J. Beritoff, Tbilisi, 335–342.

Herzen, A., 1864. Expériences sur les centres modérateurs de l'action réflexe, Turin.

Hess, W., 1956. Hypothalamus and Thalamus: Documentary pictures. Stuttgart, Thieme.

Heubel, E., 1877. Über die Abhängigkeit der wachen Gehirnzustandes von äusseren Er-regungen. Pflügers Arch. ges. Physiol. *14*, 158–210.

Hoffmann, P., 1934. Die physiologischen Eigenschaften der Eigenreflexe. Ergebn. Physiol. *36*, 15–110.

Hughes, J., and Gasser, H., 1934a. Some properties of the cord potentials evoked by a single afferent volley. Am. J. Physiol. *108*, 295–306.

Hughes, J., and Gasser, H., 1934b. The response of the spinal cord to two different afferent volleys. Am. J. Physiol. *108*, 307–321.

Ioseliani, T., 1958. The effects of stimulation of the substantia gelatinosa of the spinal cord. Bull. Acad. Sc. Georgian S.S.R. *21*, 599–605.

Ioseliani, T., 1959. The role of substantia gelatinosa Rolando in reflex activity of the spinal cord. Thesis, University of Tbilisi.

Jasper, H., 1949. Diffuse projection systems: the integrative action of the thalamic reticular system. EEG Clin. Neurophysiol. *1*, 405–420.

Jasper, H. 1954. Functional properties of the thalamic reticular system. In: Brain Mechanisms and Consciousness. Springfield, Ill., Charles C Thomas, 374–401.

Jasper, H., Naquet, R., and King, E., 1955. Thalamo-cortical recruiting responses in sensory receiving areas in the cat. EEG Clin. Neurophysiol. 7, 99–114.

Jasper, H., Ricci, F., and Doane, B., 1958. Microelectrode analysis of cortical cell discharge during avoidance conditioning in the monkey. Moscow. International Colloquium on EEG of Higher Nervous Activity, October 6-11. Moscow, Gosisdat.

Johannes, T., 1930. Zur Funktion des sensiblen Thalamus. Pflügers Arch. ges. Physiol. *224*, 372–385.

Kaada, B., 1951. Somatomotor, autonomic, and electrocorticographic responses to electrical stimulation of "rhinencephalic" and other structures in primates, cat and dog. Acta Physiol. Scandinav. *24*, Suppl. 83.

Kaada, B., Jansen, J., and Andersen, P., 1954. Stimulation of the amygdaloid nuclear complex in unanesthetized cats. Neurology 4, 48.

Kato, G., 1934. Microphysiology. Tokyo, Maruzen.

Kempinsky, W., 1951. Cortical projection of vestibular and facial nerves in cat. J. Neurophysiol., *14*, 203–210.

Kennard, M. A., 1944. Experimental analysis of the function of the basal ganglia in monkeys and chimpanzees. J. Neurophysiol. 7, 127–148.

Khananashvili, M., 1956. Recent data on differentiation of spatial conditioned stimuli. In: Ejhegodnik (Year-Book) Leningrad, Inst. exper. Med. Acad. Med. Sc. 36–40.

Khechinashvili, S., 1958. Vestibular Function. Tbilisi, Georgian Acad. Sc.

Khojava, Z., 1951. Problems of habit in psychology. Thesis, University of Tbilisi.

Klosovsky, G., and Volgina, H., 1956. On the functional role of caudati. In: Problems of Neurosurgery, Moscow, Medgis *1*, 8–14.

Kogan, A., 1949. Electrophysiological investigation of central mechanisms of some compound reflexes. Moscow, Medgit.

Kogan, A., 1960. Study of the structural basis of the nature of temporary connections. Gagra Colloquium, *3*, 191–212.

Köhler, W., 1925. The Mentality of Apes. New York, Harcourt, Brace and Company.

Kölliker, A., 1902. Weitere Beobachtungen über die Hofmann'schen Kerne am Mark der Vögel. Anat. Anz. *21, 3/4,* S.81.

Kölliker, A., 1902. Ueber die oberflächlichen Nervenkerne im Mark der Vögel und Reptilien. Ztschr. Wiss. Zool. *72,* 1, S.126.

Konorski, J., 1950. Mechanisms of learning. In: Physiological Mechanisms in Animal Behaviour, Symposium Soc. Exper. Biol. IV. Cambridge. New York, Academic Press, 409–431.

Kostyuk, P., 1956. On the autogenetic inhibition of muscle. In: Problems of Modern Physiology of the Nervous and Muscle Systems. Symposium dedicated to J. Beritoff, Tbilisi, 129–140.

Kostyuk, J., 1958a. Electrical manifestation of the reciprocal excitation and inhibition in single motoneurons. Doklady Acad. Sc. U.S.S.R. *119,* 1255–1258.

Kostyuk, P., 1958b. Electrical manifestations of the reciprocal excitation and inhibition in single internuncial neurons. Doklady Acad. Sc. U.S.S.R. *120,* 219–222.

Kravkov, S., 1948. The Interrelation of Sensory Organs. Moscow-Leningrad, Gosisdat.

Kravkov, S., 1950. Eye and Its Work. Moscow, Gosisdat, 180–192.

Kreps, E., 1933. Formation of a conditioned reflex with an unconditioned stimulus preceding a conditioned stimulus. Trans. Pavlov Physiol. Lab. *5,* 5–20.

Krestovnikov, A., 1913. Essential conditions during the elaboration of conditioned reflexes. Trans. Soc. Russian Physicians *80* Petersburg.

Kupalov, P., 1938. Environment and activity of the cortex. J. Physiol. Petersburg U.S.S.R. *24,* 228–234.

Kupalov, P., 1947. The mechanism of associative function of the cerebrum. J. Physiol. U.S.S.R. *33,* 699–708.

Kupalov, P., 1948. Qualitative peculiarities of higher cortical nervous processes and the answer to critics of Pavlov's study. Bull. Biol. Méd. exper., Moscow, *26,* 401–413.

Landau, W., 1956. An analysis of the cortical response to antidromic pyramidal tract stimulation in the cat. EEG Clin. Neurophysiol. *8,* 445–456.

Laptev, I., 1949. Environment as a complex conditioned stimulus. In: Problems of Higher Nervous Activity. P. K. Anokhin, ed., Moscow, 461–475.

Lashley, K., 1938. The thalamus and emotion. Psychol. Rev. *45,* 42–61.

Lazarev, P., 1918. Interaction between visual and auditory organs. Bull. (Izwestija) Russian Acad. Sc. 1306.

Lenhossek, M., 1895. Der feinere Bau des Nervensystems. In: Fisscher's Medicin, Ed. 2. Berlin, H. Kornfeld.

Lentz, A., 1934. Conditioned salivary reflexes in man and their relationship to the awareness of the subject. J. Physiol. U.S.S.R. *17,* 1197– 1215.

Leontyev, A., 1948. Psychology. Moscow, Gosisdat.

Leontovitch, T.A., 1958. Particularities of interneuronal connections in the subcortical ganglia of mammals. Arch. Anat. Hist. & Embryol. Leningrad, 35, 2, 17–25.

Li, Choh Luh, and Jasper, H., 1953. Microelectrode studies of the electrical activity of the cerebral cortex in the cat. J. Physiol. *121*, 117–140.

Lissak, K., and Grastyán, E., 1957. The significance of activating systems and the hippocampus in the conditioned reflex. Congress Internat. EEG, 445

Lissak, K., and Grastyán, E., 1958. Changes of the electrical activity of hippocampus during the formation of temporary connections. Moscow, Inter. Coll. EEG Higher Nerv. Activity, October 6-11. Moscow, Gosisdat.

Lissak, K. E., Grastyán, X., Csanaky, A., Keresi, F., and Vereby, G., 1957. A Study of Hippocampal Function in the Waking and Sleeping Animal with Chronically Implanted Electrodes. Acta Physiol. Pharmacol. Néerand. *6*, 89.

Livanov, M., 1958. Concerning the establishment of temporary connections. Moscow, Int. Coll. EEG Higher Nerv. Activity, October 6-11. Moscow, Gosisdat.

Livingston, R., Hernandez Peon, R., and French, J., 1953. Corticofugal projections to the brain stem activating system. Fed. Proc. *12*, 89.

Lorente de Nó, R., 1933, 1934. Studies on the structure of the cerebral cortex. I, II. J. Psychol. Neurol. *45*, p. 381.

Lorente de Nó, R., 1944. Cerebral cortex: architecture, intracortical connections, motor projections. In: Fulton, J., Physiology of the Nervous System, New York, Oxford University Press, 274–313.

Luckina, A. M., 1925. Training of the associative motor reflex to a complex color stimulation. In New Contributions to Reflexology and Physiology of the Central Nervous System. Moscow-Leningrad, Gosisdat.

Macharashvili, D., 1955. On the origin of differentiation of the conditioned reflex. Thesis, University of Tbilisi.

MacLean, P., 1948. The limbic system and its hippocampal formation. J. Neurosurg. *11*, 29.

Magnus, R., 1924. Körperstellung. Berlin, J. Springer.

Magnus, R., 1909a. Zur Regelung der Bewegungen durch das Zentralnervensystem. I. Mitteilung, Pflügers Arch. J. ges. Physiol. *130*, 219.

Magnus, R., 1909b. Zur Regelung der Bewegungen durch das Zentralnervensystem. II. Mitteilung, Pflügers Arch. ges. Physiol. *130*, 253.

Magnus, R., 1910a. Zur Regelung der Bewegungen durch das Zentralnervensystem. III. Mitteilung, Pflügers Arch. ges. Physiol. *134*, 545.

Magnus, R., 1910b. Zur Regelung der Bewegungen durch das Zentralnervensystem. IV. Mitteilung, Pflügers Arch. ges. Physiol. *134*, 584.

Magoun, H. W., 1963. The Waking Brain, 2nd Ed. Springfield, Ill., Charles C Thomas.

Makarov, P., 1952. Neurodynamics of Visual System of a Man. Leningrad, Medgis.

Makarov, P., 1960. Tuning of excitability, lability and brain rhythmicity during formation of a temporary connection. Gagra Colloquium 3, 299–316.

Mangold, E., and Eckstein, A., 1919. Die Reflexerregbarkeit inder tierischen Hypnoze. Pflügers Arch. ges. Physiol. *177*, 1–37.

Masserman, J., 1943. Behavior and Neurosis. Chicago, University of Chicago Press.

Maximow, A., 1930. A Text-book of Histology. Bloom, W., Ed. Philadelphia, W. B. Saunders Co.

McCleary, R., and Lazarus, R., 1949. Autonomic discrimination without awareness. J. Pers. *18*, 171–179.

McLardy, T., 1948. Projection of the centromedian nucleus of the human thalamus. Brain *71*, 290–303.

McRioch, D., and Brenner, C., 1938. Experiments of the corpus striatum and rhinencephalon. J. Comp. Neurol. *68*, 491.

Meltzer, J., 1882. Das Schluckzentrum und seine Irradiation. Inaugural Dissertation, Berlin.

Mettler, F., Ades, H., Lipman, E., and Culler, E., 1939. The extrapyramidal system. Arch. Neurol. & Psychiat. *41*, 984–995.

Michailow, S., 1909. Versuch einer systematischen Untersuchung der Leitungsbahnen des sympathischen Nervensystems. Pflügers Arch. ges. Physiol. *128*, 283–397.

Mickle, W., and Ades, H., 1954. Rostral projection pathway of the vestibular system. Am. J. Physiol. *176*, 243–246.

Missischev, V., 1925. Typical variations in conditioned motor reflexes in man. In: New Contributions to Reflexology and Physiology of the Central Nervous System. Moscow-Leningrad, Gosisdat.

Morgan, C. L., 1900. Animal Behavior. London, Arnold.

Morgan, C. L., 1913. Instinct und Erfahrung. Berlin.

Moruzzi, G., 1950. Problems in Cerebellar Physiology. Springfield, Charles C Thomas.

Moruzzi, G., and Magoun, H., 1949. Brain stem reticular formation of the EEG. EEG Clin. Neurophysiol. *1*, 455–473.

Motsny, P., 1956. On the influence of polarization of motor centers on spinal reflexes in warm blooded animals in connection with the study of the nature of reciprocal inhibition. In: Problems of Modern Physiology of the Nervous and Muscle Systems. Symposium dedicated to J. Beritoff, Tbilisi, 213–223.

Narikashvili, S., 1936. On the role of proprioceptive and cutaneous stimulation in central coordination. In: Problems of Nervous Physiology and Behavior. Symposium dedicated to J. Beritoff, Tbilisi, 413–426.

Narikashvili, S., 1937. Über die Rolle des Hirnstammes in der Reflexreaction der Tiere. Tbilisi, Trans. Beritashvili Physiol. Inst. *3*, 463–478.

Narikashvili, S., 1956. The primary responses of different parts of the auditory area of the cerebral cortex of a cat and changes in them depending on the intensity and frequency of acoustic stimuli. Tbilisi, Trans. Beritashvili Physiol. Inst. *10*, 73–101.

Natishvili, A., Veshapeli, N., Abdousheli, M., Gogitidze, E., Tsibadze, D., Georbenadze, A., Tvaladze, G., Sakvarelidze, S., and Jgenti, V., 1936. The microcephalic girl "Peta" and her clinical and morphological peculiarities. Problems of Nervous Physiology and Behavior. Symposium dedicated to J. Beritoff, Tbilisi, 427–501.

Nemilov, A., 1913. Histological structure of dorsal roots and the white matter of the spinal cord. Petersburg.

Nutsubidze, M., 1960. Role of gyrus hippocampi in emotional reactions in the cat. Trans. Georgian S.S.R. Acad. Sc.

Olds, J., 1958. Self-stimulation of the brain. Its use to study local effects of hunger, sex, and drugs. Science *127*, 315.

O'Leary, J., 1941. Structure of the area striata of the cat. J. Comp. Neurol. *25*, 131–164.

O'Leary, J., and Bishop, G., 1938. The optically excitable cortex of the rabbit. J. Comp. Neurol. *68*, 423–478.

Ordzhonikidze, T., and Nutsubidze, M., 1959a. On the behavior of cats devoid of the neocortex. Trans. Inst. Physiol. Georgian Acad. Sc. *12*, 85–93.

Ordzhonikidze, T., and Nutsubidze, M., 1959b. The role of paleocortex in emotional reactions in cats. Trans. Inst. Physiol. Georgian Acad. Sc. *12*, 94–105.

Ordzhonikidze, T., and Nutsubidze, M., 1959c. The role of the neocortex in emotional reactions in cats. Bull Acad. Sc. Georgian S.S.R., 187–192.

Osipova, V., 1926. Speed of formation of conditioned reflexes in school children. In: New Contributions to Reflexology and Physiology of the Central Nervous System, vol. 2. Leningrad, Gosisdat.

Pavlov, I., 1923. Process of differentiation of stimuli in hemispheres. In: Twenty Years' Study of Higher Nervous Activity in Animals — Conditioned Reflexes. Moscow-Leningrad Gosisdat, 113–124.

Pavlov, I., 1949a. Conditioned Reflex. Complete Works, vol. 3, Moscow-Leningrad Akad. Sc. U.S.S.R., 557–575.

Pavlov, I., 1949b. Physiological mechanisms of so-called voluntary movements. Complete Works, vol. 3, Moscow-Leningrad Akad. Sc. U.S.S.R., 553–556.

Pavlov, I., 1949c. Objective investigations of higher nervous activity in animals. Complete Works, vol. 3, Moscow-Leningrad Akad. Sc. U.S.S.R., 188–198.

Pavlov, I., 1949d. The answer of the physiologist to psychologists. Complete Works, vol. 3, Moscow-Leningrad Akad. Sc. U.S.S.R., 428–455.

Pavlov, I., 1949e. On the Wedensky conception of the processes of excitation and inhibition. Discussion of Orbeli's opinion on the refractory phase. "Pavlovskie sredy," Moscow-Leningrad Akad. Sc. U.S.S.R., 2, 91–96.

Pavlov, I., 1949f. Physiological role of motor region of the cortex. Physiological mechanisms involved in the experiments of Konorski and Miller. "Pavlovskie sredy," Moscow-Leningrad Akad. Sc. U.S.S.R., 2, 480–490.

Pavlov, I., 1951. Some problems on the physiology of hemispheres. Complete Works, vol. 3, part 2, Moscow-Leningrad Akad. Sc. U.S.S.R., 89–105.

Pavlova, V., 1933. Will a conditioned reflex be formed when an unconditioned stimulus precedes an indifferent stimulus? Trans. Pavlov Physiol. Lab. 5, 21–31.

Pearson, A., 1952. Role of gelatinous substance of spinal cord in conduction of pain. Arch. Neurol. & Psychiat. *68*, 515–529.

Peele, T., 1942. Cytoarchitecture of individual parietal areas in the monkey (Macaca mulata) and the distribution of the efferent fibers. J. Comp. Neurol. *77*, 693.

Penfield, W., 1952. Epileptic automatism and the centrencephalic integrating system. A. Res. Nerv. & Ment. Dis. Proc. *30*, 519–525.

Penfield, W., 1952. Epileptic automatism and the centrencephalic integrat- and the conditioning effect of habitual seizures. Amer. J. Physiol. *16*, 255–281.

Penfield, W., and Jasper, H., 1954. Epilepsy and the Functional Anatomy of the Human Brain. Boston, Little, Brown.

Philippson, M., 1905. L'automatie et la centralisation dans le système nerveux des animaux. Bruxelles, Falk Fils.

Pimenoff, P., 1907. Special group of conditioned reflexes. Petersburg, Thesis Medical Academy.

Poljakov, G., 1953. On the fine peculiarities of structure of a human cerebral cortex and the functional interactions between the neurons. Moscow-Leningrad, Arch. anat. histol. embryol. *30*, 5, 48.

Poljakov, G., 1956. On the ratio of main types of neurons in the cerebral cortex of a man. Moscow, J. Higher Nervous Activity, *6*, 469–478.

Poljakov, G., 1958. Recent data concerning neurons and interneuronal connections in the central nervous system. Reports at Sixth Kiev All Union Cong. anat. histol. & embryol. Moscow, Medgiz, 73–83. Kharkov.

Poljakov, G., and Sarkisov, S., 1949. Neurons and interneuronal connections of cerebral cortex. In: Cytoarchitectonics of the Cerebral Cortex in Man. Moscow, Medgiz, 102–120.

Popov, N., 1950. Characterstics of the functions of the cortex and subcortex in dog and monkey after total removal of the cerebral cortex. Bull. Biol. et Méd. exper. *30*, N7, 12, Moscow.

Popov, N. 1953. Investigation of Physiology of the Cerebral Cortex. Moscow, Soviet Science.

Popova, N., 1960. Comparative study of nervous processes in acoustic and visual analyzers of the dog; related structural data. Moscow, Thesis Brain Institute Acad. Med. Sc. (Mimeographed).

Portugalov, V., *et al.*, 1958a. Histological Methods in Normal and Pathological Morphology. Moscow, Medgis. 1–247.

Portugalov, V., 1958b. The peculiarities of chemical topography of central nervous system. Reports at Sixth Kiev All Union Cong. anat., histol. & embryol. Kharkov, Medgiz. 84–88.

Pressman, J., 1938. Conditioned motor defensive reflexes in dogs with disconnected localization areas. J. Physiol. U.S.S.R. *24*, 844–854.

Purpura, D. P., 1946. Observation on the cortical mechanism of EEG activation accompanying behavioural arousal. Science *123*, 804.

Rabinovich, M., and Trofimov, L., 1957. Dominant focus of excitation during the formation of conditioned reflex. Moscow, Bull. Biol. & Méd. exper. *43*, 2, 3–8.

Ramon y Cajal, S., 1893. La rétine des vertébrés. La cellule 9, 119. Quoted by Ariens Kappers, 1936.

Ramon y Cajal, S., 1899. Nuevos observaciones sobre la estructura de la medula espinal de los mamíferos. Barcelona.

Ramon y Cajal, S., 1955. Histologie du système nerveux de l'homme et des vertébrés. T.2. Trans. par L. Azoulay, Madrid.

Ranson, S., 1915. Unmyelinated nerve-fibers as conductors of protophotic sensation. Brain *38*, 381–389.

Ranson, S., and Billingsley, P., 1916. Conduction of painful afferent impulses in the spinal cord. Am. J. Physiol. *40*, 571–584.

Ranson, S., and Ranson, S., Jr., 1942. Efferent fibers of the corpus striatum. Res. Publ. A. Nerv. & ment. Dis. *21*, 69.

Ranson, S., Ranson, S., Jr., and Ranson, M., 1941. Fiber connections of corpus striatum as seen in Marchi preparations. Arch. Neurol. & Phychiat. *46*, 230–249.

Rexed, B., 1954. A cytoarchitectonic atlas of spinal cord in the cat. J. Comp. Neurol. *100*, 297–379.

Richet, C., 1883. Deux expériences d'inhibition sur la grenouille et quelques autres traits relativs à l'inhibition. Bull. Soc. biol. *35*, 456–549.

Roberts, W., 1958. Both rewarding and punishing effects from stimulation of posterior hypothalamus of cat with same electrode at same intensity. J. Comp. & Physiol. Psychol. *51*, 400–405.

Roginski, G., 1948. Habits and Rudiments of Intellectual Action in Anthropoids (Chimpanzée). Leningrad, Gosisdat.

Roitbak, A., 1950a. Oscillographic analysis of inhibition of spinal reflexes during stimulation of trigeminal nerve. Doklady Acad. Sc. U.S.S.R. *72*, 603–606.

Roitbak, A., 1950b. The characteristics and origin of electric potentials of ventral and dorsal root potentials in frogs during trigeminal stimulation. Trans. Beritashvili Physiol. Inst. *8*, 93–133.

Roitbak, A., 1953. Oscillographic study of foci increased excitability in the cerebral cortex. Trans. Inst. Physiol. Georgian Acad. Sc. *9*, 97–131.

Roitbak, A., 1955. Bioelectrical Phenomena in the Cerebral Cortex. Tbilisi, Georgian S.S.R. Acad. Sc.

Roitbak, A., 1956. Dendrites and the process of inhibition. Gagra Colloquium, Tbilisi, *2*, 165–200.

Roitbak, A., 1957. On the nature of the extinction of orientation reflexes. Naukovi Zapiski *16*, 17, 167–174. Symposium dedicated to D. S. Woronzow, Kiev State Univ., no. 10.

Roitbak, A., 1958a. Analysis of electrical phenomena in the cerebral cortex during the extinction of orientation and conditioned reflexes. Moscow, Internat. Colloquium EEG Soc. October 6–11. Moscow, Gosisdat.

Roitbak, A., 1958b. Concerning the mechanism of extinction of orientation and conditioned reflexes. Physiol. Bohemoslov. *7*, 125–134.

Rossi, G., 1912. Ricerche sull'eccitabilità della corteccia cerebrale in cani sottoposti ad emiestirpazione cerebellare. Arch. di fisiol. *10*, 251–260. Quoted by Moruzzi, G., Problems in Cerebellar Physiology, Springfield, Ill., Charles C Thomas, 1950.

Rozhanski, N., 1913. Some Data on the Physiology of Sleep. Petersburg, Thesis of St. Petersburg.

Ruwaldt, M., and Snider, R., 1956. Projections of vestibular areas of cerebellum to cerebrum. J. Comp. Neurol. *104*, 387–401.

Sager, O., 1960. Role of rhinencephalon in the formation of temporary connections. Unpublished paper read at the Institute of Physiology, Georgian S.S.R. Acad. Sc. Oct. 22.

Sager, O., and Butkhusi, S. M., 1963. Interaction of the hippocampus, dorsomedial nucleus of thalamus and amygdala. Unpublished observations.

Sakhiulina, G., 1955. Some data on the electrophysiology of conditioned reflexes. Moscow, Eighth All-Union Cong. Physiol. 533–535.

Samojloff, A., and Kisseleff, M., 1927. Zur Charakteristik der zentralen Hemmungsprozesse. Pflügers Arch. ges. Physiol. *215*, 699–715.

Sarkisov, S., 1948. Some Peculiarities of the Structure of Neural Connections in the Cerebral Cortex. Moscow, Gosisdat.

Savich, A., 1913. Further Data on the Interaction of Food Reflexes. Petersburg, Thesis University of St. Petersburg.

Scherrer, H., and Hernández Peón, R., 1958. Hennung postsynaptischer Potentiale in Nucleus gracilis. Pflügers Arch. ges. Physiol. *267*, 434–445.

Schnirmann, A., 1925. Zur Frage über Möglichkeit der Erziehung d. motorischen Assotiationsreflexes vermittels der retrospinalen Kombinationen. Herausgegeben von Prof. W. Bechterew. Beitr. Reflexol. u. Physiol. Nervensystems *1*, 218.

Sepp, E., 1949. The History of the Development of the Nervous System in Vertebrates. Moscow, Gosisdat.

Serkov, F., and Palamarchuk, J., 1958. Changes in electrical activity of the cerebral cortex and some subcortical formations during food and defensive reflexes. Gagra Colloquium *3*, 363–371, Tbilisi.

Setchenov, I., 1863. Physiologische Studien über die Hemmungsmechanismen für die Reflextätigkeit des Rückenmarks in Gehirn des Frosches. Berlin, Reprinted Selected Works, vol. 3, Moscow, 1952.

Setchenov, I., 1868. On Electrical and Chemical Stimulation of sensitive Nerves of the Frog. Petersburg, Reprinted Selected Works, vol. 3, Moscow, 1952.

Setchenov, I., 1873. By whom and how is psychology to be worked out. Reprinted Selected Works, vol. 1, Moscow Gosisdat, 1952, 172–267.

Setchenov, I., 1878. Elements of thought. Reprinted Selected Works, vol. 1, 1952, 272–426.

Setchenov, I., and Paschutin, B., 1865. Neue Versuche am Hirn und Rückenmark des Frosches. Berlin, 1–95.

Sherrington, C., 1894. On the anatomical constitution of nerves of skeletal muscles; with remarks on recurrent fibers in the ventral spinal nerve-root. J. Physiol. *17*, 211–258.

Sherrington, C., 1906. The Integrative Action of the Nervous System, New Haven, Yale University Press, 1947.

Shimamoto, T., and Verzeano, M., 1954. Relations between caudate and diffusely projecting thalamic nuclei. J. Neurophysiol. *17*, 278–288.

Shkolnik-Yarros, E., 1954. On the morphology of the visual analyzer. Moscow, J. Higher Nervous Activity *4*, 289–304.

Shkolnik-Yarros, E., 1958a. Efferent pathways of the visual cortex. Moscow, J. Higher Nervous Activity *8*, 123–136.

Shkolnik-Yarros, E., 1958b. The peculiarities of neurons and interneuronal connections in the visual analyzer. Sixth Kiev, All Union Cong. anat. histol. & embryol., 436.

Skoglund, C., 1945. Transsynaptic and direct stimulation of postfibers in the artificial synapse formed by severed mammalian nerve. J. Neurophysiol. *8*, 365–376.

Sperry, R., 1947. Cerebral regulation of motor coordination in monkeys following multiple transection of sensorimotor cortex. J. Neurophysiol. *10*, 275–294.

Sperry, R., and Miner, N., 1955. Pattern perception following insertion of mica plates into visual cortex. J. Comp. & physiol. Psychol. *48*, 463–470.

Spiegel, E., 1919. Die Kerne im Vorderhirn der Säuger. Arb. neurol. Inst. Wien. Univ. *22*, 418.

Spiegel, E., 1932. Rindenerregung (Auslösung epileptsformer Anfälle) durch Labyrinthreizung. Versuch einer Lokalisation der cortikalen Labyrinthzentren. XVII. Ztschr. ges. Neurol. Psychiat. *138*, 178–196.

Spiegel, E., Szekely, E., and Baker, W., 1956. Afferent thalamo-striopallidal mechanisms. Am. Neurol. A. 71–73.

Spiegel, E., Szekely, E., and Baker, W., 1957. Electrographic study of thalamic impulses to the striatum and pallidum. EEG Clin. Neurophysiol. *9*, 291–299.

Sprague, J., 1958. The distribution of dorsal root fibers on motor cells in the lumbosacral spinal cord of the cat and site of excitatory and inhibitory terminals of monosynaptic pathways. Proc. Royal Soc. London s.B *937*, 538–556.

Sukhanov, S. A., 1899. Contribution to the question of beadlike formation of protoplasmic processes of the cortical nerve cells. Thesis, University of Moscow.

Svaetichin, G., 1951. Electrophysiological investigations on single ganglion cells. Acta Physiol. Scandinav. *24*, suppl. 86, 1–57.

Ten Cate, J., 1934. Akustische und optische Reaktionen der Katzen nach teilweisen und totalen Extirpationen des Neopalliums. Arch. néerland. Physiol. *19*, 191–264.

Ten Cate, J., and Herk, A., 1933. Beobachtungen an Kaninchen nach Extirpationen im Neopallium. Arch. néerland. Physiol. *18*, 337–386.

Teplov, B., 1949. Psychology. Moscow Gosisdat.

Tevzadze, B., 1951. Effect of n. trigeminus on reflex reactions. Trans. Tbilisi Stalin State University *42*, 25-42.

Thorpe, W., 1950. The concepts of learning and their relation to those of instinct. In: Physiological Mechanisms in Animal Behaviour. Cambridge, Symp. Soc. Exper. Biol. *4*, 387-408.

Tower, S., 1937. Function and structure in the chronically isolated lumbosacral spinal cord of the dog. J. Comp. Neurol. *67*, 109-131.

Tvaladze, G., 1936. The cortex cytoarchitectonics of Peta's brain. Problems of Nervous Physiology and Behavior, Symposium dedicated to J. Beritoff, Tbilisi, 478-490.

Tvaladze, G., 1939. Postembryonic development of the brain from birth to 15 years. Dissertation from the Bechterew Brain Institute.

Tvaladze, G., 1942. Anthropometrical and encephalographical data of the brain in the postembryonic period of life. Collected works of the Zooveterinary Institute of the Georgian S.S.R.

Tvaladze, G., 1952. Postembryonic growth of the cerebral fissures in length. Batumi, Rustaveli State Pedagogical Institute *2*, 313-349.

Tzkipuridze, L., and Chichinadze, N., 1944a. On the central inhibition of the pain in the case of causalgia. Bull. Acad. Sc. Georgian S.S.R. *5*, 311-320.

Tzkipuridze, L., and Chichinadze, N., 1944b. On the central inhibition of some kinds of pain. Bull. Acad. Sc. Georgian S.S.R. *5*, 439-448.

Uchtomsky, A., 1911. Über die Abhängigkeit der kortikalen motorischen Reaktionen von zentralen Nervenwirkungen. Tr. Soc. Natur. *41*, Lief 2. (Trans. Physiol. Lab. Petersburg Univ. *5*.)

Umrath, K., 1933. Der Erregungsvorgang in den Motoneuronen von Rana esculenta. Pflügers Arch. ges. Physiol. *233*, 357-370.

Umrath, K., 1934. Aktionsströme vom Zentralnervensystem des Frosches. Pflügers Arch. ges. Physiol. *234*, 562-569.

Ursin, H., and Kaada, B., 1960a. Functional localization within the amygdaloid complex in the cortex. Electroencephalog. & Clin. Neurophysiol. *12*, 1-20.

Ursin, H., and Kaada, B., 1960b. Subcortical structures mediating the attention response induced by amygdala stimulation. Exper. Neurol. *2*, 109-122.

Uznadze, D., 1930. Einstellungsumschau als Grundlage der Kontrasttäuschungen. Ninth International Congress of Psychology, Proceedings and Papers, 453-454.

Uznadze, D., 1939. Untersuchungen zur Psychologie der Einstellung. Acta Psychol. *4*, 326-360.

Uznadze, D., 1941. Fundamentals of the theory of set. Tbilisi, Trans. Stalin State University (In Georgian) p. 17.

Uznadze, D., 1949. Experimental basis of psychology of attitude. Tbilisi, Trans. Psychol. Inst. Acad. Sc. Georgian S.S.R. *6*.

Vatsuro, E., 1947. On certain new principles in the concept of higher nervous activity. J. Physiol. U.S.S.R. *33*, 327-334.

Voytonis, N., 1945. Forms of expression of attitudes in animals, apes in particular. Psychologia, vol. 3, dedicated to D. Uznadze, Tbilisi, 121–140.

Vrba, R., 1956. On the role of proteins of cerebral nervous tissue in excitatory and inhibitory processes. Progr. modern Biol., Moscow (Uspekhi sovr. Biol.), *41*, 322–352.

Walberg, F., and Brodal, A., 1953. Pyramidal tract fibers from temporal and occipital lobes. An experimental study in the cat. Brain *76*, 491–508.

Walker, A., 1938. An oscillographic study of the cerebello-cerebral relationships. J. Neurophysiol. *1*, 16–23.

Walzl, E., and Mountcastle, V., 1949. Projection of vestibular nerve of cerebral cortex of the cat. Am. J. Physiol. *159*, 595.

Wedensky, N., 1903. Die Erregung, Hemmung und Narkose. Pflügers Arch. ges. Physiol. *100*, 1–144.

Wedensky, N., 1920. Accessory electrotonic alterations of excitability. Perielectrotonus. Petersburg, Bull. Acad. Impér. Sc. *14*, ser. VI, 332–359.

Woodworth, R., 1906. The cause of a voluntary movement. In studies in philosophy and psychology by former student of Garman. Boston, Houghton Mifflin, 351–392.

Woodworth, R., 1939. Psychological Issues. New York, Henry Holt.

Woolsey, C., and Chang, H., 1948. Activation of the cerebral cortex by antidromic volleys in the pyramidal tract. In The Frontal Lobes, Baltimore, Williams and Wilkins, 146–162.

Worchal, P., and Dollenbach, K. M., 1947. "Facial vision"; perception of obstacles by the deaf-blind. Am. J. Psychol. *60*, 502.

Worchal, P., Manness, I., and Andrew, J., 1950. Perception of obstacles by the blind. J. Exper. Psychol. *40*, 746–751.

Yoshii, N., 1957. Principles methodologiques de l'investigation électroencephalagraphique du comportement conditionnel. EEG Clin. Neurophysiol. Suppl. 6, *9*, 75–88.

Yoshii, N. and Hockaday, W., 1958. Conditioning of frequency specific repetitive EEG response with intermittent photic stimulation. EEG Clin. Neurophysiol. *10*, 487–502.

Yoshii, N., and Matsumoto, D., 1958. Electroencephalographic study of internal inhibition on saliva and defensive conditioned reflexes in dogs. Moscow, Internat. Colloquium on Electroencephalography and Conditioned Reflexes, October 6–11. Moscow, Gosisdat.

Yoshii, N., Matsumoto, J., and Hori, Y., 1958. Electroencephalographic study of conditioned reflex in animals. Quoted from Magoun, H., The Waking Brain. Springfield, Ill., Charles C Thomas, 111–112.

Zavarsin, A., 1941. Essays on the Evolution of Histology of the Nervous System. Moscow-Leningrad, Medgiz.

Zeliony, G., 1911–1912. A dog with removed cerebral hemispheres. I, II. trans. Soc. Russian Physicians, *80*, 50, 471.

Zeliony, G., 1929. Effets de l'ablation des hemispheres cerebraux. Rev. méd. *2*, 191.

Zeliony, G., 1930. Die Resultate der Grosshirnhemisphärenentfernung. Moscow-Leningrad, J. med. biol. *1–2*, 3–18.

Zhukova, G., 1953. On the problem of the development of the cortical end of motor analyzer. Moscow, Arch. anat. histol. & embryol. *30*, I, 32–38.

Zurabashvili, A., 1951. Synapses and the Reversible Changes of Nerve. Moscow, Medgiz.

INDEX